FACTOR ANALYSIS

A SYNTHESIS OF FACTORIAL METHODS

THE UNIVERSITY OF CHICAGO PRESS · CHICAGO

THE BAKER & TAYLOR COMPANY, NEW YORK; THE CAMBRIDGE UNIVERSITY
PRESS, LONDON; THE MARUZEN-KABUSHIKI-KAISHA, TOKYO, OSAKA,
KYOTO, FUKUOKA, SENDAI; THE COMMERCIAL PRESS, LIMITED, SHANGHAI

FACTOR ANALYSIS

A SYNTHESIS OF FACTORIAL METHODS

By

KARL J. HOLZINGER

AND

HARRY H. HARMAN

THE UNIVERSITY OF CHICAGO PRESS
CHICAGO · ILLINOIS

PREFACE

The chief purpose of this volume is to present a general treatment of factor analysis including an objective basis for comparing various forms of solution. To accomplish this a thorough examination has been made of the logical and mathematical foundations underlying the methods of analysis employed. The treatment throughout has been made as rigorous as possible with the hope that factor analysis would emerge as a sound branch of statistical theory rather than as a series of disconnected methods of application. A considerable amount of mathematics has been found necessary for such rigorous treatment. The text, however, has been made self-contained in large measure by the treatment of such subjects as higher dimensional geometry and the fundamentals of matrix theory.

Another aim of the text is the practical one of supplying the methods of analysis in a very simple, readable form for the worker who is not concerned with the rigorous foundation. Such an analyst would need only a general knowledge of the various forms of solution, as described in the text, and he could then follow the detailed outlines for computation, which are given in the appropriate appendixes. Complete checks on all the arithmetical processes are also given throughout these appendixes.

In Part I the analytic and geometric bases for factor analysis are set forth. Certain fundamental statistics are introduced in Chapter II, the most important of which include the assumed factorial composition of variables and the distinction between patterns and structures. Inasmuch as geometry is a convenient form not only for presenting the basic theorems of factor analysis but also for clarifying many ideas in the actual solutions, Chapter III is devoted entirely to that subject. The fundamental theorems basic to the various methods are given in Chapters III and IV. A new approach to the determination of the common-factor space is presented in Chapter IV.

In order to furnish an objective basis for selecting a given form of solution, a set of statistical criteria are enumerated in Chapter V. When certain of these standards are postulated, several "preferred" solutions are disclosed. These are presented formally in Chapter V, and the distinguishing characteristics of each type are indicated in detail. The practical analyst who does not desire to read the complete development of each method should become thoroughly acquainted with the properties of the types of solution treated in this chapter (and also the oblique form of solution of Chap. XI) so that he can make an intelligent choice of a particular form.

Chapter V is of fundamental importance for a clear understanding of the problem of choice of a particular type of factor solution, and the synthetic treatment of this chapter should add unity to the subject of factor analysis.

The complete theoretical development of the preferred types of solution is given in Parts II and III. The theory underlying each form is presented, and this is followed by illustrative examples. Among the new methods introduced in the present text are the averoid modification of the centroid method in Chapter VIII and the objective procedure for oblique solutions of Chapter XI. Sampling formulas of factor coefficients and for residuals have also been developed in Chapter VI. Complete forms of analysis, including detailed steps of procedure for each method, have been given in Appendixes C, D, and E. These should be of chief value to the nonmathematical student who may find portions of the theoretical treatment somewhat difficult.

The evaluation of factors and relationships among factors are dealt with in Part IV. A synthetic treatment of several methods for estimating factors from the observed variables is given in Chapter XII. The relative advantages and disadvantages of each method are indicated, so that the most desirable procedure can be readily selected. A routine scheme for the estimation of factors is given in Appendix G. In the final chapter the relationships between two factor solutions obtained by different methods of analysis are discussed. Then, to assist the practical analyst in employing the various methods described throughout the book, a general outline of procedure is suggested in **13.4**.

The last part of the book consists of eight appendixes, the contents of some of which have already been indicated. In Appendix B a number of proofs of some of the fundamental theorems of the text are presented. These have been placed in the Appendix because of their mathematical complexity. These proofs are required for complete rigor, but the nonmathematical reader, who may accept the theorems without proof, can read the text without them. In Appendix H tables are presented for facilitating the calculation of the standard errors derived in Chapter VI.

The student whose background includes college mathematics through the calculus and a good course in statistics should be able to follow the entire treatment without supplementary reading. Since matrix theory may be unfamiliar, this topic has been treated in Appendix A. This contains the definitions, rules, and simple illustrations of the parts of this theory required for an understanding of the present text. The student who desires to learn only the forms of solution and the required routine analysis may omit much of the theoretical development and still have a good practical knowledge of factor analysis. The instructor who uses this volume as a text will probably want to exercise his judgment as to the portions to be omitted. It is suggested, however, that all basic theorems be considered and illustrated even though the proofs are omitted.

No attempt has been made to give a historical account of the development of factor analysis. This has been omitted partly because of the greatly added bulk and partly because such an account would involve both statistical method and psychological theories and thus would be outside the scope of the present general statistical treatment. For similar reasons it has also been found necessary to omit the treatment of a number of alternative approaches to factor analysis such as the "Sampling Theory of Intelligence," "Cluster Analysis," and "Inverted Factor Analysis."

A number of practical illustrations of all the methods are presented throughout the text. Complete calculations are exhibited in order to clarify the various procedures. No additional exercises have been included, but it is planned to supplement the present volume with an exercise manual. This will include simple exercises, practical applications, and questions designed to increase the usefulness of the present volume as a textbook. For purposes of reference a bibliography of contributions to the methods of factor analysis is also presented. This includes not only works on factorial methods and some of their major applications but also related mathematical treatises.

Each section in the text is distinguished by a number in bold-face type consisting of the number of the chapter in which the section occurs, prefixed to the number of the section in that chapter and separated from it by a period; e.g., **2.10** indicates the tenth section of the second chapter. Similarly tables, figures, and equations are distinguished first with the number of the chapter in which they occur and then, separated by a period, with their serial number within the chapter; e.g., Table 7.3 refers to the third table of Chapter VII and "equation (6.2)" refers to the second equation of Chapter VI. A few page references are also included, but the above notation will be found convenient for rapid cross-reference.

The authors are greatly indebted to the Social Science Research Committee of the University of Chicago for grants which made possible the research required for the present volume. They are especially indebted to Professor Louis Wirth for his suggestion that the present synthetic treatment be undertaken and for his advice and encouragement during the lengthy preparation of the manuscript. To the penetrating criticisms of Dr. A. L. O'Toole are due many improvements in the manuscript. The writers are also indebted to Dr. L. R. Wilcox for criticism of Chapter III on geometry and for his suggestion of the set-theory notations. To Dr. Lee J. Cronbach, who read several chapters of the original manuscript, they are grateful for helpful suggestions and criticisms.

KARL J. HOLZINGER
HARRY H. HARMAN

UNIVERSITY OF CHICAGO
May 1941

TABLE OF CONTENTS

PART I. ANALYTIC AND GEOMETRIC
BASES FOR FACTOR ANALYSIS

TABLE OF CONTENTS

PART I

ANALYTIC AND GEOMETRIC BASES
FOR FACTOR ANALYSIS

CHAPTER I

INTRODUCTION

1.1. *Nature of Factor Analysis*

Factor analysis is a branch of statistical theory concerned with the resolution of a set of descriptive variables in terms of a small number of categories or factors. This resolution is accomplished by the analysis of the intercorrelations of the variables. A satisfactory solution will yield factors which convey all the essential information of the original set of variables. The chief aim is thus to attain scientific parsimony or economy of description.

This aim should not be construed to mean that factor analysis necessarily attempts to discover the "fundamental" or "basic" categories in a given field of investigation such as psychology. It would be very desirable, of course, to base such an analysis upon a set of variables which measures all possible mental aspects of a given population as completely and accurately as possible. Even in such a case, however, the factors would not be completely fundamental because of the omission of important measures which were not yet devised. While the goal of complete description cannot be reached theoretically, it may be approached practically in a limited field of investigation where a relatively small number of variables is considered exhaustive. In all cases, however, factor analysis does give a simple interpretation of a given body of data and thus affords a fundamental description of the particular set of variables analyzed.

The essential purpose of factor analysis has been well expressed by Professor Truman L. Kelley: "There is no search for timeless, spaceless, populationless truth in factor analysis; rather, it represents a simple, straightforward problem of description in several dimensions of a definite group functioning in definite manners, and he who assumes to read more remote verities into the factorial outcome is certainly doomed to disappointment."*

1.2. *Applications and Problems*

The applications of factor analysis up to the present time have been chiefly in the field of psychology, because the methods were invented by psychologists for dealing with certain of their problems. A factor analysis

---

* "Comment on Wilson and Worcester's 'Note on Factor Analysis,' " *Psychometrika*, 1940, p. 120.

may lead to some theory suggested by the form of the solution, and conversely one may formulate a theory and verify it by an appropriate form of factorial solution. The latter approach is illustrated by Professor Charles Spearman's theory that *"all branches of intellectual activity have in common one fundamental function (or group of functions) whereas the remaining or specific elements of the activity seem in every case to be wholly different from that in all others."** He showed that if certain relationships (the tetrads defined in **4.3**) exist among the correlations, all the variables can be resolved into linear expressions involving only one general factor and an additional factor unique to each variable. These relationships furnish the statistical verification of the "Two-Factor Theory." If a set of psychological variables yields correlation coefficients which do not satisfy the preceding relationships, then a more complex theory may be postulated. This may require several common factors in the statistical description of the variables.

Recently, Kelley has described a method involving factor analysis which may well be used in the selection and classification of army personnel.† Of fundamental importance for this analysis is the selection of variables which have definite social significance. Two types of variables are involved: first, those which are measures of social *utility* and, second, those which are concerned with measuring the *well-being* of the individual. The former measures are selected because of their bearing on vocational success, while the latter are chosen to reflect individual happiness. From such a set of variables several factors are obtained. Then the profile of an individual can be compared with that of the average participant in the type of job being considered. Kelley's primary purpose was not "to suggest the measures to be employed, nor even the detailed principles for their selection, but to give a method for utilizing them to their fullest . . . . in the service of a State dedicated to the preservation of human liberties and rights."‡

Psychologists are planning experiments employing the techniques of factor analysis to determine a small number of psychological tests to describe the human mind as completely as possible. The approach consists of a factorial analysis of a large battery of tests in order to identify a few common factors. Then the tests which best measure these factors, or, preferably, revised tests based upon these, may be selected as direct measures of the "factors of mind." However, only to the extent to which psychologists

---

* "General Intelligence, Objectively Determined and Measured," *Amer. J. Psychol.*, 1904, p. 201.

† *Talents and Tasks: Their Conjunction in a Democracy for Wholesome Living and National Defense*, 1940.

‡ *Ibid.*, p. 48.

agree that the tests selected are the "right tests" can they be said to be actual measures of the factors. Such "factor tests" should be of a "pure" nature, differing widely from one another so as to cover the entire range of mental activity. To the present time, several major studies* have been undertaken to identify factors from large sets of tests. The tests which best measure each of the factors, however, are still far from being "pure." A great deal of research in test construction is still required before tests can be found which can be regarded as even approximating the "factors of the mind."

The methods of factor analysis have been successfully applied, in recent years, not only in psychology but also in such varied fields as political science, business, and medicine. Sometimes, in the study of a particular problem, variables from several different fields may be employed. Thus, in an attempt to discover the underlying causes for poor reading, psychological, physical, and medical evidence has been pooled for factorial analysis. In a widely different field a physicist has turned to factor analysis to discover some simple explanation of the intensity of cosmic rays under varying conditions of temperature and air pressure at different altitudes. A factor analysis of stock prices of railroad equipment, automotive parts, and oils has been made to arrive at the fundamental indices of this type of business activity. It has also been proposed to employ factor analysis in medicine in order to obtain a simple functional classification of substances producing allergy. These are only a few of the types of practical applications that may be expected as the methods of factor analysis become more widely known.

The foregoing applications of factor analysis are concerned mainly with testing hypotheses in scientific investigations. Another use, considered by some to be the chief value of factor analysis, is to supplement conventional statistical techniques. By means of factor analysis the computation of multiple correlation coefficients, partial correlation coefficients, and regression coefficients can be greatly simplified when many variables are involved. In the problem of studying the relationship between two sets of variables factor analysis can again be employed. The best linear function of the variables in each set is obtained by factorial methods, and then the correlation between these composites gives what is known as the *canonical correlation*.† Such a correlation is the maximum possible between the two sets of variables. This technique should be of great value in test construction, inasmuch as it furnishes the investigator with improved methods for obtaining more valid and reliable pools of subtests.

---

* L. L. Thurstone, *Primary Mental Abilities*, 1938; K. J. Holzinger, *Preliminary Reports on Spearman-Holzinger Unitary Trait Study*, Nos. 1–9, 1934–36.

† Harold Hotelling, "Relations between Two Sets of Variates," *Biometrika*, 1936.

The present text is concerned primarily with the exposition of various procedures in factor analysis. These methods are completely illustrated by numerical examples taken from psychology, biometry, and political science. These examples are used chiefly to clarify the theoretical treatment rather than to exhibit the practical usefulness of factor analysis in the broader type of application mentioned above.

1.3. *Scientific Theories*

Factor analysis, like all statistics, is a branch of applied mathematics. It employs observed data, which necessarily include discrepancies, and hence may lead to several different mathematical formulations of a given problem. In general, an applied mathematical theory consists of the following parts:

SCIENTIFIC THEORY IN A GIVEN FIELD
1. Observed data (with discrepancies)
2. Mathematical theory
   Postulates
   Definitions
   Theorems
3. Verification with data

Any such applied science involves some mathematical theory as its basis, plus a set of observations, and, finally, the check of the particular mathematical theory with the original data. In all problems of applied mathematics there may be a number of mathematical theories which explain the phenomena in a satisfactory manner. A misunderstanding of the relationship between a mathematical theory and observed data is frequently encountered. When a theory has been successfully employed in describing a set of data, there is a tendency to accept this law as the only correct one for describing the observations.

Furthermore, it is sometimes inferred that nature behaves in precisely the way which the mathematics indicates. As a matter of fact, nature never does behave in this way, and there are *always more mathematical theories than one* whose results depart from a given set of data by less than the errors of observation.

.   .   .   .

The danger is always when a theory has been found to be convenient and effective over a long period of time, that people begin to think that nature herself behaves precisely in the way which is indicated by the theory. This is never the case, and the belief that it is so may close our minds to other possible theories and be a serious impedence to progress in the development of our interpretations of the world around us.*

* G. A. Bliss, "Mathematical Interpretations of Geometrical and Physical Phenomena," *Amer. Math. Monthly*, 1933, pp. 472, 477. (Italics ours.)

The above observations may be illustrated in several different fields. One of the simplest cases arises in the problem of surveying a small tract of land. For this purpose either of two mathematical theories, plane or spherical trigonometry, may be applied. Thus, in surveying a city lot the results by either theory would be equally satisfactory, and the engineer would prefer the plane theory because of its greater simplicity. In this instance, however, there is no doubt as to the greater accuracy of the spherical theory since the earth is essentially spherical.

In the field of astronomy there are two theories describing the solar system. The Ptolemaic and Copernican theories, with suitable modification of the former, describe the motions of the planets with equal accuracy. "There is really no advantage for either of these theories as compared with the other, as far as their adaptability to explain numerically the facts of the solar system is concerned. The Copernican theory is, however, much the simpler geometrically and mathematically. For this reason it has been adapted and developed until astronomers can predict coming celestial events with most surprising accuracy."*

Even the subject of geometry, which might seem to depend on a unique mathematical theory, can be described by means of many different theories. Thus, the physical configurations in a plane can be interpreted in the light of Euclidean geometry, Riemannian geometry, or various other types of non-Euclidean geometry. Therefore, the applied science of geometry can have several alternative theories as its basis.

As in the foregoing illustrations there are different theories, or forms of solution, which may arise in the factorial analysis of a particular set of data. The usefulness of factor analysis as a scientific tool has been questioned by some workers because of this indeterminacy. It should be evident, however, that this is tantamount to indicting all applied sciences because they do not depend upon unique theories.

Since the beginning of this century, psychologists and statisticians have developed several types of factorial solutions. The proponent of each system of analysis has urged its suitability for the interpretation of psychological data. These varying points of view have been wittily described by Cureton as follows:

Factor theory may be defined as a mathematical rationalization. A factor-analyst is an individual with a peculiar obsession regarding the nature of mental ability or personality. By the application of higher mathematics to wishful thinking, he always proves that his original fixed idea or compulsion was right or necessary. In the process he usually proves that all other factor-analysts are dangerously insane, and that the only salvation for them is to undergo his own brand of analysis in

* *Ibid.*, pp. 477–78.

order that the true essence of their several maladies may be discovered. Since they never submit to this indignity, he classes them all as hopeless cases, and searches about for some branch of mathematics which none of them is likely to have studied in order to prove that their incurability is not only necessary but also sufficient.*

The factor analyst must recognize the fact that methods other than his own must have some merit. This attitude can be expressed in a manner analogous to that employed by Barclay in his discussion of the various bidding systems in contract bridge.† The argument in the following two paragraphs is essentially that of Barclay with the phrases "bidding systems" replaced by "types of factorial solutions" and "players" by "analysts."

It is a positive fact that every one of the types of factorial solutions in extensive use today is an efficient one. When known thoroughly, a skilled analyst can apply any one of them to produce fine results in a desired situation. The enthusiastic partisan who depreciates the efficacy of some other method and calls it a poor one thereby furnishes indisputable proof of one of two things—either his own sincerity or his own ignorance. Not just ignorance of the details of the other method, but general ignorance. Any person of intelligence should know that it is highly improbable that any of the brilliant psychologists and statisticians who have worked on these problems for the last thirty years would produce and advocate a "rotten" system.

The analyst who learns all the leading factorial methods and becomes familiar with them in actual use will be able to defend any method that someone may endeavor to ridicule. When some authority makes light of another method of analysis, it is quite likely that the man advocating a particular system is extremely earnest in believing that he is offering his followers the very best procedures, but it may also be that the man has not given enough study to the other's method to realize its fine points as well as its deficiencies. Since no one factor method can cover all types of data which the analyst might like to describe, he should be familiar with all the methods so that he can select that one which is most suitable in a particular problem.

The various types of factorial solutions correspond to the different mathematical theories in the description of a particular scientific problem. Five preferred forms of solution are presented in the text, any one of which may be selected by the analyst for dealing with a given body of data. The exposi-

* Edward E. Cureton, "The Principal Compulsions of Factor-Analysts," *Harvard Educational Review*, 1939, p. 287.

† Shepard Barclay, *Win at Contract with Any Partner*, 1933, pp. viii–ix.

tion of these methods and their comparison are the primary aims of the present text.

The properties and statistical criteria underlying each of the preferred types are presented in Chapter V. These standards reveal the salient features of the preferred solutions, indicating their advantages and limitations. When an analyst has selected a particular form of factor solution for the description of a given problem, he should realize that there are other methods which might afford an equally satisfactory interpretation of the data.

CHAPTER II

BASIC STATISTICS

2.1. *Introduction*

In this chapter certain elementary statistical notions are introduced. These ideas are essential for much of the subsequent analysis and are therefore presented in detail for the sake of rigor and completeness. The definitions are so formulated that they are applicable in any field, such as education, psychology, or commerce. Consequently, the formulas based on these definitions are general in their application.

After the preliminary definitions of some elementary statistical concepts have been presented, the composition of a statistical variable is treated. Then a fundamental distinction between two necessary parts of a factor solution, *pattern* and *structure*, is developed. A brief discussion of the statistical adequacy of a factor solution follows. The general arbitrariness of any scientific theory is exhibited here by the indeterminacy of factor solutions. Finally, methods of organizing data for subsequent analysis are presented. In illustrating these methods a set of psychological variables is employed.

2.2. *Statistical Variables*

Any statistical study involves a selection of a group of N individuals with a number of common attributes. In a particular investigation the group of individuals might consist of such objects as persons, schools, cities, or commercial enterprises. Various aspects of such individuals may be measured and referred to as *statistical variables*. These will be designated by X_j $(j = 1, 2, \ldots, n)$, or more briefly j, where n is the number of variables in a set which is employed in describing the N individuals. Particular values of a variable X_j for individual i will be represented by X_{ji}. These will be called *observed values* inasmuch as they are measured from an arbitrary origin and by an arbitrary unit.

The sum of all N values for a variable X_j is written in the form

$$\sum_{i=1}^{N} X_{ji},$$

but this may be put more simply in the form

$$\Sigma X_{ji},$$

where it is understood that the summation extends over all values of the variable. This convention for the summation with respect to the number of observations of a particular variable will be observed throughout the text. Furthermore, the index i will be reserved explicitly to refer to the individuals, that is, for the range 1 to N. The mean of the N values of X_j is then given by

$$M_j = \frac{\Sigma X_{ji}}{N}.$$

Derived values of each variable can be obtained by fixing the origin and the unit. When the origin is taken at the mean, a particular value

$$x_{ji} = X_{ji} - M_j$$

will be called a *deviate*. The standard deviation of a variable X_j is defined by

(2.1) $$\sigma_j = \sqrt{\frac{\Sigma x_{ji}^2}{N}},$$

where, of course, the summation is over the N values of i. By taking the standard deviation as the unit of measurement, *standardized values* may be defined as follows:

(2.2) $$z_{ji} = \frac{x_{ji}}{\sigma_j}.$$

The set of all values z_{ji} ($i = 1, 2, \ldots, N$) will be designated as a statistical variable z_j in *standard form*. Obviously the *variance* (standard deviation squared) of z_j is equal to unity.

The product-moment coefficient of correlation for any two variables j and k is defined by

(2.3) $$r_{jk} = \frac{\Sigma x_{ji} x_{ki}}{\sqrt{\Sigma x_{ji}^2}\ \sqrt{\Sigma x_{ki}^2}}$$

or, making use of (2.1) and (2.2),

(2.3′) $$r_{jk} = \frac{\Sigma x_{ji} x_{ki}}{N \sigma_j \sigma_k} = \frac{\Sigma z_{ji} z_{ki}}{N}.$$

The intercorrelations between all possible pairs of variables in a set constitute the basic data for factor analysis. It will be assumed here, as in all other cases where the product-moment correlation coefficient is employed, that it is most useful in case all regression lines are sensibly linear and all variables are normally distributed in the population and approximately so in the sample.

2.3. *Composition of Variables*

The simplest mathematical expression for describing a variable in terms of several others is a linear one. This form is the one frequently employed in ordinary regression methods, although more elaborate expressions are also used for a small number of variables. For a large set of variables, however, a simple approximation becomes almost imperative, and hence linear expressions are used. Similarly, in factor analysis the simple linear form is taken to represent a variable z_j in terms of a number of underlying *factors*, or hypothetical variables, which are taken to be in standard form for convenience. A factor may be said to be in standard form if in the population its mean is zero and its standard deviation is unity. Furthermore, it is assumed that these properties also hold for a given sample. The factors are also assumed to be normally distributed.

Several types of factors may be employed. *Common factors* are those which are involved in more than one variable of a set. Two instances of common factors arise: a *general factor*, present in all variables, and a *group factor*, present in more than one but not in all variables. A factor which appears exclusively in the description of a particular variable is said to be *unique*. Common factors are necessary in order to account for the intercorrelations of the n variables. Each unique factor represents that portion of a variable not ascribable to its correlations with other variables in the set.

Employing the notation $F_1, F_2, \ldots, F_m$ for m common factors, and $U_1, U_2, \ldots, U_n$ for the unique factors, the complete linear expression for any variable z_j ($j = 1, 2, 3, \ldots, n$) may then be written in the form

$$(2.4) \qquad z_j' = a_{j1}F_1 + a_{j2}F_2 + a_{j3}F_3 + \ldots + a_{jm}F_m + a_jU_j \, ,$$

where the prime is used to indicate the theoretical form of the observed variable. For simplicity the prime will usually be dropped hereafter in the linear expression for the variable. There are, of course, n equations of this form—one for each of the n variables. Equation (2.4) might be written explicitly for the value of variable z_j for a particular individual i ($i = 1, 2, \ldots, N$), i.e.,

$$(2.5) \qquad z_{ji} = a_{j1}F_{1i} + a_{j2}F_{2i} + a_{j3}F_{3i} + \ldots + a_{jm}F_{mi} + a_jU_{ji} \, .$$

In this expression it is assumed that there are N values of each of the factors, corresponding to the N individuals of the sample. The basic problem of factor analysis is to determine the coefficients, $a_{j1}, \ldots, a_{jm}$, of the common factors. This determination is made by the various methods described in Parts II and III, employing the observed intercorrelations of the n variables. After these coefficients have been determined, the factors for the individuals can be evaluated by the methods of Chapter XII.

The contributions of the factors to the total variance of any variable z_j will next be shown. To express the variance of z_j in terms of the coefficients of the factors, square both sides of (2.5), sum over the N values of the respective variables, and divide by N, and obtain, upon expanding,

$$\frac{\Sigma z_{ji}^2}{N} = a_{j1}^2 \frac{\Sigma F_{1i}^2}{N} + a_{j2}^2 \frac{\Sigma F_{2i}^2}{N} + \ldots + a_{jm}^2 \frac{\Sigma F_{mi}^2}{N} + a_j^2 \frac{\Sigma U_{ji}^2}{N}$$

$$+ 2\left(a_{j1}a_{j2} \frac{\Sigma F_{1i}F_{2i}}{N} + \ldots + a_{j,m-1}a_{jm} \frac{\Sigma F_{m-1,i}F_{mi}}{N} \right.$$

$$+ a_{j1}a_j \frac{\Sigma F_{1i}U_{ji}}{N} + \ldots + a_{jm}a_j \frac{\Sigma F_{mi}U_{ji}}{N} \left.\right).$$

Now, since the variance of a variable in standard form is equal to unity, and all variables (including the factors) are assumed to be in standard form for any sample, the last equation may be written

$$(2.6) \quad \begin{cases} 1 = \sigma_{z_j}^2 = a_{j1}^2 + a_{j2}^2 + \ldots + a_{jm}^2 + a_j^2 + 2(a_{j1}a_{j2}r_{F_1F_2} \\ \qquad\qquad\qquad\qquad\qquad + \ldots + a_{jm}a_j r_{F_mU_j}) . \end{cases}$$

If the factors are uncorrelated,* this expression simplifies to

$$(2.7) \qquad 1 = \sigma_{z_j}^2 = a_{j1}^2 + a_{j2}^2 + \ldots + a_{jm}^2 + a_j^2 .$$

The terms on the right represent the portions of the unit variance of z_j ascribable to the respective factors. For example, a_{j2}^2 is the contribution of the factor F_2 to the variance of z_j. The total contribution of F_2 to the variances of all the variables is given by

$$a_{12}^2 + a_{22}^2 + a_{32}^2 + \ldots + a_{n2}^2 ,$$

and, in general, the *total contribution* of a factor F_t is defined to be $\displaystyle\sum_{j=1}^{n} a_{jt}^2$.

For any variable z_j the sum of the squares of the common-factor coefficients is known as its *communality* h_j^2. The last term in (2.7), which is the contribution of the unique factor, is called the *uniqueness* of z_j and indicates the extent to which the common factors fail to account for the total variance of the variable. The uniqueness of a variable may be separated into two portions due to the selection of the variables and their measurement. If additional variables are added to a given set, their correlations with the latter may make it necessary to postulate further common factors. For a

---

* The case of correlated factors is treated in Chap. XI.

fixed set of variables such potential linkages of any one of them with others can be expressed only as a portion of its uniqueness. This portion is termed the *specificity* of the variable. The remaining portion of the uniqueness may be ascribed to imperfections of measurement. The consistency with which a variable measures whatever it measures is called its *reliability*. The reliability of a variable may be expressed by the correlation of repeated measurements or of parallel forms of the variable. In either case, the two evaluations will be represented by z_j and z_J, and their correlation r_{jJ} will be called the reliability of the variable.

When the unique factors are conceived as decomposed into the two types, described above, the expression (2.4) for any variable may be written in the form

$$(2.8) \qquad z_j = a_{j1}F_1 + a_{j2}F_2 + \ldots + a_{jm}F_m + b_j S_j + c_j T_j$$
$$(j = 1, 2, \ldots, n).$$

Here S_j and T_j are the *specific* and *unreliable factors*, respectively, and b_j and c_j their coefficients. Now, if the variance of z_j is obtained in terms of the coefficients of (2.8) and compared with the expression (2.7), it is evident that

$$(2.9) \qquad\qquad\qquad a_j^2 = b_j^2 + c_j^2 \,.$$

From the preceding analysis it is apparent that the total unit variance of a variable may be resolved into three portions, attributable to common, specific, and unreliable factors. The first portion has been called the communality, while the last two portions of the variance of any variable have been named specificity and unreliability. On combining the specificity and unreliability, the uniqueness is obtained; or, again, the sum of the communality and specificity gives the reliability of a variable. A recapitulation of these ideas may be expressed in the following form:

$$(2.10) \quad \left\{ \begin{array}{ll} b_j^2 = \text{specificity}\,, & S_j = \text{specific factor}\,, \\[2mm] c_j^2 = \text{unreliability}\,, & T_j = \text{unreliable factor}\,, \\[2mm] h_j^2 = \displaystyle\sum_{s=1}^{m} a_{js}^2 = \text{communality}\,, & F_s = \text{common factor}\,, \\[2mm] a_j^2 = b_j^2 + c_j^2 = \text{uniqueness} = 1 - h_j^2\,, \\[2mm] h_j^2 + b_j^2 = \text{reliability} = 1 - c_j^2 = r_{jJ}\,. \end{array} \right.$$

By factorial methods the communality h_j^2 and the uniqueness a_j^2 of a set of variables are obtained. The uniqueness of each variable may be split into the specificity and unreliability, but this is independent of the factorial solution and follows such a solution. If the reliability r_{jJ} of a variable z_j is known (it may be obtained by experimental methods), then the unreliability may be obtained by means of the equation

$$(2.11) \qquad c_j^2 = 1 - r_{jJ} .$$

Then, of course, knowing the unreliability, the specificity is given by the "Pythagorean" relation (2.9), or

$$(2.12) \qquad b_j^2 = a_j^2 - c_j^2 ,$$

where the uniqueness a_j^2 is known from the factorial solution. From the last expression in (2.10) it follows that

$$(2.13) \qquad h_j^2 = r_{jJ} - b_j^2 \leqq r_{jJ} .$$

In other words, the communality of any variable is less than or equal to the reliability of the variable, and equals the reliability only when the specificity vanishes.

An *index of completeness of factorization* may then be expressed in the following form:

$$(2.14) \qquad H_j = \frac{100 h_j^2}{h_j^2 + b_j^2} = 100 \frac{\text{communality}}{\text{reliability}} .$$

This index shows the percentage of the reliability variance accounted for by the common factors. If it is desirable to find the total communality, $\sum_{j=1}^{n} h_j^2$, instead of the separate communalities for each variable, and also the total specificity, then the *complete index of factorization*, which is defined by

$$(2.15) \qquad H = \sum_{j=1}^{n} H_j ,$$

may be obtained. The index H plays the same role for the total set as H_j does for the individual variable z_j.

The index H_j is always less than 100 and approaches 100 only when the specificity b_j^2 vanishes. Any method of analysis for determining the coefficients a_{js} should not be carried to the point where no specificity is present when it is known that some specificity exists.

Some workers may not care to assume specific or even unreliable factors as indicated by (2.8). In this case the factors S_j and T_j are not postulated, and the number m of statistically significant common factors may be less than, or equal to, the number of variables n. In the opinion of the authors, however, the hypotheses of factors indicated by (2.8) appears most tenable even for variables which appear to describe a set of objects very completely and with great precision.

2.4. *Factor Patterns and Structures*

The factor problem will now be dealt with more generally, and for this purpose correlated factors will be postulated. The uncorrelated factors may then be considered as a special case of these. A set of equations of the form

$$
(2.16) \quad
\begin{cases}
z_1 = a_{11}F_1 + a_{12}F_2 + \ldots + a_{1m}F_m + a_1U_1 \\
z_2 = a_{21}F_1 + a_{22}F_2 + \ldots + a_{2m}F_m \qquad + a_2U_2 \\
\cdot \; \cdot \; \cdot \; \cdot \; \cdot \; \cdot \; \cdot \; \cdot \; \cdot \; \cdot \; \cdot \; \cdot \; \cdot \; \cdot \\
z_n = a_{n1}F_1 + a_{n2}F_2 + \ldots + a_{nm}F_m \qquad\qquad + a_nU_n ,
\end{cases}
$$

expressing n variables in terms of m common factors and n unique factors, will be defined as a *factor pattern*, or, more briefly, *pattern*. As indicated above, the common factors F_s ($s = 1, 2, \ldots, m$) may be correlated or uncorrelated, but the unique factors U_j ($j = 1, 2, \ldots, n$) are always assumed to be uncorrelated among themselves and with all common factors. In the linear description of a given variable any number of common factors $\mu(\mu \leq m)$ may be involved. This number is called the *complexity* of the variable.

Factor analysis yields not only patterns but also correlations between the variables and the factors. A set of such correlations will be defined as a *factor structure*, or merely a *structure*. Both a structure and a pattern are necessary in order to furnish a complete solution. The functional relationships between the elements of a structure and the coefficients of a pattern will now be shown.

Multiplying any one of equations (2.16) by the respective factors, summing over the number of observations N, and dividing by N, produces

$$
(2.17) \quad
\begin{cases}
r_{z_jF_1} = a_{j1} \qquad\quad + a_{j2}r_{F_1F_2} + \ldots + a_{js}r_{F_1F_s} + \ldots + a_{jm}r_{F_1F_m} , \\
r_{z_jF_2} = a_{j1}r_{F_2F_1} + a_{j2} \qquad\quad + \ldots + a_{js}r_{F_2F_s} + \ldots + a_{jm}r_{F_2F_m} , \\
\cdot \; \cdot \; \cdot \; \cdot \; \cdot \; \cdot \; \cdot \; \cdot \; \cdot \; \cdot \; \cdot \; \cdot \; \cdot \; \cdot \; \cdot \; \cdot \\
r_{z_jF_s} = a_{j1}r_{F_sF_1} + a_{j2}r_{F_sF_2} + \ldots + a_{js} \qquad\quad + \ldots + a_{jm}r_{F_sF_m} , \\
\cdot \; \cdot \; \cdot \; \cdot \; \cdot \; \cdot \; \cdot \; \cdot \; \cdot \; \cdot \; \cdot \; \cdot \; \cdot \; \cdot \; \cdot \; \cdot \\
r_{z_jF_m} = a_{j1}r_{F_mF_1} + a_{j2}r_{F_mF_2} + \ldots + a_{js}r_{F_mF_s} + \ldots + a_{jm} ,
\end{cases}
$$

and

$$(2.18) \quad r_{z_jU_j} = a_j .$$

Equation (2.18) shows that the elements $r_{z_jU_j}$ of a factor structure are the coefficients of the unique factors in the pattern. When no confusion can arise, the table of correlations of variables with common factors only, i.e., the table of $r_{z_jF_s}$, will be referred to as the factor structure. The matrix formulation of the relationship between a factor pattern and structure is given in Appendix **B.11**.

In a numerical problem equations (2.17) may be used to evaluate the correlations of the variables with the factors when the coefficients of the pattern and the intercorrelations of the factors are known. More frequently, however, these equations are used to obtain the values of the pattern coefficients when the correlations between variables and factors and the correlations between the factors themselves are known.

Formally the equations (2.17) may be considered as constituting n sets of m linear equations in the unknowns a_{js} ($j = 1, 2, \ldots, n$; $s = 1, 2, \ldots, m$), with the left-hand members as known quantities. It is then possible to solve* for the m coefficients a_{js} in each of the n sets, that is, for each value of j. Here it has been assumed that the elements of the factor structure and the correlations between factors are known, and so the coefficients of the factor pattern may be obtained. The result is

$$(2.19) \qquad a_{js} = \frac{A_{js}}{A},$$

where A is the determinant of coefficients of the a_{js} and A_{js} is the determinant obtained from A by replacing the elements of the sth column by the elements $r_{z_jF_1}, r_{z_jF_2}, \ldots, r_{z_jF_m}$. It has thus been shown that a pattern can be constructed from a known structure.

It is interesting to note† that the values a_{js} in the above solution turn out to be regression coefficients, so that equations (2.16) are in the form of regression equations with the errors of estimate included. These errors are represented by the unique factors. A plus-or-minus sign may be placed in front of the a_j because the unique-factor coefficients in a pattern are usually obtained, after all the other coefficients are known, in such a manner as to bring the variance of each variable up to unity. This procedure involves a square root and thus leads to the indeterminacy of sign.

Since the unique factors are of minor interest in factor analysis, it is convenient to write that portion of a factor pattern which involves only the common factors. For similar reasons, a table of coefficients of the common factors may be referred to as a factor pattern, when there is no ambiguity.

---

* Maxime Bocher, *Introduction to Higher Algebra*, 1935, p. 43. See also Appen. **G.1** for a simplified method of solving a set of simultaneous equations.

† See Appen. **B.2**.

From equations (2.17) it is apparent that the elements $r_{z_jF_s}$ of a structure are generally different from the coefficients a_{js} of a pattern. In case the common factors F_s are uncorrelated, that is, $r_{F_sF_t} = 0 (s \neq t)$, then equations (2.17) reduce to

$$(2.20) \qquad r_{z_jF_s} = a_{js} \qquad\qquad (j = 1, 2, \ldots, n; \; s = 1, 2, \ldots, m) \,.$$

Thus, only in the case of uncorrelated factors are the elements of a structure identical with the corresponding coefficients of a pattern. In an analysis involving uncorrelated factors, a complete solution is furnished merely by a factor pattern inasmuch as the correlations of the variables with the factors are given by the respective coefficients.

As already indicated, both structure and pattern should be produced in making a complete factor analysis. The structure reveals the correlations of variables and factors, which are useful for the identification of factors and for subsequent estimates of the latter. The pattern shows the linear composition of variables in terms of factors in the form of regression equations. It may also be used for reproducing the correlations between variables to determine the adequacy of the solution. In comparing different systems of factors for a given set of variables, patterns are again useful.

2.5. *Statistical Basis for Adequacy of Solution*

The manner in which a set of factors account for the intercorrelations in a set of variables will be considered next. The variables are assumed to be linearly composed of the factors as given by the pattern (2.16). Since the factors are assumed to be in standard form, the correlations between variables may then be reproduced from the factor pattern by the following procedure: multiply any equation (2.16) of a variable by the equation of another, sum over the number of individuals N, and divide by N. For any two variables z_j, z_k $(j, k = 1, 2, \ldots, n)$ their correlation may be written in the form*

$$(2.21) \quad \begin{cases} r'_{jk} = a_{j1}a_{k1} + a_{j2}a_{k2} + a_{j3}a_{k3} + \ldots + a_{jm}a_{km} \\ \qquad + (a_{j1}a_{k2} + a_{k1}a_{j2})r_{F_1F_2} + (a_{j1}a_{k3} + a_{k1}a_{j3})r_{F_1F_3} + \ldots \\ \qquad + (a_{j1}a_{km} + a_{k1}a_{jm})r_{F_1F_m} + (a_{j2}a_{k3} + a_{k2}a_{j3})r_{F_2F_3} + \ldots \\ \qquad + (a_{j2}a_{km} + a_{k2}a_{jm})r_{F_2F_m} + \ldots + a_{j1}a_k r_{F_1U_k} + a_{k1}a_j r_{F_1U_j} + \ldots \\ \qquad + a_{jm}a_k r_{F_mU_k} + a_{km}a_j r_{F_mU_j} + a_j a_k r_{U_jU_k} , \end{cases}$$

---

* Holzinger and Harman, "Relationships between Factors Obtained from Certain Analyses," *Journal of Educational Psychology*, 1937, p. 324.

where the *reproduced correlation* (computed from the pattern) is written r'_{jk} to distinguish it from the observed correlation r_{jk}. This distinction will be made throughout the text.

The unique factors have been assumed to be uncorrelated with the common factors and among themselves, hence $r_{F_s U_j} = r_{F_s U_k} = r_{U_j U_k} = 0$. If the common factors are uncorrelated, equation (2.21) simplifies still further. The correlations $r_{F_s F_t}$ $(s \neq t; s, t = 1, 2, \ldots, m)$ are then zero, and everything below the first line of the equation vanishes. For the case of uncorrelated common factors, any correlation is thus reproduced from the factor pattern by an equation of the following form:

$$(2.22) \qquad r'_{jk} = a_{j1}a_{k1} + a_{j2}a_{k2} + \ldots + a_{jm}a_{km}$$
$$(j \neq k; j, k = 1, 2, \ldots, n) .$$

This expression is merely the sum of the products of corresponding pattern coefficients of the two variables correlated.

Equation (2.22) may be represented, perhaps more simply, by use of matrix notation.* Let the matrix of coefficients of the common factors of the pattern be represented by $\mathbf{A}$, that is,

$$(2.23) \qquad \mathbf{A} = \begin{Vmatrix} a_{11} & a_{12} & a_{13} & \cdots & a_{1m} \\ a_{21} & a_{22} & a_{23} & \cdots & a_{2m} \\ \cdot & \cdot & \cdot & \cdots & \cdot \\ a_{j1} & a_{j2} & a_{j3} & \cdots & a_{jm} \\ \cdot & \cdot & \cdot & \cdots & \cdot \\ a_{n1} & a_{n2} & a_{n3} & \cdots & a_{nm} \end{Vmatrix} ,$$

which will be referred to as the *pattern matrix*. Then the product of $\mathbf{A}$ by its transpose $\mathbf{A}'$, i.e., the matrix obtained from $\mathbf{A}$ by interchanging its rows and columns, is the matrix of reproduced correlations $\mathbf{R}^\dagger$. This result may be put in the form†

$$(2.24) \qquad \mathbf{R}^\dagger = \mathbf{A}\mathbf{A}' ,$$

* For an elementary account of the theory of matrices which is essential for the present text see Appen. A.

† Equation (2.24) has been called "the fundamental factor theorem" by L. L. Thurstone (*Vectors of Mind*, 1935, Chap. II). In the case of correlated factors, which will be treated in Chap. XI, the expression corresponding to (2.24) is

$$\mathbf{R}^\dagger = \mathbf{A}\boldsymbol{\phi}\mathbf{A}' ,$$

where $\boldsymbol{\phi}$ is the matrix of the intercorrelations of the common factors. This relation was first presented, in expanded form, by Holzinger and Harman, *op. cit.* More recently, it was formulated in matrix notation by Tucker, "The Role of Correlated Factors in Factor Analysis," *Psychometrika*, 1940.

or, writing the matrices in detail, as follows:

$$\left\| \begin{array}{cccccc} h_1^2 & r_{12}' & \cdots & r_{1j}' & \cdots & r_{1n}' \\ r_{21}' & h_2^2 & \cdots & r_{2j}' & \cdots & r_{2n}' \\ \cdot & \cdot & \cdots & \cdot & \cdots & \cdot \\ r_{j1}' & r_{j2}' & \cdots & h_j^2 & \cdots & r_{jn}' \\ \cdot & \cdot & \cdots & \cdot & \cdots & \cdot \\ r_{n1}' & r_{n2}' & \cdots & r_{nj}' & \cdots & h_n^2 \end{array} \right\|$$

$$\|$$

$$\mathbf{R}^\dagger$$

$$= \left\| \begin{array}{cccc} a_{11} & a_{12} & \cdots & a_{1m} \\ a_{21} & a_{22} & \cdots & a_{2m} \\ \cdot & \cdot & \cdots & \cdot \\ a_{j1} & a_{j2} & \cdots & a_{jm} \\ \cdot & \cdot & \cdots & \cdot \\ a_{n1} & a_{n2} & \cdots & a_{nm} \end{array} \right\| \cdot \left\| \begin{array}{cccccc} a_{11} & a_{21} & \cdots & a_{j1} & \cdots & a_{n1} \\ a_{12} & a_{22} & \cdots & a_{j2} & \cdots & a_{n2} \\ \cdot & \cdot & \cdots & \cdot & \cdots & \cdot \\ a_{1m} & a_{2m} & \cdots & a_{jm} & \cdots & a_{nm} \end{array} \right\|$$

$$\|$$

$$= \quad\quad \mathbf{A} \quad\quad \cdot \quad\quad \mathbf{A}'.$$

The correlations (2.22) are merely elements in the matrix $\mathbf{R}^\dagger$. The diagonal elements h_j^2 $(j = 1, 2, \ldots, n)$ are the communalities of the respective variables and may also be obtained by setting $j = k$ in equation (2.22). It may be noted from (2.21) that the algebraic signs of all the entries in any column of a pattern matrix $\mathbf{A}$ may be reversed without affecting the reproduced correlations.

Evidently the factor problem is concerned with the correlations of a set of variables. These correlations are reproduced, when a pattern of the form (2.16) is assumed, by means of the coefficients of the common factors. The diagonal elements of $\mathbf{R}^\dagger$ should also be reproduced from this portion of the factor pattern. Thus if, in a matrix of observed correlations, numbers approximating the communalities are put in the diagonal, the factor solution will be of the form (2.16) and the observed data (including the diagonal entries) will be closely reproduced by equation (2.24). On the other hand, if unity is in each diagonal cell of the observed correlation matrix, the factor solution necessarily would involve only common factors in order that equation (2.24) may reproduce ones in the diagonal. In this case there is obviously no allowance made for unique factors. If other values between the communalities and unity (such as reliabilities) are employed, then the form of solution would involve common and unreliability factors, but the specificity would be included in the common-factor variance. From these considerations it is clear that the values put in the diagonal of the observed correlation matrix determine what portions of the unit variances are being factored.

The general problem of relating the reproduced to the observed correlations, regardless of the diagonal entries, will be considered next. The correlations reproduced by the factor pattern, as given most generally in (2.21) or for the case of uncorrelated factors in matrix $\mathbf{R}^\dagger$, should not agree exactly with the observed correlations because allowance must be made for sampling and experimental errors. It is a commonly accepted scientific principle that a theoretical law should be simpler than the observed data upon which it is based, and hence discrepancies between the law and the data are to be expected. In the case of factor analysis, functions (the correlations r'_{jk}) of the assumed linear composition of variables should be expected to vary somewhat from the observed values.

After a factor pattern has been obtained, its adequacy as a description of the intercorrelations of the variables is determined by "removing the factors." This is done by forming the correlations from the pattern as given by equation (2.21). These values are then subtracted from the corresponding observed correlations, and the resulting differences are known as *residual correlations*. Such residuals are defined by the following formula:

$$(2.25) \qquad\qquad \bar{r}_{jk} = r_{jk} - r'_{jk} ,$$

where r_{jk} is the observed correlation and r'_{jk} is the correlation reproduced from the pattern.

In case the common factors are uncorrelated, it has been shown that the lengthy expression (2.21) for reproducing the correlations reduces to the simple form (2.22). The residuals then reduce to the form

$$(2.26) \qquad \bar{r}_{jk} = r_{jk} - (a_{j1}a_{k1} + a_{j2}a_{k2} + \ldots + a_{jm}a_{km}) .$$

The question then arises as to how nearly the correlations reproduced from a factor pattern should fit the observed ones.* The agreement may

---

* Up to the present time a good standard for "when to stop factoring" has not been developed. This problem is discussed in Chaps. VI, VII, and VIII.

be judged by the size and distribution of the residuals $\bar{r}_{jk}$. The magnitude of the residuals should, of course, be approximately zero. When all common factors have been removed in forming the residuals, then no further linkages between variables exist. It might, therefore, be expected that the distribution of residuals would be similar to that of a zero correlation in a sample of equal size. The standard error of such a zero correlation is given by the formula

$$\sigma_{r=0} = \frac{1}{\sqrt{N-1}},$$

or, since N is usually large,

(2.27) $$\sigma_{r=0} = \frac{1}{\sqrt{N}}.$$

A standard for judging adequacy of fit then may be taken to be

(2.28) $$\sigma_{\bar{r}} \leqq \frac{1}{\sqrt{N}},$$

where $\sigma_{\bar{r}}$ is the standard deviation of the series of residuals. This standard is a tentative one since it depends only on the size of the sample, whereas experiments have shown that the size of residuals depends also on other characteristics, especially the number of variables. More exact sampling error formulas will be developed in Chapter VI.

On the basis of the size of the sample alone, the following conclusions from the criterion (2.28) may be drawn. If $\sigma_{\bar{r}}$ is appreciably greater than $1/\sqrt{N}$, it may be concluded that there are further significant linkages between variables, and a modification of the form of solution is required. In case $\sigma_{\bar{r}}$ is considerably less than $1/\sqrt{N}$, it would appear that unjustified linkages between variables have been included in the solution. When the standard deviation of the residuals is just below that of a zero correlation, the solution may be regarded as acceptable in the light of the above standard. A standard equivalent to (2.28) has been given by Kelley,[*] and substantially the same basis for judging the adequacy of fit of a factor solution has also been given by Thurstone.[†]

---

[*] Truman L. Kelley, *Essential Traits of Mental Life*, 1935, p. 12, formula (7).

[†] *Op. cit.*, p. 147.

2.6. *Indeterminacy of Solution*

In any scientific field the observed phenomena can be described in a great variety of ways which are mutually consistent. The choice of a particular interpretation must then depend upon its utility. This arbitrariness or indeterminacy of description has been recently emphasized by F. R. Moulton in comparing various approaches to the measurement of the velocity of light. In conclusion he says:

All this illustrates Poincaré's thesis that every set of phenomena can be interpreted consistently in various ways, in fact, in infinitely many ways. It is our privilege to choose among the possible interpretations the ones that appear to us most satisfactory, whatever may be the reasons for our choice. If scientists would remember that various equally consistent interpretations of every set of observational data can be made, they would be much less dogmatic than they often are, and their beliefs in a possible ultimate finality of scientific theories would vanish.*

The basic phenomena for factor analysis are the correlations of a set of variables. An explanation of these correlations can be made in the form of a factor solution in an infinite number of ways.† This indeterminacy is exhibited by the fact that various systems of factors may be selected, yielding solutions which reproduce the observed correlations equally well. In order to remove this indeterminacy, certain statistical criteria may be introduced. A number of such standards are given in Chapter V which lead to a few types of preferred factor solutions.

2.7. *B-Coefficients*

One of the fundamental problems in factor analysis is the selection of the descriptive variables. These should be chosen so as to measure the aspects of the group which are significant for a particular problem, i.e., the set of variables should be valid as a whole. This criterion implies that generally the intercorrelations will be positive throughout, or else can be put in this form (see **5.7**). The variables should also be selected in such a way as to make possible the identification of the underlying factors. For this purpose it is necessary to choose at least three or four variables of a kind which appear to measure the same factor. The variables in each group of this type should not be mere parallel forms but should be distinct in content. This *hypothetical design* of the variables is tested by the factor analysis, which

---

* "The Velocity of Light," *Scientific Monthly*, 1939, p. 484.

† For proof see Appen. **B.3**. It is shown there that this indeterminacy corresponds to the infinite number of rotations from one system of reference axes to another.

gives evidence for retaining or rejecting the original groupings of the variables.

In actual practice the above groupings are usually based on previous research in which some of the factors have already been identified. The design can then be extended to include other groups of variables used to identify additional factors. In some cases it may be desirable to take a portion of a previous design and add new variables to obtain more refined measures of the factors already identified. The success of the factorial analysis depends in a large measure on the skill with which the variables in such groups have been selected.

If no design can be predetermined when the set of variables is compiled and the matrix of correlations obtained, the grouping of the variables may be indicated by an objective procedure. This method is based on the assumption that the variables of a group identifying a factor should have higher intercorrelations than with other variables in the set. To this end, the *B-coefficient*, or *coefficient of belonging*, may be employed. This coefficient is defined as *100 times the ratio of the average of the intercorrelations of a subset or group of variables to their average correlation with all remaining variables.* The group of variables for which B is computed is referred to as the "argument of B," while the remaining group of variables is called the "complementary subset." The number of variables in the argument of B increases, beginning with two, at successive stages, and the value of the B-coefficient at each stage may vary accordingly. It is evident that the value of B for a given group of variables is independent of the order in which the variables are involved in the argument of B. On the other hand, the time when a particular variable enters into the argument of B is relevant to the value of B. For example, the B-coefficient of z_1, z_3, z_4, which is written $B(z_1, z_3, z_4)$, or, more briefly, $B(1, 3, 4)$, has the same value no matter what order the three variables assume. The value of B may differ, however, depending on the sequence in which another variable, say z_2, is added. For concreteness, the value of $B(1, 3, 2)$ is usually different from $B(1, 3, 4, 2)$.

To define the B-coefficient more rigorously and thus obtain a formula for its computation, the following notation will be employed:

(2.29)

n = total number of variables in a set,

u = the subset of variables in the argument of B,

p = number of variables in the subset u,

j, k = indices ranging over u,

cu = the complementary subset of variables, that is, those variables of the original set which are not in u,

a = index ranging over cu,

$S = \sum\limits_{j<k} r_{jk}$ = sum* of intercorrelations of variables in the subset u,

$T = \sum\limits_{j, a} r_{ja}$ = sum† of correlations of variables in u with those in cu,

$\binom{p}{2} = \dfrac{p(p-1)}{2}$ = number of combination of p elements taken two at a time;‡ here, the number of correlations involved in the sum S,

$p(n-p)$ = number of correlations involved in the sum T.

* The symbol $\sum\limits_{j<k} r_{jk}$ means the sum of all the correlations r_{jk} for the specified range of j and k under the condition that j is always less than k. In the present section the summation extends over all the $p(p-1)/2$ combinations $j < k$ of the p numbers taken two at a time. An illustration of such a sum in evaluating $B(1, 2, 3, 4)$ may be written fully as follows:

$$S = \sum\limits_{j<k} r_{jk} = r_{12} + r_{13} + r_{14} + r_{23} + r_{24} + r_{34} .$$

† An example of a sum T for a total set of 6 variables in the evaluation of $B(1, 2, 3, 4)$ follows:

$$T = \sum\limits_{j, a} r_{ja} = r_{15} + r_{16} + r_{25} + r_{26} + r_{35} + r_{36} + r_{45} + r_{46} .$$

In this example, $n = 6$, $u = (1, 2, 3, 4)$, $p = 4$, j, k range over 1, 2, 3, 4, $cu = (5, 6)$, and a ranges over 5, 6.

‡ The symbol $\binom{n}{r}$ is used throughout the text in place of the conventional C_r^n to designate the number of combinations of n things taken r at a time.

The B-coefficient of the subset of variables u is then defined by

$$(2.30) \qquad B(u) = 100 \frac{\left(\dfrac{\binom{S}{p}}{2}\right)}{\left(\dfrac{T}{p(n-p)}\right)} = \frac{200(n-p)S}{(p-1)T} .$$

For purposes of computation of B-coefficients it is perhaps more convenient to write the formula for T in another form. Since the sums of the correlations of the respective variables with all others are usually obtained at the outset of any analysis, they may be used in the evaluation of T for any B-coefficient. Thus,

$$(2.31) \qquad T = \sum_{j,a} r_{ja} = \sum_{j \neq e} r_{je} - 2 \sum_{j<k} r_{jk} = \sum_{j \neq e} r_{je} - 2S ,$$

where the index e ranges over the entire set of variables.* The symbol $\sum_{j \neq e} r_{je}$ stands for the sum of the correlations of the variables in u with all other variables. Then to obtain T it is necessary to subtract twice the intercorrelations of the variables in u.

Another aid in the computation of the B-coefficients is the sum of the correlations of the last variable added to the group with the preceding ones. Letting l denote the last variable added to the group, the proposed sum may be written

$$(2.32) \qquad L = \sum_{j \neq l} r_{jl} ,$$

where the summation extends over the variables in the subset u. If a subscript p is appended to the sums L, S, and T to designate their values for

---

* An illustration of formula (2.31) for the example of the last footnote follows:

$$T = \sum_{j \neq e} r_{je} - 2 \sum_{j<k} r_{jk} ,$$

$$= (r_{12} + r_{13} + r_{14} + r_{15} + r_{16}) + (r_{21} + r_{23} + r_{24} + r_{25} + r_{26})$$
$$+ (r_{31} + r_{32} + r_{34} + r_{35} + r_{36}) + (r_{41} + r_{42} + r_{43} + r_{45} + r_{46})$$
$$-2(r_{12} + r_{13} + r_{14} + r_{23} + r_{24} + r_{34}) ,$$

$$= r_{15} + r_{16} + r_{25} + r_{26} + r_{35} + r_{36} + r_{45} + r_{46} .$$

Although this formula for T seems to be more complex than that given in (2.29), its application to actual data is more effective than the latter.

p variables in the argument of B, then successive values of S and T may be obtained by means of the following recurrence formulas:

$$(2.33) \qquad S_p = S_{p-1} + L_p$$

and

$$(2.34) \qquad T_p = T_{p-1} + \sum_{e \neq l} r_{el} - 2L_p,$$

where $\displaystyle\sum_{e \neq l} r_{el}$ is the sum of the correlations of l with all the other variables in the set.

The value $B(u) = 100$ indicates that the variables of the subset u have the same average intercorrelation as their average correlation with all remaining variables. Such variables would not be regarded as "belonging together," since they belong just as much with the other variables of the total set. As a tentative standard of belonging together, the B-coefficient of a group of variables should be at least 130.

The B-coefficients are used to sort the variables on the basis of their intercorrelations. The grouping is begun by selecting the two variables which have the highest correlation. To these is added the variable for which the sum of the correlations with the preceding is highest. This process is continued, always adding a variable which correlates highest with those already in the argument of B, until a sharp drop appears in the value of B. When this occurs, the last variable added is withdrawn from the group. Another variable may be inserted in its place, but, if the drop in B is still large, it should be withdrawn. Thus a group of variables that belong together is determined. Then, excluding the variables that have already been assigned to such a group, the two others which have the highest remaining correlation are selected to start another group. To these variables are added others, exclusive of those that have already been assigned to groups, until a significant drop appears in B, at which stage another group is formed. It is desirable to start each new group with a B-coefficient as large as possible so as to have clearly defined groups. For this purpose it may be necessary to obtain the B-coefficients for more than one pair of variables without completing the groups. The pair yielding the highest B value may then be used to introduce the next group. This process is continued until all variables have been assigned to groups or else do not fit into any group.

At the present time no sampling error formula is available by which to judge the significance of the difference between two successive values of B. One basis is to use all possible knowledge about the variables. It is a sound scientific principle to use all the facts about the data of an experiment. The original hypothesis about the nature of the set of variables may thus aid in deciding whether a drop in B is "significantly" large. More objectively, some properties of the B-coefficient will now be presented.

Since the B-coefficient is the ratio of two averages, its properties may be studied by means of them. The average of the intercorrelations of the variables u (the numerator of B) tends to decrease as the number of variables in B increases, since the variables are added on the basis of highest correlation with those already in the argument of B. Similarly, the average of the correlations of the variables u with those in cu (the denominator of B) tends to decrease with an increase in p. The decrease in the numerator is relatively greater, however, than that in the denominator.

To the numerator, which usually consists of a small number of correlations, are added a few additional correlations which are lower in value than the others and thus steadily decrease its value. On the other hand, from the large number of correlations in the denominator a small number of the larger values is taken away. The value of the denominator is decreased, but not so noticeably as that of the numerator. Thus the B-coefficient decreases, in general, as more variables are added to its argument.

An exception to this may occur with the addition of a variable to the subset u which has relatively high correlations with the preceding variables but a low sum of correlations with those in cu. In this case the decrease in the numerator is relatively smaller than that in the denominator, and B increases. Similar reasoning accounts for the fact that a variable can be rejected from a group because of a large drop in the value of B and then appear in the group later, after several others have been added to the subset u.

As the number of variables in the argument of B increases, the decreases in the above averages become less and these averages tend toward stability. A consequence of this is that an actual difference between two successive B values has a greater relative significance as the number of variables p increases.

It is convenient to refer to the variables which are found to belong together by the B-coefficients as constituting a *group* G_s $(s = 1, 2, \ldots, m)$. The serial numbers s may be assigned in order to the groups of variables which best measure the respective factors (other than a general factor). Thus, the variables at the head of the set that are found to belong together may be given the group number 1 and be said to belong to G_1. The factor which is predominantly measured by this group of variables may be symbolized by F_1. Similarly for the other groups of variables, the final subset forms the group G_m, and the factor it measures is denoted F_m. If a solution involves a general factor F_0, the variables which measure it (i.e., all the variables) may be referred to as constituting a group G_0.

2.8. *Illustrative Example*

In order to illustrate and clarify factorial methods, a numerical example is given here. This example is employed throughout the text whenever possible. Various factor solutions will be obtained for the same data, and comparisons made of different systems of factors.

TABLE 2.1

MEANS, STANDARD DEVIATIONS, AND
RELIABILITY COEFFICIENTS

Test j	Mean M_j	Standard Deviation σ_j	Reliability Coefficient r_{jJ}
1.........	29.60	6.90	.756
2.........	24.84	4.50	.568
3.........	15.65	3.07	.544
4.........	36.31	8.38	.922
5.........	44.92	11.75	.808
6.........	9.95	3.36	.651
7.........	18.79	4.63	.754
8.........	28.18	5.34	.680
9.........	17.24	7.89	.870
10.........	90.16	23.60	.952
11.........	68.41	16.84	.712
12.........	109.83	21.04	.937
13.........	191.81	37.03	.889
14.........	176.14	10.72	.648
15.........	89.45	7.57	.507
16.........	103.43	6.74	.600
17.........	7.15	4.57	.725
18.........	9.44	4.49	.610
19.........	15.24	3.58	.569
20.........	30.38	19.76	.649
21.........	14.46	4.82	.784
22.........	27.73	9.77	.787
23.........	18.82	9.35	.931
24.........	25.83	4.70	.836

The data employed for this purpose include a set of twenty-four psychological variables (or tests), described briefly in Appendix **B.1.** In Table 2.1 the means, standard deviations, and reliability coefficients are presented. These statistics are essential for the factorial methods that are treated.

The intercorrelations of these variables, which form the basic data for subsequent analyses, are presented in Table 2.2. The complete set of correlations could be presented in the form of a symmetric matrix with the elements in the principal diagonal omitted. Obviously only half of this matrix is necessary for its complete description, and it is therefore presented in this form for simplicity. The correlations for any variable j are located by reading across the row j to the diagonal and then down the column j. Then

TABLE 2.2

Intercorrelations of Twenty-four Variables

Test j	1	2	3	4	5	6	7	8	9	10	11	12	13	14	15	16	17	18	19	20	21	22	23	24
1																								
2	.318																							
3	.403	.317																						
4	.468	.230	.305																					
5	.321	.285	.247	.227																				
6	.335	.234	.268	.327	.622																			
7	.304	.157	.223	.335	.656	.722																		
8	.332	.157	.382	.391	.578	.527	.619																	
9	.326	.195	.184	.325	.723	.714	.685	.532																
10	.116	.057	.075	.099	.311	.203	.246	.285	.170															
11	.308	.150	—	.110	.344	.353	.232	.300	.280	.484														
12	.314	.145	.140	.160	.215	.095	.181	.271	.113	.585	.428													
13	.489	.239	.321	.327	.344	.309	.345	.395	.280	.408	.535	.512												
14	.125	.103	.177	.066	.280	.292	.236	.252	.260	.172	.350	.131	.195											
15	.238	.131	.065	.127	.229	.251	.172	.175	.248	.154	.314	.173	.139	.370										
16	.414	.272	.263	.322	.187	.291	.180	.296	.242	.124	.362	.119	.281	.412	.325									
17	.176	.005	.177	.187	.208	.273	.228	.255	.274	.289	.350	.278	.194	.341	.345	.324								
18	.368	.255	.211	.251	.263	.167	.159	.250	.208	.317	.350	.349	.323	.201	.334	.344	.448							
19	.270	.112	.312	.137	.190	.251	.226	.274	.274	.190	.290	.110	.263	.206	.192	.258	.324	.358						
20	.365	.292	.297	.339	.398	.435	.451	.427	.446	.173	.202	.246	.241	.302	.272	.388	.262	.301	.167					
21	.369	.306	.165	.349	.318	.263	.314	.362	.266	.405	.399	.335	.425	.183	.232	.348	.273	.357	.331	.413				
22	.413	.232	.250	.380	.435	.386	.396	.357	.483	.160	.304	.193	.279	.243	.246	.283	.273	.317	.342	.463	.374			
23	.474	.348	.383	.335	.435	.431	.405	.501	.504	.262	.251	.350	.382	.242	.256	.360	.287	.272	.303	.509	.451	.503		
24	.282	.211	.203	.248	.420	.433	.437	.388	.424	.531	.412	.414	.358	.304	.165	.262	.326	.405	.374	.366	.448	.375	.434	
$\sum r_{je}$ (e≠j)	7.528	4.751	5.309	6.045	8.242	8.182	7.909	8.306	8.156	5.666	7.089	5.877	7.584	5.443	5.079	6.609	6.009	6.808	5.754	7.755	7.606	7.693	8.678	8.220

the sum of the twenty-three correlations of a variable j with all the others is given by the total of the entries in the row and column for test z_j. This sum is represented by $\sum_{e \neq j} r_{je}$, where j is fixed and e ranges over the twenty-four variables under the restriction $e \neq j$. The sum of the correlations for each variable with all others is also given in Table 2.2.

2.9. Application of B-Coefficients

To illustrate the method of grouping variables outlined in **2.7**, the example of **2.8** will be employed. The analysis into groups is begun by selecting the two tests—5 and 9—which have the highest correlation, namely, $r_{59} = .723$. The value of $B(5, 9)$ is computed by means of formula (2.30) in Table 2.3. The tests u, comprising the argument of B, are for this case z_5 and z_9, and their correlation appears as the value of L and S, since there is only this one correlation in each of the sums. The value T is given by

$$T = \Sigma r_{5e} + \Sigma r_{9e} - 2r_{59} = 8.242 + 8.156 - 2(.723) = 14.952 \,,$$

where the sums of the correlations are taken from Table 2.2. Then the value of the B-coefficient is

$$B(5, 9) = \frac{200(n - p)S}{(p - 1)T} = \frac{4400(.723)}{14.952} = 213 \,.$$

The form of computation indicated by Table 2.3 will be found very convenient for machine calculation. In addition, the use of the sum L, defined in (2.32), and the recurrence formulas (2.33) and (2.34) will greatly facilitate the calculation of successive B values.

To illustrate the use of these formulas, the value B (17, 18, 19, 15, 16) will be calculated, showing all details. Here, $p = 5$, and the last variable added, l, is 16. From definition (2.32)

$$L = L_5 = \sum_{j \neq 16} r_{j,16} = r_{17,16} + r_{18,16} + r_{19,16} + r_{15,16} = 1.251 \,,$$

the individual correlations being given in Table 2.2. The sum S, or S_5, may be obtained from the value S_4 by means of equation (2.33) as follows:

$$S = S_5 = S_4 + L_5 = 2.001 + 1.251 = 3.252 \,.$$

It should be noted that there are two S_4 values but that one has been rejected as indicated by note (10). The next entry is merely

$$200(n - p) = 200(24 - 5) = 3,800 \,.$$

TABLE 2.3

CALCULATION OF B-COEFFICIENTS

u	p	L	S	$200(n-p)$	T	$(p-1)T$	$B(u)=\dfrac{200(n-p)S}{(p-1)T}$	Notes
(5, 9)...............	2	.723	.723	4400	14.952	14.952	213	.....
(5, 9, 7)............	3	1.341	2.064	4200	20.179	40.358	215	.....
(5, 9, 7, 6)..........	4	2.058	4.122	4000	24.245	72.735	227	.....
(5, 9, 7, 6, 8)........	5	2.256	6.378	3800	28.039	112.156	216	.....
(5, 9, 7, 6, 8, 23).....	6	2.276	8.654	3600	32.165	160.825	194	(1)
(10, 12).............	2	.585	.585	4400	10.373	10.373	248	.....
(10, 12, 13).........	3	.920	1.505	4200	16.117	32.234	196	(2)
(10, 12, 11).........	3	.912	1.497	4200	15.638	31.276	201	(3)
(10, 12, 11, 13).......	4	1.455	2.952	4000	20.312	60.936	194	(4)
(10, 12, 11, 13, 24)....	5	1.715	4.667	3800	25.102	100.408	177	(5)
(10, 12, 11, 13, 21)....	5	1.584	4.536	3800	24.750	99.000	174	(6)
(20, 23).............	2	.509	.509	4400	15.415	15.415	145	(7)
(1, 4)...............	2	.468	.468	4400	12.637	12.637	163	(8)
(1, 4, 3)............	3	.708	1.176	4200	16.530	33.060	149	.....
(1, 4, 3, 2)..........	4	.865	2.041	4000	19.551	58.653	139	.....
(1, 4, 3, 2, 21).......	5	1.189	3.230	3800	24.779	99.116	124	(9)
(17, 18).............	2	.448	.448	4400	11.921	11.921	165	.....
(17, 18, 19).........	3	.682	1.130	4200	16.311	32.622	145	.....
(17, 18, 19, 16).......	4	.926	2.056	4000	21.068	63.204	130	(10)
(17, 18, 19, 15).......	4	.871	2.001	4000	19.648	58.944	136	.....
(17, 18, 19, 15, 16)....	5	1.251	3.252	3800	23.755	95.020	130	.....
(17, 18, 19, 15, 16, 14).	6	1.530	4.782	3600	26.138	130.690	132	.....
(17, 18, 19, 15, 16, 14, 24)...............	7	1.836	6.618	3400	30.686	184.116	122	(11)
(17, 18, 19, 15, 16, 14, 22)...............	7	1.704	6.486	3400	30.423	182.538	121	(12)
(20, 23).............	2	.509	.509	4400	15.415	15.415	145	.....
(20, 23, 22)..........	3	.966	1.475	4200	21.176	42.352	146	.....
(20, 23, 22, 21).......	4	1.238	2.713	4000	26.306	78.918	138	.....
(20, 23, 22, 21, 24)....	5	1.623	4.336	3800	31.280	125.120	132	.....
(20, 23, 22, 21, 24, 18).	6	1.652	5.988	3600	34.784	173.920	124	(13)
(20, 23, 22, 21, 24, 16).	6	1.641	5.977	3600	34.607	173.035	124	(13)

NOTES ON TABLE 2.3

(1) Test 23 is rejected because of 22 points' drop in B for $p=6$.

(2) Test 13 is rejected because 52 points' drop in B seems to be too great even for $p=3$.

(3) Test 11 is retained although it causes a drop of 47 points in B. The drop in B is not so significant when $p=3$ as it is when p is larger. Furthermore, Test 11 is of the same general nature as Tests 10 and 12.

(4) Test 13 is retained, although it was previously rejected from the group. After Test 11 was put in the group, Test 13 seemed to belong together with the others, causing a drop of only 7 points in the value of B for $p=4$.

(5) Test 24 is rejected because of 17 points' drop in B for $p=5$.

(6) Test 21 is rejected because of 20 points' drop in B for $p=5$.

(7) Before continuing with the group which starts with Tests 20 and 23, another pair of tests will be tried to see if they yield a value of B greater than 145.

(8) Tests 1 and 4, although having a lower correlation than the pair 20 and 23, produce a higher value of the B-coefficient. Hence the next group is started with Tests 1 and 4.

(9) Test 21 is rejected because of 15 points' drop in B for $p=5$ and seemingly different nature of Test 21 from Tests 1, 2, 3, and 4.

(10) Test 16 is rejected because of 15 points' drop in B to see if some other test will cause a smaller drop in B. If some other test cannot be found which causes a smaller drop in B, then Test 16 will be retained in the group at this stage because a drop of 15 points for $p=4$ does not seem to be definitely significant.

(11) Test 24 is rejected because of 10 points' drop in B for $p=7$.

(12) Test 22 is rejected because of 11 points' drop in B for $p=7$.

(13) Tests 18 and 16, although they had previously been allocated to another group, are put into the argument of B along with 20, 21, 22, 23, 24 to see if the latter group of tests must be extended to other tests in the battery. The drop in B in each case, along with the seemingly different nature of Tests 18 and 16, seems to warrant their rejection from this group.

The sum T, or T_5, is given by formula (2.34) in terms of the preceding value T_4, which is in the row (17, 18, 19, 15) for $p = 4$, not in the row (17, 18, 19, 16). Its value is

$$T = T_5 = T_4 + \sum_{e \neq 16} r_{e,16} - 2L_5 = 19.648 + 6.609 - 2(1.251) = 23.755 \,,$$

where the sum of the correlations of Test 16 with all other tests is taken from Table 2.2. Then

$$(p - 1)T = 4(23.755) = 95.020 \,,$$

and

$$B(17, 18, 19, 15, 16) = \frac{200(n - p)S}{(p - 1)T} = \frac{3800(3.252)}{95.020} = 130 \,.$$

Following the procedure outlined in **2.7**, all the variables are grouped by means of B-coefficients. The groups G_s ($s = 1, 2, 3, 4, 5$), as determined in Table 2.3, may be defined by

(2.35)
$$\begin{cases} G_1 = (1, 2, 3, 4) \,, \\ G_2 = (5, 6, 7, 8, 9) \,, \\ G_3 = (10, 11, 12, 13) \,, \\ G_4 = (14, 15, 16, 17, 18, 19) \,, \\ G_5 = (20, 21, 22, 23, 24) \,. \end{cases}$$

The grouping by B-coefficients adheres to the original design of this set of tests because most of these tests had been used in factor experiments before and because the abilities they measured were quite well known. This may not be true in general. In a number of published studies the B-coefficients and the succeeding factor solutions failed to verify some postulated factors.*

2.10. *Correlations of Sums*

It is often convenient for subsequent analysis (e.g., Chaps. XI and XII) to consider a series of variables combined to form a single variable. Such new *composite variables* may then be put in standard form, and the correlation between two such variables obtained.† Thus it may be useful to combine the respective series of variables of each group G_s ($s = 1, 2, \ldots, m$), so that in place of the original n variables there will be only m composites.

The reduction to composite variables and the intercorrelations between such derived variables may be done in the following manner. Consider two series—$z_1, z_2, \ldots, z_q$ and $z_I, z_{II}, \ldots, z_Q$—consisting of q and Q variables, respectively.‡ Each variable involves N values and is in standard form, i.e., has zero mean and unit standard deviation. Let the sums of these series of variables be denoted by the following composite variables:

$$(2.36) \qquad \begin{cases} v = z_1 + z_2 + \ldots + z_q, \\ w = z_I + z_{II} + \ldots + z_Q, \end{cases}$$

the values of which are obtained by substituting the corresponding values of the observed variables on the right. It is apparent that these new variables are also measured from their means as origin. Since different letters

---

* An example of this appeared in the factor solution obtained by Holzinger and Harman, "Comparison of Two Factorial Analyses," *Psychometrika*, 1938, pp. 45–60. In preparing the test battery, Professor Thurstone had postulated that "verbal reasoning, numerical reasoning, and space reasoning would be separate factors and that these would be different from verbal abstraction and visual imagery" (see L. L. Thurstone, "The Perceptual Factor," *Psychometrika*, 1938, p. 11). Both his and the authors' factor solutions cut across these predetermined groupings that had guided the test construction and revealed some different factors.

† Charles Spearman, "Correlations of Sums and Differences," *British Journal of Psychology*, 1913, pp. 417–26.

‡ The variables $z_I, z_{II}, \ldots, z_Q$ should not be interpreted as denoting parallel forms of some others. The roman subscripts are used here merely as a convenient way of designating a second series of variables, distinct from the series $z_1, z_2, \ldots, z_q$.

are used to denote the two composite variables, no subscripts are necessary to distinguish them, and a single subscript is sufficient to represent the individual values of these variables. Thus,

(2.37)
$$\begin{cases} v_i = z_{1i} + z_{2i} + \ldots + z_{qi} \\ w_i = z_{Ii} + z_{IIi} + \ldots + z_{Qi} \end{cases}$$

give the N values of the composite variables.

The correlation between the composite variables is given by

(2.38)
$$r_{vw} = \frac{\Sigma v_i w_i}{N \sigma_v \sigma_w} .$$

To obtain an expression for r_{vw} involving the correlations between the original variables, a formula for the standard deviation of a sum of variables is first required. By definition,

$$\sigma_v = \sqrt{\frac{\Sigma v_i^2}{N}} = \sqrt{\frac{\Sigma(z_{1i} + z_{2i} + \ldots + z_{qi})^2}{N}} .$$

Expanding the square, this expression becomes

$$\sigma_v = \sqrt{\frac{\Sigma z_{1i}^2}{N} + \frac{\Sigma z_{2i}^2}{N} + \ldots + \frac{\Sigma z_{qi}^2}{N} + 2\left(\frac{\Sigma z_{1i} z_{2i}}{N} + \ldots + \frac{\Sigma z_{q-1, i} z_{qi}}{N}\right)} .$$

Now, since

(2.39)
$$\frac{\Sigma z_{ji}^2}{N} = \sigma_j^2 = 1 \quad \text{and} \quad \frac{\Sigma z_{ji} z_{ki}}{N} = r_{jk} ,$$

the last formula reduces to

(2.40)
$$\sigma_v = \sqrt{q + 2\sum_{j<k=1}^{q} r_{jk}} .$$

Similarly the standard deviation of the variable w may be written

(2.40′)
$$\sigma_w = \sqrt{Q + 2\sum_{J<K=I}^{Q} r_{JK}} .$$

Returning to formula (2.38), it is seen that there remains $\Sigma v_i w_i / N$ to be expressed in terms of correlations between the original variables. Inserting the values of v_i and w_i into this formula, there results

$$\frac{1}{N} \Sigma v_i w_i = \frac{1}{N} \sum_{i=1}^{N} \left(\sum_{j=1}^{q} z_{ji} \right) \left(\sum_{J=I}^{Q} z_{Ji} \right) .$$

If the sums in the parentheses are expanded and the indicated multiplication performed, this expression can be rearranged in the following form:

$$\frac{\Sigma v_i w_i}{N} = \frac{\displaystyle\sum_{i=1}^{N} \left(\sum_{j=1}^{q} \sum_{J=I}^{Q} z_{ji} z_{Ji} \right)}{N} ,$$

which, in turn, upon summing for i reduces to

$$(2.41) \qquad\qquad \frac{\Sigma v_i w_i}{N} = \sum_{j=1}^{q} \sum_{J=I}^{Q} r_{jJ} .$$

Substituting the values from (2.40), (2.40'), and (2.41) into (2.38), the following expression for the correlation between two sums of variables is obtained:

$$(2.42) \qquad\qquad r_{vw} = \frac{\displaystyle\sum_{j=1}^{q} \sum_{J=I}^{Q} r_{jJ}}{\sigma_v \sigma_w} .$$

This formula gives the correlation between any two composite variables in terms of the correlations between the individual variables comprising the derived ones.

As a special case of (2.42), the correlation of a variable z_0, in standard form, with a composite variable v may be considered. It is readily seen that the correlation in this case is given by

$$(2.43) \qquad\qquad r_{0v} = \frac{\displaystyle\sum_{j=1}^{q} r_{0j}}{\sqrt{q + 2 \displaystyle\sum_{j<k=1}^{q} r_{jk}}} .$$

It may be instructive to give a diagrammatic representation of formula (2.42). Consider the following table of intercorrelations between the original variables involved in v and w:

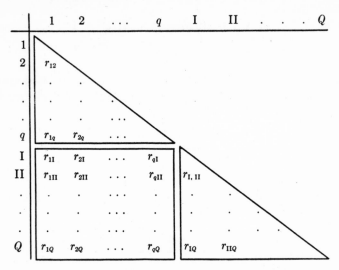

Let $\triangle q$ represent the sum of the elements in the upper triangle, that is, the sum of the intercorrelations of the q variables making up the composite variable v. Similarly, let $\triangle Q$ represent the sum of the elements in the lower triangle; and $\square qQ$ those in the rectangle, that is, the sum of the intercorrelations of the variables involved in v with those in w. Then formula (2.42) may be written symbolically in the form

$$(2.44) \qquad r_{vw} = \frac{\square qQ}{\sqrt{q + 2\triangle q}\,\sqrt{Q + 2\triangle Q}}.$$

2.11. *Application of Correlations of Sums*

To indicate the use of the formulas just developed, they will be applied to the groups of tests defined in (2.35). The composite variables arising from these groups are

$$(2.45) \quad v_1 = \sum_{j=1}^{4} z_j, \quad v_2 = \sum_{j=5}^{9} z_j, \quad v_3 = \sum_{j=10}^{13} z_j, \quad v_4 = \sum_{j=14}^{19} z_j, \quad v_5 = \sum_{j=20}^{24} z_j,$$

where a single letter v with varying subscripts is employed to distinguish the variables.

The standard deviations of these new variables may be computed by means of (2.40), the result being

$$(2.46) \quad \begin{cases} \sigma_{v_1} = \sqrt{4 + 2(2.041)} = \sqrt{8.082} = 2.843 \,, \\ \sigma_{v_2} = \sqrt{5 + 2(6.378)} = \sqrt{17.756} = 4.214 \,, \\ \sigma_{v_3} = \sqrt{4 + 2(2.952)} = \sqrt{9.904} = 3.147 \,, \\ \sigma_{v_4} = \sqrt{6 + 2(4.782)} = \sqrt{15.564} = 3.945 \,, \\ \sigma_{v_5} = \sqrt{5 + 2(4.336)} = \sqrt{13.672} = 3.698 \,. \end{cases}$$

TABLE 2.4

INTERCORRELATIONS OF FIVE
COMPOSITE TESTS

Composite Test	v_1	v_2	v_3	v_4	v_5
v_1........	......	......	......	......	......
v_2........	.464	......	......	......	......
v_3........	.334	.398	......	......	......
v_4........	.425	.427	.460	......	......
v_5........	.594	.649	.545	.588	......

TABLE 2.5

CORRELATIONS OF ORIGINAL WITH
COMPOSITE TESTS

Test	v_1	v_2	v_3	v_4	v_5
z_1........	......	.384	.390	.403	.515
z_2........	......	.244	.188	.223	.376
z_3........	......	.309	.152	.305	.351
z_4........	......	.381	.221	.276	.446
z_5........	.380	......	.386	.344	.544
z_6........	.409	......	.305	.387	.527
z_7........	.358	......	.319	.304	.542
z_8........	.444	......	.398	.381	.550
z_9........	.362	......	.268	.382	.574
z_{10}........	.069	.288	......	.316	.414
z_{11}........	.232	.358	......	.483	.424
z_{12}........	.267	.208	......	.294	.421
z_{13}........	.484	.397	......	.354	.456
z_{14}........	.166	.313	.269	......	.345
z_{15}........	.197	.255	.224	......	.317
z_{16}........	.447	.284	.266	......	.444
z_{17}........	.192	.294	.357	......	.357
z_{18}........	.382	.248	.425	......	.447
z_{19}........	.292	.288	.271	......	.410
z_{20}........	.455	.512	.274	.429	......
z_{21}........	.418	.361	.503	.412	......
z_{22}........	.448	.490	.297	.432	......
z_{23}........	.542	.540	.396	.436	......
z_{24}........	.332	.499	.545	.465	......

Then, applying formula (2.42), the intercorrelations of the composite tests are readily obtained. They are presented in Table 2.4.

Besides the intercorrelations of composite tests, there will be occasion to use the correlations of the original twenty-four tests with the composite ones. Such correlations may be computed by means of formula (2.43). In Table 2.5 are given the correlations of each test z_j ($j = 1, 2, \ldots, 24$) with the composite tests v_s ($s = 1, 2, 3, 4, 5$) which do not include the test z_j.

CHAPTER III

GEOMETRIC FORMULATION OF THE FACTOR PROBLEM

3.1. *Introduction*

For a complete understanding of the various factor methods for analyzing a set of variables it is very helpful to resort to geometry to supplement and extend the algebraic ideas. The geometric foundation to be developed in this chapter will furnish a basis for subsequent analysis and comparison of methods. It will then be possible to use geometric ideas freely and also to pass from these to equivalent algebraic expressions. The geometry which is most useful for factor analysis is that of higher dimensions. The concept of extending the idea of dimensionality has been confined to the comparatively small class of mathematicians and philosophers, but psychologists and educators have now come to rely on this concept as a very useful tool in analyzing mental traits, the total number of dimensions required being certainly greater than three.

After a very brief exposition of the nature of higher dimensional geometry, a coordinate system is introduced, so that the succeeding development can be made analytically. Then the notion of linear dependence is developed, which paves the way for one of the most fundamental theorems of factor analysis. Before the application of these geometric ideas to the factor problem is made, however, certain formulas for distance and angle are necessary. These are developed, first, in terms of rectangular coordinates and, then, for general coordinates. The theory of transformations for rectangular coordinates forms the basis upon which some actual analyses are obtained in later chapters. The formulas in terms of general coordinates are included so that a geometric interpretation of less common forms of factorial solutions may be made.

In **3.7** a statistical variable is interpreted as a point, or a vector, in higher dimensional space. The standard deviation of the variable then becomes a distance, and the correlation between two variables is the cosine of the angle between the two vectors representing the variables. The direct application of the geometric theorems to the fundamental problems of factor analysis is made in the final section. There it is shown that the dimension of the smallest space which contains the vectors representing a given set of variables is equal to the rank of the matrix of correlations with communalities in the diagonals.

3.2. *Geometry of N Dimensions*

The concept of higher dimensions is arrived at by geometric and algebraic means. The notions of point, line, and plane may be generalized to higher dimensional objects, and extended geometric interpretations of algebraic relationships may be given. The deductions made in the higher dimensional spaces are based upon the analogous theory in three-dimensional space and supplementary logical reasoning.

The basic axioms* for Euclidean geometry may be assumed and such modifications made as are necessary to insure that the space has a sufficiently high dimensionality. The point, straight line, and plane are taken as undefined elements, and later corresponding elements of higher dimensional space may be defined in terms of these.

Starting with four given non-coplanar points, all the points, lines, and planes can be obtained which constitute a three-dimensional space. The space, or manifold, determined by these points is essentially ordinary space of three dimensions. If the existence of at least one point not in this set is postulated, then all the elements of a four-dimensional space can be obtained (with the help of the basic axioms). The three-dimensional region does not now constitute the whole of space but merely a subspace of the space of four dimensions. The three-dimensional region will be called a *hyperplane* lying in the four-space, analogous to a plane lying in a three-space. A hyperplane in a space of four dimensions is determined by four non-coplanar points, a point and a plane, or by two skew lines.

Some of the elementary geometrical properties of the elements in a three- and four-dimensional projective space may now be enumerated.† In a three-dimensional space two planes intersect in a line; a line cuts a plane in a point; and any three planes have a point in common. In a four-dimensional space two hyperplanes intersect in a plane, three hyperplanes intersect in a line, and four in a point, while five do not in general have any point in common; a hyperplane cuts a plane in a line, and a line in a point; two planes have in general only one point in common, and a plane and a line in general have no point in common.

The notion of dimensionality may be viewed in another manner. A point in a line is said to have one degree of freedom (of motion); in a plane, two; and in ordinary space, three. The point being taken as element, a line is said to be of one dimension; a plane, two; and ordinary space, three. These

---

* D. M. Y. Sommerville, *An Introduction to the Geometry of N Dimensions*, 1929, Chap. I. See Appen. **B.4** for list of basic axioms.

† By postulating a projective space the statement of the geometric properties is greatly simplified by not having to deal with special parallel instances. See Appen. **B.4** for the projective axiom.

spaces are called *linear spaces*, or *flat spaces*, i.e., a plane is a *two-flat* and ordinary space is a *three-flat*. An $(N-1)$-flat in an N-space will generally be called a *hyperplane*. The linear spaces point, line, plane, three-flat, . . . , hyperplane, N-flat are manifolds determined by one, two, three, four, . . . , N, $N+1$ points,* respectively, and having zero, one, two, three, . . . , $N-1$, N dimensions.

3.3. *Cartesian Coordinate System*

The geometric ideas are found to be most useful and easily formulated when they are given analytic representation. A point P may thus be represented by a *vector* $(x_1, x_2, \ldots, x_N)$, which is a matrix with one row (or column). Each x_i is a real number, and all N numbers may be called a *system* or *N-tuple*. By a "point" is meant simply one of the undefined elements of the space which is characterized by a given set of axioms, so that a set of points is really an arbitrary set of any whatever elements. On the other hand, the N-tuple $(x_1, x_2, \ldots, x_N)$ may be called an "arithmetic point." A correspondence between a set of "geometric points" and a set of "arithmetic points" is called a *coordinate system*.† The numbers, $x_1, x_2, \ldots, X_N$, which constitute the representation of P, are called the coordinates of P. For purposes of factor analysis, the distinction between a "geometric" and the corresponding "arithmetic" point is not essential, and the word "point" will be used for either one. The notation $P : (x_i)$ will frequently be used to designate the point and its coordinates.

An N-dimensional Euclidean space will be assumed, and in this space a non-homogeneous *Cartesian coordinate system* will be set up. The points $O : (0, 0, \ldots, 0)$, and $E_1 : (1, 0, \ldots, 0)$, $E_2 : (0, 1, 0, \ldots, 0)$, . . . , $E_N : (0, \ldots, 0, 1)$ will be called the origin and unit points, respectively. The N lines Ox_i $(i = 1, 2, \ldots, N)$, each passing through the origin and one of the unit points, will be called the *coordinate axes*. The N hyperplanes‡ $\pi_i = Ox_1x_2 \ldots)x_i(\ldots x_N$, each passing through O and containing $N-1$ axes, will be called the *coordinate hyperplanes*. A hyperplane π_i is

* It is understood that the set of p points, which determine a $(p-1)$-flat, do not lie in a $(p-2)$-flat.

† The coordinate systems that will be introduced in this volume will always produce a one-to-one correspondence between the geometric and arithmetic points. This restriction may be removed, however. A correspondence may carry each point P into a set of arithmetic points, as, for example, in a homogeneous coordinate system. A theory of factor analysis based on such a system, or an even more general geometric foundation, may prove to be very important, but thus far such research has not been undertaken.

‡ The inverted parentheses are used in the designation of any hyperplane to indicate the omitted coordinate axis.

said to be "opposite" to the axis Ox_i. The *coordinates* $(x_1, x_2, \ldots, x_N)$ of any point P are equal, respectively, to its distances from each coordinate hyperplane measured along a line parallel to the opposite axis; or, in other words, the distance cut off on each axis by a hyperplane parallel to the respective opposite coordinate hyperplane. For example, the coordinate x_1 is equal to the distance (denoted by x_1) cut off on the Ox_1 axis by a hyperplane parallel to the coordinate hyperplane π_1.

3.4. *Linear Combination and Dependence*

The N-tuple $(x_1, x_2, \ldots, x_N)$ which represents a point P may be considered as a vector equivalent to the point P. Such a vector which joins the origin O to the point P is sometimes called a "radius vector." Two fundamental operations in vector algebra are multiplication by a number and addition of vectors. More precisely, if P is a point represented by the vector $(x_1, x_2, \ldots, x_N)$ and c is a number, then cP is the point

$$(cx_1, cx_2, \ldots, cx_N),$$

while, if $P_1 : (x_{11}, x_{12}, \ldots, x_{1N})$ and $P_2 : (x_{21}, x_{22}, \ldots, x_{2N})$ are two points,* then $P_1 + P_2$ is the point

$$(x_{11} + x_{21}, x_{12} + x_{22}, \ldots, x_{1N} + x_{2N}).$$

In general, any linear combination of m points, $P_1 : (x_{11}, x_{12}, \ldots, x_{1N})$, $\ldots, P_m : (x_{m1}, x_{m2}, \ldots, x_{mN})$, may be defined by combining the two previous operations, as follows:

$$t_1 P_1 + t_2 P_2 + \ldots + t_m P_m,$$

where the t's are any numbers. By taking varying values of the t's, different linear combinations of the original m points can be obtained. Any one of these new points may be denoted† $P(t)$ or $P(t_1, t_2, \ldots, t_m)$, with coordinates given by

$$(3.1) \qquad\qquad x_i = \sum_{s=1}^{m} t_s x_{si} \qquad\qquad (i = 1, 2, \ldots, N),$$

---

* The double subscript notation is used on the coordinates in order to distinguish the points. Thus x_{si} designates the ith coordinate of the point P_s.

† The symbol $P(t)$, or $P(t_1, t_2, \ldots, t_m)$, is the conventional function notation which is to be read, "P is a function of t (in this case, a set of t's), or P is a function of $t_1, t_2, \ldots, t_m$." On the other hand, $P : (x_i)$ is the notation for a point P with coordinates x_i.

and are said to be *linearly dependent* on the original points $P_1, P_2, \ldots, P_m$. Each coordinate x_i of a point $P(t)$ is expressed as a linear combination of the corresponding coordinates $x_{1i}, x_{2i}, \ldots, x_{mi}$ of the m points $P_1, P_2, \ldots, P_m$.* A set of two or more points is said to be *linearly independent* if no one of them is dependent on the rest. According to these definitions, the origin is linearly dependent on any set of points and a single point is linearly independent if it is not the origin.

The preceding definitions can be made, alternatively, by giving a direct definition of linear independence. Thus, a set of points $P_1, \ldots, P_m$ is linearly independent if the conditions

$$(3.2) \qquad \sum_{s=1}^{m} t_s x_{si} = 0$$

imply that $t_1 = t_2 = \ldots = t_m = 0$. This is readily seen to be consistent with the definition (3.1). For if one of the coefficients were different from zero, say $t_1 \neq 0$, then (3.2) could be written in the form

$$x_{1i} = -\frac{t_2}{t_1} x_{2i} - \frac{t_3}{t_1} x_{3i} - \ldots - \frac{t_m}{t_1} x_{mi};$$

and, according to (3.1), the point P_1 would be one of the points $P(t)$ which is linearly dependent on the points $P_2, P_3, \ldots, P_m$. Having a positive definition of independence, the definition of linear dependence is given by its negation, that is, a set of m points is linearly dependent if the conditions (3.2) hold for the coefficients not all zero.

When a set of points is given, it may be of interest to know how many of them are linearly independent. Let $P_1 : (x_{11}, x_{12}, \ldots, x_{1N})$, $P_2 : (x_{21}, x_{22}, \ldots, x_{2N}), \ldots, P_n : (x_{n1}, x_{n2}, \ldots, x_{nN})$ be any set of n points. Either all

* To clarify some of these ideas, consider the special case of $N = 3$ and two points $P_1 : (x_{11}, x_{12}, x_{13})$ and $P_2 : (x_{21}, x_{22}, x_{23})$. All the points $P(t)$ which are linearly dependent on the points P_1 and P_2 are given by the following coordinates:

$$P(t_1, t_2) : \begin{cases} x_1 = t_1 x_{11} + t_2 x_{21} \\ x_2 = t_1 x_{12} + t_2 x_{22} \\ x_3 = t_1 x_{13} + t_2 x_{23} \end{cases}$$

for varying values of t_1 and t_2. For particular values of t_1 and t_2, the first coordinate of $P(t)$ is a linear combination of the first coordinates of P_1 and P_2; the second coordinate is the same linear combination of the second ones; and the third coordinate is again the same linear combination of the third ones. For example, if the coordinates of P_1 are (1, 3, 4) and those of P_2 are (2, 1, 5) and $t_1 = 1$, $t_2 = 2$, then $P(t)$ is given by the coordinates $x_1 = 5$, $x_2 = 5$, $x_3 = 14$.

these points coincide with the origin or at least one of them, say P_1, is independent. Of the remaining points, either they will all depend upon P_1 or at least one of them, say P_2, will be independent of P_1. Proceeding in this way an independent set of points, say $P_1, P_2, \ldots, P_m$, will be obtained upon which all the points $P_1, P_2, \ldots, P_n$ will be linearly dependent. A criterion for determining m may be obtained by means of the matrix

$$\|x_{ji}\| = \begin{Vmatrix} x_{11} & x_{12} & x_{13} & \ldots & x_{1N} \\ x_{21} & x_{22} & x_{23} & \ldots & x_{2N} \\ x_{31} & x_{32} & x_{33} & \ldots & x_{3N} \\ \cdot & \cdot & \cdot & \ldots & \cdot \\ x_{n1} & x_{n2} & x_{n3} & \ldots & x_{nN} \end{Vmatrix},$$

whose rows are the n points. An important result for linear dependence of points, and which will be utilized later to determine the number of common factors necessary to describe a set of variables, may be stated as

THEOREM 3.1. *If m is the rank of the matrix $\|x_{ji}\|$, the points $P_1, P_2, \ldots, P_n$ are all dependent upon m of them, which are themselves independent.**

Subspaces of the N-space may now be given analytical representation. If $P_1, P_2, \ldots, P_k$ are k linearly independent points, the set of all points linearly dependent on them is called a *linear k-space* and is defined by the equations

$$(3.3) \qquad\qquad x_i = \sum_{j=1}^{k} t_j x_{ji} \qquad\qquad (i = 1, 2, \ldots, N),$$

where the t's are a set of k parameters, and for each set of values $(t_1, t_2, \ldots, t_k)$ there is a corresponding point of the linear k-space. Any one of the original k linearly independent points is, of course, given by definition (3.3); for example, P_2 is given by $t_2 = 1$ and $t_1 = t_3 = \ldots = t_k = 0$. The k points $P_1, P_2, \ldots, P_k$ are said to determine the linear k-space. A linear 1-space

---

*For a proof of this theorem see Appen. **B.5**. An application may be made to the example of the last footnote. The matrix of the three points is

$$\begin{Vmatrix} 1 & 3 & 4 \\ 2 & 1 & 5 \\ 5 & 5 & 14 \end{Vmatrix},$$

which is readily seen to be of rank two; for the third-order determinant is zero while a second-order determinant (e.g., the one in the upper left-hand corner) can be found which is different from zero. Since the matrix is of rank two, the three points are dependent upon two of them, which are themselves independent. Then the three points are contained in a plane, but not in a line, as will be evident from Theorem 3.2.

consists of the points whose coordinates are proportional to those of a given point $P_1 : (x_{11}, x_{12}, \ldots, x_{1N})$, and may be called a line through the origin. Its equations are given by

$$(3.4) \qquad\qquad x_i = t_1 x_{1i} \qquad\qquad (i = 1, 2, \ldots, N).$$

These are a set of N *parametric equations* of a line through the origin, where t_1 is known as the parameter.

The transitive law for linear dependence may now be indicated. All points linearly dependent on m points $P_1, \ldots, P_m$ in a linear k-space are contained in that k-space. The coordinates of the m points are given by equations of the form (3.3), and any point linearly dependent on $P_1, \ldots, P_m$ is then obviously dependent on $P_1, \ldots, P_k$.

Furthermore, if the points $P_1, \ldots, P_k$ determine a linear k-space, there is no other linear k-space containing these points. A linear k-space is thus determined by any set of k independent points contained in it, and a linear k-space does not contain a set of l independent points, where $l > k$. For, by definition (3.1), it is implied that any k points in a set of l independent points are themselves independent, and hence determine a linear k-space containing the larger set. Theorem 3.1 may then be stated as follows:

THEOREM 3.2. *If m is the rank of the matrix $\|x_{ji}\|$, the points $P_1, P_2, \ldots, P_n$ are all contained in a linear m-space but not in a linear μ-space, where $\mu < m$.*

A geometric interpretation of linear dependence can now be given. The m vectors $P_s : (x_{s1}, x_{s2}, \ldots, x_{sN})$, $(s = 1, 2, \ldots, m)$, employed in the definition (3.1), determine an m-dimensional subspace of the original N-space, and if $OP_1, OP_2, \ldots, OP_m$ are taken as the coordinate axes, then $t_1, t_2, \ldots, t_m$ in (3.1) are the coordinates of x_i.

A linear k-space, as defined by equations (3.3), always contains the origin, since the origin is linearly dependent on any set of points. The notion of subspaces of the N-dimensional space may be generalized to spaces which do not include the origin. For this purpose, a *translation* of coordinates,

$$(3.5) \qquad\qquad y_i = x_i + c_i,$$

is defined. Then any set of points which corresponds, under a translation, to a linear k-space may be called a *flat k-space*, or merely a *k-flat*. As noted in **3.2**, a 0-flat is a single point; a 1-flat is a straight line; a 2-flat is a plane; and an $(N - 1)$-flat is a hyperplane.

The geometric theorems developed in this section will be applied specifically to the factor problem in **3.8**. First, certain fundamental formulas for distance and angle will be developed and applied to correlational theory.

3.5. *Elementary Formulas in Rectangular Coordinates*

When the coordinate axes are mutually orthogonal, i.e., at right angles to one another, the reference system set up in section **3.3** is called a *rectangular Cartesian system*. Some elementary formulas in *rectangular* coordinates will be presented in this section.

For any two vectors or points $P_1 : (x_{11}, x_{12}, \ldots, x_{1N})$ and $P_2 : (x_{21}, x_{22}, \ldots, x_{2N})$, their *scalar product** is defined by

$$(3.6) \qquad\qquad P_1 \cdot P_2 = \Sigma x_{1i} x_{2i} ,$$

where summation with respect to i is understood. Then the *norm* of P_1 is defined as the positive square root of the inner product of P_1 with itself, that is,

$$(3.7) \qquad\qquad N(P) = \sqrt{P_1 \cdot P_1} = \sqrt{\Sigma x_{1i}^2} ,$$

and the *distance* between P_1 and P_2 is defined by

$$(3.8) \qquad D(P_1 P_2) = N(P_1 - P_2) = \sqrt{\Sigma (x_{1i} - x_{2i})^2} .$$

It is readily seen that the norm of a point is the distance from the origin to the point, that is, $N(P) = D(OP)$. The distance function satisfies the following familiar conditions of elementary geometry:

$$(3.9) \qquad \begin{cases} D(P_1 P_1) = 0 , \\ D(P_1 P_2) \neq 0 \text{ if } P_1 \neq P_2 , \\ D(P_1 P_2) = D(P_2 P_1) , \\ D(P_1 P_2) + D(P_2 P_3) \geq D(P_1 P_3) . \end{cases}$$

The first three of these relations are obvious. The fourth, however, requires some proof. It may be noted that distances are invariant under translations. Thus if two points P_1, P_2 are translated into two points P_1', P_2', then $D(P_1 P_2) = D(P_1' P_2')$, which may be verified by applying (3.5). The fourth formula of (3.9) will therefore be unaltered if the points P_1, P_2, and P_3 are transformed by a translation which carries P_2 into the origin. Then, putting in the distances by means of (3.7) and (3.8), the inequality of (3.9) becomes

$$(3.10) \qquad \sqrt{\Sigma x_{1i}^2} + \sqrt{\Sigma x_{3i}^2} \geq \sqrt{\Sigma (x_{1i} - x_{3i})^2} ,$$

which may be verified algebraically.

---

* This is sometimes called the *inner* or *dot* product.

Now the equality occurs in (3.10) if, and only if,

$$x_{3i} = -t_1 x_{1i} \qquad (i = 1, 2, \ldots, N),$$

where t_1 is a positive constant. These equations are of the form (3.4) and so represent a straight line through the origin with the points P_1 and P_3 on opposite sides of the origin. Hence, equality occurs in the fourth relation of (3.9) if, and only if, the coordinates of P_1, P_2, and P_3 are related by equations of the form

$$(3.11) \qquad A(x_{1i} - x_{2i}) + B(x_{3i} - x_{2i}) = 0,$$

where A and B are constants of like sign and not both zero. If the condition (3.11) is satisfied, and if $P_1 \neq P_2$ and $P_2 \neq P_3$, then P_2 is said to lie *between* P_1 and P_3.

Of special interest to factor analysis are some theorems of elementary geometry which have to do with transformations which leave distances invariant. Such transformations, in which any point $P_1 : (x_{1i})$ is carried into $Q_1 : (y_{1i})$ and $P_2 : (x_{2i})$ is carried into $Q_2 : (y_{2i})$, have the following property

$$(3.12) \qquad \Sigma(x_{1i} - x_{2i})^2 = \Sigma(y_{1i} - y_{2i})^2.$$

From the condition that a point P_2 is between two others, P_1 and P_3, if, and only if,

$$D(P_1 P_2) + D(P_2 P_3) = D(P_1 P_3),$$

it follows that a transformation which leaves distances unaltered carries straight lines into straight lines. Now, by a fundamental theorem of geometry,* the transformation is linear, that is, of the form

$$(3.13) \qquad y_{ji} = \sum_{k=1}^{N} a_{ik} x_{jk} + c_i$$

$$(i = 1, 2, \ldots, N; j = 1, 2, 3, \ldots).$$

Upon substituting the values of y_{1i} and y_{2i} from (3.13), equation (3.12) becomes

$$(3.14) \qquad \sum_{i=1}^{N} (x_{1i} - x_{2i})^2 = \sum_{i=1}^{N} \left[\sum_{k=1}^{N} a_{ik}(x_{1k} - x_{2k}) \right]^2.$$

---

* The theorem states that *any nonsingular transformation of an N-space into itself is linear if it carries straight lines into straight lines.* For a proof of this theorem see Oswald Veblen and J. H. C. Whitehead, *The Foundations of Differential Geometry*, 1932, pp. 12–15.

It now remains to find the conditions which the a's must satisfy in order that (3.14) should hold, and then the most general transformation which preserves distance will be specified. The right-hand side of (3.14) can be written as follows:

$$\sum_{i=1}^{N} \{ a_{i1}^2(x_{11} - x_{21})^2 + a_{i2}^2(x_{12} - x_{22})^2 + \ldots + a_{iN}^2(x_{1N} - x_{2N})^2$$
$$+ 2[a_{i1}a_{i2}(x_{11} - x_{21})(x_{12} - x_{22}) + \ldots$$
$$+ a_{i,N-1}a_{iN}(x_{1,N-1} - x_{2,N-1})(x_{1N} - x_{2N})] \} ,$$

or simplified to

$$\sum_{i=1}^{N} \sum_{k=1}^{N} \sum_{l=1}^{N} a_{ik}a_{il}(x_{1k} - x_{2k})(x_{1l} - x_{2l}) .$$

Hence, equation (3.14) is satisfied when

(3.15) $$\Sigma a_{ik}a_{il} = \delta_{kl} ,$$

where δ_{kl} is the Kronecker delta which is equal to unity if $k = l$ and equal to zero if $k \neq l$. Any linear homogeneous transformation,

(3.16) $$y_{ji} = \sum_{k=1}^{N} a_{ik}x_{jk} ,$$

whose coefficients satisfy (3.15) is called *orthogonal*, and its matrix an *orthogonal matrix*. The following theorem has thus been established:

THEOREM 3.3. *The distance between any two points is an invariant under a general rigid motion, that is, an orthogonal transformation followed by a translation.*

Other geometric ideas that are useful in factor analysis center around the notion of the angle between two lines. The only characteristic of a point is its position, as given by its coordinates in a frame of reference. A line is ordinarily distinguished not by coordinates but by its inclinations to the respective coordinate axes. The angles which a line OP makes with the axes, i.e., $\theta_i = POx_i$, are called the *direction angles* of the line, and their cosines are called *direction cosines*. If the norm $N(P)$, i.e., the distance $D(OP)$, is denoted by ρ, then

(3.17) $$x_i = \rho \cos \theta_i \qquad (i = 1, 2, \ldots, N) .$$

By (3.7),

$$\rho^2 = \Sigma x_i^2 ,$$

and substituting the value of x_i from (3.17), gives

$$\rho^2 = \Sigma \rho^2 \cos^2 \theta_i \,,$$

so that

(3.18) $\Sigma \cos^2 \theta_i = 1 \,.$

This property, that the sum of the squares of the direction cosines of a line in N-space is equal to unity, is a direct extension of the one in ordinary space.

The parametric equations of a line through the origin O and a fixed point $P_1 : (x_{1i})$ are given by (3.4). The coordinates of any point $P : (x_i)$ on a line through the origin with the direction cosines

$$\lambda_i = \cos \theta_i$$

are given by (3.17). When ρ is taken as a parametric variable along the line, the N equations (3.17) can be regarded as the equations of the line, which may be written

$$\rho = \frac{x_i}{\lambda_i} \qquad\qquad (i = 1, 2, \ldots, N) \,.$$

Upon equating the N expressions for ρ, the following $N - 1$ equations arise:

(3.19) $\dfrac{x_1}{\lambda_1} = \dfrac{x_2}{\lambda_2} = \ldots = \dfrac{x_N}{\lambda_N} \,.$

If $P : (x_1, x_2, \ldots, x_N)$ is taken as a variable point on the line, (3.19) can be regarded as the equations of the line.

By means of a translation, of the form (3.5), the equations of a line AP through an arbitrarily fixed point $A : (a_1, a_2, \ldots, a_N)$ and with the direction cosines λ_i are transformed from (3.19) to

(3.20) $\dfrac{x_1 - a_1}{\lambda_1} = \dfrac{x_2 - a_2}{\lambda_2} = \ldots = \dfrac{x_N - a_N}{\lambda_N} \,.$

Moreover, if

(3.21) $\lambda_i = bl_i \qquad\qquad (i = 1, 2, \ldots, N) \,,$

where b is a constant different from zero, the equations of the line AP may be written in the form

(3.22) $\dfrac{x_1 - a_1}{l_1} = \dfrac{x_2 - a_2}{l_2} = \ldots = \dfrac{x_N - a_N}{l_N} \,,$

where the l_i are not now equal to, but only proportional to, the direction cosines. The numbers l_i are called *direction numbers* of the line.

The actual direction cosines of a line can readily be obtained from the numbers proportional to them. For, squaring both sides of (3.21) and summing for i, this equation becomes

$$b^2 \Sigma l_i^2 = \Sigma \lambda_i^2 = 1 \,,$$

where the last equality follows from (3.18). Then the constant of proportionality is

$$b = \frac{1}{\sqrt{\Sigma l_i^2}} \,,$$

and the direction cosines are given by

$$(3.23) \qquad\qquad \lambda_i = \frac{l_i}{\sqrt{\Sigma l_i^2}} \,.$$

Hence equations (3.22) may be taken as the general form of the $(N - 1)$ equations of a line in N-space.

The coordinates of any point $P : (x_i)$ on a line through $A : (a_i)$ with direction numbers l_i are

$$(3.24) \qquad\qquad x_i = a_i + tl_i \qquad\qquad (i = 1, 2, \ldots, N) \,,$$

where t is the repeated value in (3.22). Equations (3.24) may be regarded as a system of parametric equations of a line through a fixed point. The distance $D(AP)$ along the line from the fixed point A up to any position of the variable point P is

$$D(AP) = \sqrt{\Sigma(x_i - a_i)^2} = t\sqrt{\Sigma l_i^2} \,,$$

so that,

$$(3.25) \qquad\qquad t = \frac{D(AP)}{\sqrt{\Sigma l_i^2}} \,.$$

It is thus evident that the parameter t in equations (3.24) is proportional to the distance from the fixed point to a variable point on the line and is equal to this distance when the equations of the line are given in terms of the direction cosines.

Now a formula for the cosine of the angle between two lines in N-space may be derived. When two lines meet in a point,* a plane can be drawn

---

* If the lines do not meet in a point, the angle between the lines may be defined as the angle which one of the lines makes with a line parallel to the second, which intersects the first line.

through the point containing the two lines, and their inclination can be obtained from the trigonometric properties of a triangle in the plane. Let the two lines through $A : (a_i)$ be represented by the equations

(3.26)
$$\begin{cases} \dfrac{x_1 - a_1}{\lambda_1} = \dfrac{x_2 - a_2}{\lambda_2} = \ldots = \dfrac{x_N - a_N}{\lambda_N}\,, \\[2mm] \dfrac{y_1 - a_1}{\mu_1} = \dfrac{y_2 - a_2}{\mu_2} = \ldots = \dfrac{y_N - a_N}{\mu_N}\,, \end{cases}$$

where the x_i and y_i are the coordinates of the variable points on the lines, and the λ_i and μ_i are the direction cosines of the lines. On the first line take any point P at a distance p from A; on the second line take any point Q at a distance q from A; and connect the points P and Q with a line, which necessarily lies in the plane. The points and lines are plotted in the plane of the two given lines in Figure 3.1.

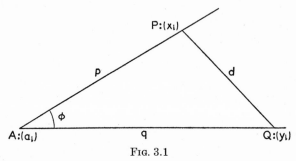

FIG. 3.1

Let ϕ = angle PAQ and let $d = D(PQ)$, then the law of cosines applied to the triangle PAQ gives

(3.27)
$$d^2 = p^2 + q^2 - 2pq \cos \phi\,.$$

The distance d is also given by formula (3.8), in which, according to (3.24), the coordinates of P are $x_i = a_i + p\lambda_i$ and those of Q are $y_i = a_i + q\mu_i$, so that

(3.28)
$$\begin{cases} d^2 = \Sigma(x_i - y_i)^2 = \Sigma(p\lambda_i - q\mu_i)^2\,, \\[1mm] \quad = p^2\Sigma\lambda_i^2 + q^2\Sigma\mu_i^2 - 2pq\Sigma\lambda_i\mu_i\,, \\[1mm] \quad = p^2 + q^2 - 2pq\Sigma\lambda_i\mu_i\,, \end{cases}$$

since $\Sigma\lambda_i^2 = \Sigma\mu_i^2 = 1$ by (3.18). When the terms of (3.28) are identified with the corresponding ones of (3.27), the following result is obtained:

(3.29)
$$\cos \phi = \Sigma\lambda_i\mu_i\,.$$

Thus the cosine of the angle of separation of two lines is given by the sum of the products of corresponding direction cosines of the lines, i.e., the scalar product of the vectors $(\lambda_1, \lambda_2, \ldots, \lambda_N)$ and $(\mu_1, \mu_2, \ldots, \mu_N)$.

If the equations of the lines are given in the form (3.22), with l_i and m_i as the direction numbers of the respective lines, the cosine of the angle of separation becomes

$$(3.30) \qquad \cos \phi = \frac{\Sigma l_i m_i}{\sqrt{\Sigma l_i^2} \sqrt{\Sigma m_i^2}} .$$

Here the cosine of the angle of separation of two lines is given in terms of numbers proportional to the direction cosines of the lines.

By means of formula (3.29) another expression for the scalar product of two vectors or points may be written in place of (3.6). The coordinates of the two points $P_1 : (x_{1i})$ and $P_2 : (x_{2i})$ may be expressed as follows:

$$x_{1i} = \rho_1 \lambda_{1i}, \quad x_{2i} = \rho_2 \lambda_{2i} \qquad (i = 1, 2, \ldots, N),$$

where ρ_1, ρ_2 are the respective distances from the origin O to the points P_1, P_2, and λ_{1i}, λ_{2i} are the direction cosines of the lines OP_1 and OP_2. Then, substituting these values in (3.6), there arises

$$P_1 \cdot P_2 = \Sigma x_{1i} x_{2i} = \rho_1 \rho_2 \Sigma \lambda_{1i} \lambda_{2i},$$

which, according to (3.29), reduces to

$$(3.31) \qquad P_1 \cdot P_2 = \rho_1 \rho_2 \cos \phi_{12},$$

where ϕ_{12} is the angle $P_1 O P_2$. Formula (3.31) states that the scalar product of two vectors is the product of the lengths of the vectors by the cosine of their angular separation. This is very often taken as the definition of the scalar product.

3.6. *Elementary Formulas in General Cartesian Coordinates*

In the preceding section various formulas were presented in terms of rectangular coordinates. Now the restriction that the coordinate axes are mutually orthogonal will be removed, and more general formulas obtained. The formulas for distance and angle will then be in terms of general Cartesian coordinates and will simplify to those of **3.5** when the angles between all pairs of reference axes are taken as 90°.

The general Cartesian coordinate system contains N reference axes Ox_i which may make any angles with one another. Then the angle between the

x_i and x_k axes may be designated θ_{ik} $(i, k = 1, 2, \ldots, N)$. As may be expected, the formulas for distance and angle in terms of general Cartesian coordinates will involve the inclinations of the reference axes.

Formulas for the distance function in general coordinates will first be given. In the plane the square of the length of the radius vector OP is readily found to be

$$\rho^2 = [D(OP)]^2 = x_1^2 + x_2^2 - 2x_1x_2 \cos(180° - \theta_{12})$$
$$= x_1^2 + x_2^2 + 2x_1x_2 \cos \theta_{12}.$$

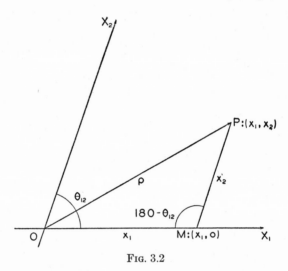

FIG. 3.2

This formula follows immediately on applying the law of cosines to the triangle POM, indicated in Figure 3.2. By induction, it can be shown that in N-space the distance ρ from the origin O to an arbitrary point $P : (x_1, x_2, \ldots, x_N)$ is given by

$$(3.32) \qquad \rho = \sqrt{\Sigma\Sigma x_i x_k \cos \theta_{ik}},$$

where $\Sigma\Sigma$ indicates summation for i and k from 1 to N. This convention for the double summation will be employed throughout this section. In a similar manner, the distance between any two points $P_1 : (x_{11}, x_{12}, \ldots, x_{1N})$ and $P_2 : (x_{21}, x_{22}, \ldots, x_{2N})$ may be shown to be given by the following formula:

$$(3.33) \qquad D(P_1P_2) = \sqrt{\Sigma\Sigma(x_{1i} - x_{2i})(x_{1k} - x_{2k}) \cos \theta_{ik}}.$$

The relations (3.32) and (3.33) reduce to the corresponding formulas (3.7) and (3.8) for distance in rectangular coordinates when the angles of inclination between pairs of axes are 90°, inasmuch as $\cos \theta_{ik} = 0$ for every $i \neq k$.

There will now be given several properties of a line in terms of more general (not necessarily rectangular) coordinates. The direction of a line OP is determined by the ratios of the coordinates of an arbitrary point $P : (x_1, x_2, \ldots, x_N)$ on the line to the length $\rho = D(OP)$. These ratios, denoted by $\lambda_i = x_i/\rho$, are called the *direction ratios* of the line OP. Then if the coordinates of P are expressed in the form

$$(3.34) \qquad x_i = \rho\lambda_i \qquad \text{or} \qquad x_k = \rho\lambda_k ,$$

and substituted in (3.32), there results

$$\rho^2 = \rho^2 \Sigma\Sigma\lambda_i\lambda_k \cos \theta_{ik} ,$$

so that

$$(3.35) \qquad \Sigma\Sigma\lambda_i\lambda_k \cos \theta_{ik} = 1 .$$

The direction ratios become the direction cosines of a line when a general Cartesian coordinate system is specialized to a rectangular one. Then formulas (3.34) and (3.35) reduce to (3.17) and (3.18), respectively.

An expression for the angle between two lines, in general coordinates, can now be deduced. For simplicity, let the two lines pass through the origin and be distinguished by the direction ratios λ_i, μ_i ($i = 1, 2, \ldots, N$), respectively. Select a point $P : (x_i)$ on the first line, and a point $Q : (y_i)$ on the second line, and let $p = D(OP)$, $q = D(OQ)$, $d = D(PQ)$, and $\phi =$ angle POQ. Then

$$d^2 = p^2 + q^2 - 2pq \cos \phi .$$

But d is also given by (3.33), in which the coordinates of P are $x_i = p\lambda_i$ and those of Q are $y_i = q\mu_i$, so that after these values are substituted, the formula becomes

$$d^2 = p^2 + q^2 - 2pq\Sigma\Sigma\lambda_i\mu_k \cos \theta_{ik} .$$

By equating the two expressions for the square of the distance, the following formula for the angle between two lines is obtained:

$$(3.36) \qquad \cos \phi = \Sigma\Sigma\lambda_i\mu_k \cos \theta_{ik} .$$

This formula reduces to (3.29) when the axes make right angles with one another.

3.7. *Geometric Interpretation of Correlation*

In this and the following section there will be presented a number of applications of the preceding geometric ideas to the factor problem. The raw data are the values of n statistical variables for each of N individuals. These data may be set down in a matrix as follows:

$$\|X_{ji}\| = \begin{Vmatrix} X_{11} & X_{12} & X_{13} & \ldots & X_{1N} \\ X_{21} & X_{22} & X_{23} & \ldots & X_{2N} \\ X_{31} & X_{32} & X_{33} & \ldots & X_{3N} \\ \cdot & \cdot & \cdot & \cdots & \cdot \\ X_{n1} & X_{n2} & X_{n3} & \ldots & X_{nN} \end{Vmatrix},$$

where any element X_{ji} represents the observed value of variable j for individual i; so that the n rows represent the variables and the N columns, the individuals. By subtracting the mean of each variable from the observed values of that variable, the matrix of deviates,

$$\|x_{ji}\| = \begin{Vmatrix} x_{11} & x_{12} & x_{13} & \ldots & x_{1N} \\ x_{21} & x_{22} & x_{23} & \ldots & x_{2N} \\ x_{31} & x_{32} & x_{33} & \ldots & x_{3N} \\ \cdot & \cdot & \cdot & \cdots & \cdot \\ x_{n1} & x_{n2} & x_{n3} & \ldots & x_{nN} \end{Vmatrix},$$

is obtained.

Each row of $\|x_{ji}\|$ consists of N real, ordered numbers, and hence may be considered as the rectangular Cartesian coordinates of a point x_j ($j = 1, 2, \ldots, n$). The variables (or points) are thus designated by an x with a single subscript, whereas the values of the variables (i.e., the coordinates of the points) are indicated by an x with two subscripts. A particular value (or coordinate) x_{ji} stands for the ith coordinate of the point x_j.

As has been remarked before, it is usually more convenient to put the variables in standard form. The matrix of standardized values may then be represented by

$$\|z_{ji}\| = \begin{Vmatrix} z_{11} & z_{12} & z_{13} & \ldots & z_{1N} \\ z_{21} & z_{22} & z_{23} & \ldots & z_{2N} \\ z_{31} & z_{32} & z_{33} & \ldots & z_{3N} \\ \cdot & \cdot & \cdot & \cdots & \cdot \\ z_{n1} & z_{n2} & z_{n3} & \ldots & z_{nN} \end{Vmatrix},$$

in which the rows may be interpreted as the rectangular Cartesian coordinates of n points z_j ($j = 1, 2, \ldots, n$) in an N-space.

The length of the radius vector to a point x_j, according to formula (3.7), is

$$(3.37) \qquad \rho_j = \sqrt{\Sigma x_{ji}^2} \,.$$

According to equation (2.1), however, the expression on the right is equal to $\sqrt{N}\sigma_j$, so that

$$(3.38) \qquad \rho_j = \sqrt{N}\sigma_j \,.$$

The standard deviation of a statistical variable may thus be interpreted as being proportional to the distance from the origin out to the point representing the variable, the constant of proportionality being $1/\sqrt{N}$.

By way of geometric representation of a set of values of two variables, x_j and x_k, it is customary to think of the x_{ji} and the x_{ki} as the coordinates of N points (x_{j1}, x_{k1}), (x_{j2}, x_{k2}), . . . , (x_{jN}, x_{kN}) in the plane x_jOx_k. This plot of points is called a *scatter diagram;* and, by means of this representation, a better understanding of the relations involved in the definition (2.3) of a coefficient of correlation can be obtained. In general, for n variables this will be referred to as the *point representation*.

Even more important in some respects is a geometric representation not by N points in a plane (for two variables) but by two points in an N-space. The two variables are then represented by the points $x_j : (x_{j1}, x_{j2}, . . . , x_{jN})$ and $x_k : (x_{k1}, x_{k2}, . . . , x_{kN})$, which may be termed "vectors" according to **3.4**. Such a configuration for n variables will be called the *vector representation*.

If the direction cosines of these vectors are denoted by λ_{ji} and λ_{ki}, respectively, then by (3.17),

$$(3.39) \qquad \lambda_{ji} = \frac{x_{ji}}{\rho_j}, \qquad \lambda_{ki} = \frac{x_{ki}}{\rho_k} \qquad (i = 1, 2, . . . , N) ,$$

where $\rho_j = D(Ox_j)$ and $\rho_k = D(Ox_k)$. Inserting these values in formula (3.29), it becomes

$$(3.40) \qquad \cos \phi_{jk} = \Sigma \lambda_{ji}\lambda_{ki} = \frac{\Sigma x_{ji}x_{ki}}{\rho_j\rho_k} ,$$

where ϕ_{jk} is the angle of separation of the two lines. Then $\cos \phi_{jk}$ may be interpreted as the scalar product of the vectors x_j and x_k divided by the product of the lengths of these vectors. Upon substituting the values for ρ_j and ρ_k from (3.38), formula (3.40) reduces to

$$(3.41) \qquad \cos \phi_{jk} = \frac{\Sigma x_{ji}x_{ki}}{N\sigma_j\sigma_k} ,$$

which, according to (2.3′), becomes

$$(3.42) \qquad\qquad r_{jk} = \cos \phi_{jk} \qquad\qquad (j, k = 1, 2, \ldots, n) \, .$$

The coefficient of correlation between two variables (measured as deviates from their respective means) is the cosine of the angle between their vectors in N-space.

3.8. *Fundamental Subspace for Factor Analysis*

By means of the geometric notions introduced in this chapter it is possible to determine the minimum number of common factors that is necessary to describe a set of variables in the sense of equations (2.16). According to Theorem 3.2, the n points whose coordinates are given in the matrix $\|z_{ji}\|$ are all contained in a linear m-space, where m is the rank of the matrix. In other words, the n vectors can be described in terms of m reference vectors.

This property can be stated in terms of the intercorrelations of the n variables by means of the following:

THEOREM 3.4. *The rank of the product of a matrix by its transpose is equal to the rank of the matrix.*[*]

The product of the matrix $\|z_{ji}\|$ by its transpose, $\|z_{ik}\|$, is given by

$$(3.43) \quad \|z_{ji}\| \cdot \|z_{ik}\| = \begin{Vmatrix} \Sigma z_{1i}^2 & \Sigma z_{1i}z_{2i} & \Sigma z_{1i}z_{3i} & \ldots & \Sigma z_{1i}z_{ni} \\ \Sigma z_{2i}z_{1i} & \Sigma z_{2i}^2 & \Sigma z_{2i}z_{3i} & \ldots & \Sigma z_{2i}z_{ni} \\ \Sigma z_{3i}z_{1i} & \Sigma z_{3i}z_{2i} & \Sigma z_{3i}^2 & \ldots & \Sigma z_{3i}z_{ni} \\ \cdot & \cdot & \cdot & \cdot & \cdot \\ \Sigma z_{ni}z_{1i} & \Sigma z_{ni}z_{2i} & \Sigma z_{ni}z_{3i} & \ldots & \Sigma z_{ni}^2 \end{Vmatrix} .$$

Recalling that $\Sigma z_{ji}^2 = N$ and $\Sigma z_{ji}z_{ki} = Nr_{jk}$, the preceding equation can be written in the form

$$(3.44) \quad \|z_{ji}\| \cdot \|z_{ik}\| = N^2 \begin{Vmatrix} 1 & r_{12} & r_{13} & \ldots & r_{1n} \\ r_{21} & 1 & r_{23} & \ldots & r_{2n} \\ r_{31} & r_{32} & 1 & \ldots & r_{3n} \\ \cdot & \cdot & \cdot & & \cdot \\ r_{n1} & r_{n2} & r_{n3} & \ldots & 1 \end{Vmatrix} = N^2 \|r_{jk}\| \, .$$

Then, according to Theorem 3.4, the rank of the correlation matrix $\|r_{jk}\|$ is equal to the rank of the matrix of standardized values, $\|z_{ji}\|$. Hence any property of the variables which is inferred only from the rank of the latter

---

[*] For a proof of this theorem see Appen. **B.6.**

matrix may be stated in terms of the correlation matrix. It therefore follows from Theorem 3.2 that *the n variables can be expressed as linear functions of not less than m factors, where m is the rank of the correlation matrix.*

In case the correlation matrix contains ones in the diagonal, its rank is n, and the variables would then be describable in terms of n common factors. If it is desired to describe the n variables in terms of less than n common factors, a pattern of the form (2.16) may be postulated. From such a pattern the correlations are reproduced, as before, but with communalities in place of ones in the diagonals. Then a factor pattern of the desired form can be obtained by employing a matrix of the form in (3.44) with the ones replaced by communalities. The rank of this matrix is generally less than the order n. By the preceding argument, it is therefore apparent that the number of common factors in the pattern is equal to m, the rank of the correlation matrix. This is the smallest number of factors that will account for the intercorrelations. Stated geometrically, the smallest space containing the n points is a flat m-space. Such a space will be referred to as the *common-factor space.* For purposes of reference the above ideas may be recapitulated in the following:

THEOREM 3.5. *If m is the rank of the correlation matrix, with communalities in the diagonal, then the smallest number of linearly independent factors which will account for the intercorrelations is m; or, the common-factor space is of m dimensions.*[*]

In order to clarify the preceding ideas, the three important spaces will be reviewed. For any variable z_j the system $(z_{j1}, z_{j2}, \ldots, z_{jN})$ of N real numbers may be considered as the rectangular Cartesian coordinates of a point in an N-dimensional space. By means of this vector representation, the configuration of two variables is merely two dimensional, i.e., in a plane, although it has to be regarded as imbedded in an N-space. In general, the configuration of n vectors may be regarded as in an n-dimensional space which is imbedded in the original N-space. For purposes of factor analysis, this space can be greatly reduced, as indicated in Theorem 3.5.

Before giving the final interpretation of the vectors representing the variables in the common-factor space, a geometric discussion of the linear expressions (2.4) which include unique as well as the common factors will be found convenient. The n vectors may then be considered in the total-factor space of the m common factors and n unique factors. The vector representation of any variable in this space is given by

$$z_j' : (a_{j1}, a_{j2}, \ldots, a_{jm}, 0, \ldots, 0, a_j, 0, \ldots, 0) ,$$

[*] This theorem is given by L. L. Thurstone, *Vectors of Mind*, 1935, p. 72.

where the prime is employed to indicate the linear description of the observed variable z_j. The first m coordinates are with respect to the common-factor axes, and the last n coordinates, consisting of only one value different from zero, are with respect to the unique-factor axes. For simplicity let it be assumed that the common factors are mutually orthogonal, and, as usual, the unique factors are orthogonal to all factors. Then the norm, or length, of such a vector, according to (3.7), is

$$(3.45) \qquad N(z_j') = \sqrt{a_{j1}^2 + \ldots + a_{jm}^2 + a_j^2} = 1 \,.$$

In other words, each of the vectors representing the variables in the total factor space is of unit length. The direction cosines of such a vector in this space are simply the coordinates of the end point. The cosine of the angle of inclination (ϕ_{jk}') of two such vectors, z_j' and z_k', then becomes

$$(3.46) \qquad \cos \phi_{jk}' = \sum_{s=1}^{m+n} \lambda_{js}' \lambda_{ks}' = \sum_{s=1}^{m} a_{js} a_{ks} = r_{jk}' \,,$$

where λ_{js}' and λ_{ks}' denote the sets of direction cosines of z_j' and z_k', respectively. Equation (3.46) shows that the reproduced correlation for any two variables is the cosine of the angle between their vectors in the total-factor space. The reproduced correlation r_{jk}' will approximate the observed correlation r_{jk} to the extent that the linear representations of the variables are adequate.

Now the final interpretation of the variables as vectors in the common-factor space can be made. The orthogonal projections of the n vectors from the total-factor space into the common-factor space of m dimensions are defined to be the vectors representing the variables in this subspace. Such a vector may be denoted by

$$z_j'' : (a_{j1}, a_{j2}, \ldots, a_{jm}) \,.$$

The coordinates of the end point of this vector are the same as the first m coordinates in the total-factor space. This property holds even if the common-factor axes are oblique, provided only that the unique-factor axes are orthogonal to the common-factor space. It will again be assumed for simplicity that the common factors are uncorrelated.

A projected vector in the m-space is usually of smaller magnitude than the corresponding vector in the total-factor space, being of the same length only if the variable has no unique variance. Likewise, the angles between pairs of vectors in the common-factor space are smaller and, consequently, their cosines larger. The length of a vector z_j'' in this space is given by

$$(3.47) \qquad N(z_j'') = \sqrt{a_{j1}^2 + a_{j2}^2 + \ldots + a_{jm}^2} = h_j \,,$$

that is, the square root of the communality h_j^2 of the variable. The direction cosines of any two vectors z_j'' and z_k'' in the common-factor space are given by

$$(3.48) \qquad \lambda_{js}'' = \frac{a_{js}}{h_j} \,, \qquad \lambda_{ks}'' = \frac{a_{ks}}{h_k} \qquad (s = 1, 2, \ldots, m) \,.$$

Putting these values into (3.29), the cosine of the angle of inclination of these vectors becomes

$$(3.49) \qquad \cos \phi_{jk}'' = \sum_{s=1}^{m} \lambda_{js}'' \lambda_{ks}'' = \frac{\sum\limits_{s=1}^{m} a_{js} a_{ks}}{h_j h_k} \,.$$

It is obvious that the expression (3.49) is generally larger than that given by (3.46), being equal to it only when $h_j h_k = 1$. Hence the angles between vectors in the common-factor space are smaller than the corresponding angles in the total-factor space.

The problem of interpreting a reproduced correlation r_{jk}' geometrically can be treated in the common-factor space. It is evident from (3.46) and (3.49) that

$$(3.50) \qquad \cos \phi_{jk}'' = \frac{r_{jk}'}{h_j h_k} \,.$$

The cosine of the angle of separation of two vectors representing variables in the common-factor space may be referred to as the correlation corrected for uniqueness. In other words, the expression (3.50) would be the value of the reproduced correlation between j and k if these variables were free from unique variance. Solving (3.50) explicitly for the reproduced correlation, there results

$$(3.51) \qquad r_{jk}' = h_j h_k \cos \phi_{jk}'' \,.$$

Thus, the reproduced correlation between two variables is given by the scalar product of their vectors in the common-factor space. Of course, the observed correlation r_{jk} differs slightly from the value given in (3.51), unless the residual is exactly zero.

A simple illustration of the foregoing ideas may be given for the case of only two factors. The common-factor space is of two dimensions, and the two (uncorrelated) factors F_1 and F_2 are represented in Figure 3.3 by unit vectors separated by a right angle. Each variable z_j of a set can be described

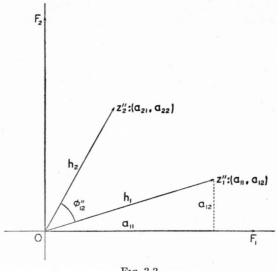

Fig. 3.3

in terms of the two common factors and a unique factor. The linear expressions for two such variables may be written as follows:

$$(3.52) \qquad \begin{cases} z_1' = a_{11}F_1 + a_{12}F_2 + a_1U_1 + 0 \cdot U_2, \\ z_2' = a_{21}F_1 + a_{22}F_2 + 0 \cdot U_1 + a_2U_2. \end{cases}$$

The geometric representation of these linear expressions for the original variables can be made in the total-factor space of four dimensions, defined by the two common factors and the two unique factors. In this space the vectors representing z_1' and z_2' are of unit length, and their correlation is given by

$$(3.53) \qquad r_{12}' = a_{11}a_{21} + a_{12}a_{22}.$$

All the essential information about the variables, i.e., the intercorrelations, can be obtained from the consideration of the common-factor space. The projections of the two vectors z_1' and z_2' into this space are indicated in

Figure 3.3 by z_1'' and z_2'', respectively, and may be written analytically in the form

(3.54)
$$\begin{cases} z_1'' = a_{11}F_1 + a_{12}F_2 \,, \\ z_2'' = a_{21}F_1 + a_{22}F_2 \,. \end{cases}$$

The lengths of these vectors are given by the square roots of their communalities, i.e.,

(3.55)
$$\begin{cases} D(Oz_1'') = \sqrt{a_{11}^2 + a_{12}^2} = \sqrt{h_1^2} \,, \\ D(Oz_2'') = \sqrt{a_{21}^2 + a_{22}^2} = \sqrt{h_2^2} \,. \end{cases}$$

The cosine of the angle (ϕ_{12}'') separating these vectors is given by formula (3.49), as follows:

(3.56)
$$\cos \phi_{12}'' = \frac{a_{11}}{h_1} \cdot \frac{a_{21}}{h_2} + \frac{a_{12}}{h_1} \cdot \frac{a_{22}}{h_2} = \frac{1}{h_1 h_2} (a_{11}a_{21} + a_{12}a_{22}) \,,$$

or, employing (3.53),

(3.57)
$$r_{12}' = h_1 h_2 \cos \phi_{12}'' \,.$$

This formula shows that the reproduced correlation of two variables is given by the product of the lengths of the two vectors by the cosine of their angle of separation in the common-factor space.

In the foregoing discussion it was necessary to employ distinct notation to clearly represent elements in the different spaces. Since it would be rather clumsy to retain primes and double primes in the remainder of this volume, they will be dropped when no confusion can arise as to the particular space involved.

CHAPTER IV

DETERMINATION OF THE COMMON-FACTOR SPACE

4.1. *Introduction*

In the preceding chapter it has been shown that the number of common factors necessary to describe a set of variables is equal to the rank of the correlation matrix. For a given set the observed correlations are known, but the communalities are unknown. The rank of the correlation matrix may then vary with the values put in the principal diagonal. It is thus possible to determine values for the communalities which make the rank of the correlation matrix as low as possible. This produces a minimum number of common factors.

The minimum number of factors for a given matrix of linearly independent correlations is obtained theoretically in **4.2.** It is then shown that, when certain relations exist among the correlations,* the set of variables can be described in terms of a smaller number of factors. These relations are developed explicitly for one factor and any number of variables in **4.3,** and for two factors in **4.4.** The general procedure for obtaining such conditions among the correlations for any number of factors is indicated in **4.5.**

When the necessary conditions among the correlations of a set of variables are satisfied for a certain rank of the matrix, the communalities can be evaluated consistently with this rank. This problem is considered in **4.6** and illustrated with a set of eight physical variables. This method of determining the communalities forms the theoretical basis for the estimation of communalities discussed in **7.2.** Such estimates are required in the principal-factor and centroid solutions which are presented in Chapters VII and VIII. Finally, to illustrate some of the methods of this chapter, a matrix of correlations of six hypothetical variables is introduced. Even more important uses of this chapter, however, are made in the methods of analysis in Chapter VI.

4.2. *Number of Common Factors*

One of the major problems in factor analysis is to determine how much the rank of the correlation matrix can be reduced by a suitable choice of

---

* When these relations exist, the property of linear independence does not hold.

the communalities when the intercorrelations are given. The correlation matrix may be written

$$\Delta = \begin{Vmatrix} h_1^2 & r_{12} & r_{13} & \ldots & r_{1n} \\ r_{21} & h_2^2 & r_{23} & \ldots & r_{2n} \\ r_{31} & r_{32} & h_3^2 & \ldots & r_{3n} \\ \cdot & \cdot & \cdot & \cdots & \cdot \\ r_{n1} & r_{n2} & r_{n3} & \ldots & h_n^2 \end{Vmatrix},$$

where the communalities, h_j^2, are unknown, and the observed correlations satisfy the property, $r_{jk} = r_{kj}$ $(j, k = 1, 2, \ldots, n)$. *The rank of the symmetric matrix Δ is m if an m-rowed principal minor Δ_{mm} is not zero and if zero is the value of every principal minor obtained by annexing to Δ_{mm} one row and the same column of Δ, and also of every principal minor obtained by annexing two rows and the same two columns.* By means of this theorem the number of linearly independent conditions that the unknown communalities must satisfy in order that the matrix Δ shall be of rank m can be determined.

There are n rows in Δ and m in the nonvanishing principal minor Δ_{mm}. This leaves $(n - m)$ rows which may be annexed, one at a time, to Δ_{mm}, or $(n - m)$ determinants which must vanish. The $(n - m)$ rows may be added two at a time in $\binom{n - m}{2}$ ways to Δ_{mm}, giving $(n - m)(n - m - 1)/2$ additional determinants which must vanish. Hence the total number of independent conditions (i.e., the number of minors set equal to zero) that the communalities must satisfy in order that Δ be of rank m is†

$$(4.1) \qquad \nu_m = (n - m) + \frac{(n - m)(n - m - 1)}{2} = \frac{(n - m)(n - m + 1)}{2}.$$

In general, the ν_m equations have solutions $h_1^2, h_2^2, \ldots, h_n^2$ only if the number of unknowns is greater than or equal to this number of conditions. If the number of unknowns is less than the number of equations, then the coefficients in the equations (the correlations) must satisfy certain relations in order that the number of independent conditions for the unknowns may be reduced to the number of unknowns.

* L. E. Dickson, *Modern Algebraic Theories*, Theorem 15, p. 79.

† The proof given here is incomplete in the sense that the ν_m equations have not been shown to be linearly independent, i.e., that none of them follows from the others. Walter Ledermann in his article, "On the Rank of the Reduced Correlational Matrix in Multiple-Factor Analysis" (*Psychometrika*, 1937, pp. 85–93), arrives at the same number of conditions for the n unknown communalities, although by a different argument, and offers a proof of the linear independence of these equations.

First, however, let it be assumed that the correlations are arbitrary values, then the set of conditions can be satisfied only if

$$(4.2) \qquad n \geq \nu_m .$$

The last inequality may be written in the following equivalent form:

$$(4.3) \qquad \phi(m) = \nu_m - n = \frac{m^2 - (2n + 1)m + n(n - 1)}{2} \leq 0 .$$

Setting the quadratic $\phi(m)$ equal to zero and solving for m, the two roots are given by

$$(4.4) \qquad m = \frac{(2n + 1) \pm \sqrt{8n + 1}}{2} .$$

Now, it can readily be shown that the plot of the quadratic function $\phi(m)$ is a parabola which opens up vertically. This curve crosses the m-axis at the two points whose abscissas are given in (4.4), and hence $\phi(m) \leq 0$ for values of m between these extremes. The rank of the correlation matrix, with unknown communalities and arbitrary correlations, may thus be reduced to the value m, which is given by

$$(4.5) \qquad \frac{(2n + 1) + \sqrt{8n + 1}}{2} \geq m \geq \frac{(2n + 1) - \sqrt{8n + 1}}{2} .$$

The smallest possible value for m is then the smallest integer greater than or equal to the value in the right-hand member of (4.5). In Table 4.1 there is listed the smallest rank that can be attained for a matrix of a given order, up to $n = 15$, when the correlations are assumed to be quite arbitrary.

TABLE 4.1

MINIMUM RANK UNDER ASSUMPTION OF
INDEPENDENT CORRELATIONS

n......	2	3	4	5	6	7	8	9	10	11	12	13	14	15
m......	1	1	2	3	3	4	5	6	6	7	8	9	10	10

Generally, the observed correlations from statistical variables cannot be considered as arbitrary or independent. The inequality in (4.2) may then be reversed, that is, the number of unknowns may be less than the number of conditions which they must satisfy. The unknown communalities are then "overdetermined" in the sense that the larger number of equations may not be consistent. In order for a solution to exist, the coefficients in the equations must satisfy at least $\phi(m)$ relations. The differences $(\nu_m - n)$, that is, the number of conditions that the correlations must satisfy so that a matrix of order n can be reduced to rank m, are given in Table 4.2.

TABLE 4.2

NUMBER OF INDEPENDENT CONDITIONS ON THE CORRELATIONS: $\phi(m)$

m \ n	2	3	4	5	6	7	8	9	10	11	12	n
1....	−1	0	2	5	9	14	20	27	35	44	54	$\binom{n-1}{2} - 1 = \dfrac{n(n-3)}{2}$
2....	−2	−2	−1	1	4	8	13	19	26	34	43	$\binom{n-2}{2} - 2 = \dfrac{n(n-5)}{2} + 1$
3....		−3	−3	−2	0	3	7	12	18	25	33	$\binom{n-3}{2} - 3 = \dfrac{n(n-7)}{2} + 3$
4....			−4	−4	−3	− 1	2	6	11	17	24	$\binom{n-4}{2} - 4 = \dfrac{n(n-9)}{2} + 6$
5....				−5	−5	− 4	− 2	1	5	10	16	$\binom{n-5}{2} - 5 = \dfrac{n(n-11)}{2} + 10$
6....					−6	− 6	− 5	− 3	0	4	9	$\binom{n-6}{2} - 6 = \dfrac{n(n-13)}{2} + 15$
m....												$\binom{n-m}{2} - m = \dfrac{n(n-2m-1)}{2} + \binom{m}{2}$

The lower left-hand corner of the table has no entries because the rank cannot exceed the order of a matrix. A negative value represents a larger number of unknowns than conditions, so that there is an infinite number of solutions in such a case, the general solution involving $(n - \nu_m)$ arbitrary parameters. A zero value represents the case of as many unknowns as equations. For a given number of variables, n, a negative or zero entry indicates the rank m which the correlation matrix can attain without any restrictions on the correlations. In these cases the inequality (4.2) is satisfied, and the conditions on the communalities are met under the assumption that the correlations are independent variables. The value of m for the first negative or zero entry, reading down a column of Table 4.2, corresponds to the value of m, for the same n, in Table 4.1.

It is important for factor analysis, however, to attain a lower rank, for any value of n, than that given in Table 4.1. In an actual factor study the investigator should select the variables on some hypothesis of underlying factors.* Then the correlation coefficients will not be independent, and, owing to the consequent relationships among them, the rank of the correlation matrix will be lower than otherwise. In other words, the number of factors, m, necessary to describe a set of n variables will be lower than the minimum value given in (4.5) if the variables are selected to fall into subgroups. This, of course, is desirable in factor analysis. If ten factors were necessary to describe fifteen variables, there would be very little gain in parsimony of thought.

4.3. *Conditions for One Common Factor*

The number of independent relationships that must exist among the correlations in order that the rank shall be lower than the minimum in (4.5) is given by the positive values in Table 4.2. Thus for $n = 3$, no relationships are necessary to attain rank one; that is, three variables can always be described in terms of one common factor. Four variables, however, cannot be described by just one factor unless their intercorrelations satisfy two (independent) conditions. These well-known conditions† are the vanishing of the *tetrads*, namely,

$$(4.6) \qquad \begin{cases} r_{12}r_{34} - r_{14}r_{23} = 0 \,, \\ r_{13}r_{24} - r_{14}r_{23} = 0 \,. \end{cases}$$

It may be well to indicate how the conditions (4.6) are arrived at when $n = 4$ and $m = 1$, so that the method of generalization will be more evident. When there are just four variables, the matrix of intercorrelations may be written

$$\Delta_4 = \begin{Vmatrix} h_1^2 & r_{12} & r_{13} & r_{14} \\ r_{21} & h_2^2 & r_{23} & r_{24} \\ r_{31} & r_{32} & h_3^2 & r_{34} \\ r_{41} & r_{42} & r_{43} & h_4^2 \end{Vmatrix}.$$

This matrix will be of rank one if all second-order minors vanish. By the selection of appropriate minors, several linear equations can be determined for the solution of each of the communalities. Thus, h_1^2 is given by any one of the following three equations:

$$\begin{vmatrix} h_1^2 & r_{13} \\ r_{21} & r_{23} \end{vmatrix} = 0 \,, \qquad \begin{vmatrix} h_1^2 & r_{14} \\ r_{21} & r_{24} \end{vmatrix} = 0 \,, \qquad \begin{vmatrix} h_1^2 & r_{14} \\ r_{31} & r_{34} \end{vmatrix} = 0 \,,$$

* See **2.7**.   † Charles Spearman, *The Abilities of Man*, 1927.

or

(4.7)
$$h_1^2 = \frac{r_{12}r_{13}}{r_{23}} = \frac{r_{12}r_{14}}{r_{24}} = \frac{r_{13}r_{14}}{r_{34}}.$$

On eliminating h_1^2, the two equations (4.6) arise. The solutions (4.7) for h_1^2 are consistent if the conditions (4.6) are satisfied.

The question arises whether new conditions are introduced when the other communalities are solved for and eliminated. According to Table 4.2, only two independent conditions on the correlations are necessary to assure rank one for a fourth-order correlation matrix. To illustrate the dependence of any other conditions on the two already obtained, the solutions for the second communality are given:

(4.8)
$$h_2^2 = \frac{r_{21}r_{23}}{r_{13}} = \frac{r_{21}r_{24}}{r_{14}} = \frac{r_{23}r_{24}}{r_{34}}.$$

These equations may be obtained by setting appropriate second-order minors of Δ_4 equal to zero or, more simply, by interchanging the indices 1 and 2 in (4.7). On eliminating h_2^2 from (4.8), the following conditions arise:

(4.9)
$$\begin{cases} r_{13}r_{24} - r_{14}r_{23} = 0 \,, \\ r_{13}r_{24} - r_{12}r_{34} = 0 \,. \end{cases}$$

The first of these equations is identical with the second of equations (4.6), and the second is the difference of equations (4.6). Hence no new (independent) conditions are introduced.

Referring to Table 4.2 again, it is seen that five relationships must exist among the intercorrelations of five variables if they are to be described in terms of only one common factor. The correlation matrix,

$$\Delta_5 = \begin{Vmatrix} h_1^2 & r_{12} & r_{13} & r_{14} & r_{15} \\ r_{21} & h_2^2 & r_{23} & r_{24} & r_{25} \\ r_{31} & r_{32} & h_3^2 & r_{34} & r_{35} \\ r_{41} & r_{42} & r_{43} & h_4^2 & r_{45} \\ r_{51} & r_{52} & r_{53} & r_{54} & h_5^2 \end{Vmatrix},$$

will be of rank one if all second-order minors vanish. The five independent conditions that the correlations must satisfy may be obtained by the preceding process.

Several linear equations for the solution of each of the communalities can be obtained by setting appropriate second-order minors of Δ_5 equal to zero. The first communality, for example, is given by any one of the six equations:

$$\begin{vmatrix} h_1^2 & r_{13} \\ r_{21} & r_{23} \end{vmatrix} = 0\,, \qquad \begin{vmatrix} h_1^2 & r_{14} \\ r_{21} & r_{24} \end{vmatrix} = 0\,, \qquad \begin{vmatrix} h_1^2 & r_{15} \\ r_{21} & r_{25} \end{vmatrix} = 0\,,$$

$$\begin{vmatrix} h_1^2 & r_{14} \\ r_{31} & r_{34} \end{vmatrix} = 0\,, \qquad \begin{vmatrix} h_1^2 & r_{15} \\ r_{31} & r_{35} \end{vmatrix} = 0\,, \qquad \begin{vmatrix} h_1^2 & r_{15} \\ r_{41} & r_{45} \end{vmatrix} = 0\,,$$

or

$$(4.10) \qquad h_1^2 = \frac{r_{12}r_{13}}{r_{23}} = \frac{r_{12}r_{14}}{r_{24}} = \frac{r_{12}r_{15}}{r_{25}} = \frac{r_{13}r_{14}}{r_{34}} = \frac{r_{13}r_{15}}{r_{35}} = \frac{r_{14}r_{15}}{r_{45}}.$$

In order that the solution for h_1^2 shall be unique, the following five conditions must be satisfied:

$$(4.11) \qquad \frac{r_{12}r_{13}}{r_{23}} = \frac{r_{12}r_{14}}{r_{24}} = \frac{r_{12}r_{15}}{r_{25}} = \frac{r_{13}r_{14}}{r_{34}} = \frac{r_{13}r_{15}}{r_{35}} = \frac{r_{14}r_{15}}{r_{45}}.$$

These conditions may be put in the equivalent form:

$$(4.12) \qquad \begin{cases} r_{13}r_{24} - r_{14}r_{23} = 0, \\ r_{13}r_{25} - r_{15}r_{23} = 0, \\ r_{12}r_{34} - r_{14}r_{23} = 0, \\ r_{12}r_{35} - r_{15}r_{23} = 0, \\ r_{13}r_{45} - r_{14}r_{35} = 0. \end{cases}$$

Any other conditions must be linearly dependent on the above equations. Thus if instead of obtaining the solutions for h_1^2, those for h_2^2 were obtained, the resulting five conditions could then be shown to be dependent on the foregoing relations.* A similar argument holds for the conditions obtained by solving and eliminating any other communality.

* As in the case of h_1^2, there are six linear equations for the solution of h_2^2, namely,

$$h_2^2 = \frac{r_{21}r_{23}}{r_{13}} = \frac{r_{21}r_{24}}{r_{14}} = \frac{r_{21}r_{25}}{r_{15}} = \frac{r_{23}r_{24}}{r_{34}} = \frac{r_{23}r_{25}}{r_{35}} = \frac{r_{24}r_{25}}{r_{45}}.$$

On eliminating h_2^2, the consistency conditions may be put in the form:

(i) $r_{23}r_{14} - r_{24}r_{13} = 0,$

(ii) $r_{23}r_{15} - r_{25}r_{13} = 0,$

(iii) $r_{12}r_{34} - r_{24}r_{13} = 0,$

(iv) $r_{12}r_{35} - r_{25}r_{13} = 0,$

(v) $r_{23}r_{45} - r_{24}r_{35} = 0.$

Now it will be shown that these equations are linear combinations of those in (4.12). Equations (i) and (ii) are equivalent to (4.12_1) and 4.12_2), respectively. Equation (iii) is the difference of (4.12_1) and (4.12_3), and equation (iv) is the difference of (4.12_2) and (4.12_4). To show that (v) is linearly dependent on (4.12), substitute $r_{13} = r_{14}r_{23}/r_{24}$, obtained from (4.12_1), into (4.12_5). The result is

$$r_{14}r_{23}r_{45} - r_{14}r_{35}r_{24} = 0,$$

which reduces to (v) by factoring out r_{14}.

According to Table 4.2, a set of n variables can be described in terms of just one common factor if $n(n-3)/2$ linearly independent relationships exist among the correlations. These conditions, whatever form they take, are equivalent to the following set:

(4.13)
$$\begin{cases} \dfrac{r_{12}r_{13}}{r_{23}} = \dfrac{r_{12}r_{14}}{r_{24}} = \cdots = \dfrac{r_{12}r_{1n}}{r_{2n}} = \dfrac{r_{13}r_{14}}{r_{34}} \\[2em] \qquad\qquad = \cdots = \dfrac{r_{13}r_{1n}}{r_{3n}} = \cdots = \dfrac{r_{1,n-1}r_{1n}}{r_{n-1,n}}. \end{cases}$$

For any variable z_e, a term of the form

$$t_{jk} = \frac{r_{ej}r_{ek}}{r_{jk}} \qquad \left(\begin{array}{l} e, j, k = 1, 2, \ldots, n \\ \quad e \neq j \neq k \end{array}\right)$$

will be called a *triad*. It is readily seen that there are $\dbinom{n-1}{2}$ triads in (4.13), or

(4.14)
$$\binom{n-1}{2} - 1 = \frac{n(n-3)}{2}$$

equations of condition for one general factor among n variables.

The number of conditions of the form (4.13) to determine whether a matrix is of rank one is considerably less than the number of tetrads. Every four variables give rise to three tetrads so that the total number of different tetrads for n variables is

(4.15)
$$3\binom{n}{4} = \frac{n(n-1)(n-2)(n-3)}{8}.$$

The difference between (4.15) and (4.14) is

(4.16)
$$\left[\frac{n(n-3)}{2}\right] \cdot \left[\frac{n(n-3)-2}{4}\right].$$

To indicate the magnitude of this number, suppose $n = 15$. The total number of tetrads is 4,095, while the number of triad conditions (4.13) is only 90. The difference (4.16) is 4,005. In other words, the labor of computing the conditions (4.13) is only about one-fortieth of that of computing the tetrads, for fifteen variables. For a larger number of variables the relative economy of labor becomes more pronounced.

4.4. *Conditions for Two Common Factors*

The necessary conditions for a matrix of correlations to attain rank two will next be considered. For five variables it is a well-known fact that one relationship must exist, namely, the following *pentad criterion*:*

$$(4.17) \quad \left\{ \begin{aligned} & r_{12}r_{23}r_{34}r_{45}r_{51} - r_{12}r_{23}r_{35}r_{41}r_{54} - r_{12}r_{24}r_{35}r_{43}r_{51} + r_{12}r_{24}r_{31}r_{45}r_{53} \\ & + r_{12}r_{25}r_{34}r_{41}r_{53} - r_{12}r_{25}r_{31}r_{43}r_{54} - r_{13}r_{24}r_{35}r_{41}r_{52} + r_{13}r_{25}r_{34}r_{42}r_{51} \\ & + r_{14}r_{23}r_{31}r_{45}r_{52} - r_{14}r_{25}r_{32}r_{43}r_{51} - r_{15}r_{23}r_{31}r_{42}r_{54} \\ & + r_{15}r_{24}r_{32}r_{41}r_{53} = 0 \,. \end{aligned} \right.$$

This condition may be obtained by the method employed before. The correlation matrix, Δ_5, must have every third-order minor equal to zero if it is to be of rank two. By selecting appropriate minors, several linear equations for the solution of each of the communalities and hence the conditions for consistency can be obtained. Accordingly, for h_1^2 the following two determinants are employed:

$$\begin{vmatrix} h_1^2 & r_{13} & r_{15} \\ r_{21} & r_{23} & r_{25} \\ r_{41} & r_{43} & r_{45} \end{vmatrix} = 0 \,, \qquad \begin{vmatrix} h_1^2 & r_{14} & r_{15} \\ r_{21} & r_{24} & r_{25} \\ r_{31} & r_{34} & r_{35} \end{vmatrix} = 0 \,.$$

Equating the two solutions for h_1^2, there results

$$\frac{r_{21}(r_{13}r_{45} - r_{15}r_{43}) - r_{41}(r_{13}r_{25} - r_{15}r_{23})}{(r_{23}r_{45} - r_{25}r_{43})}$$
$$= \frac{r_{21}(r_{14}r_{35} - r_{15}r_{34}) - r_{31}(r_{14}r_{25} - r_{15}r_{24})}{(r_{24}r_{35} - r_{25}r_{34})} \,,$$

or

$$(4.18) \quad \left\{ \begin{aligned} & [r_{24}r_{35} - r_{25}r_{34}][r_{21}(r_{13}r_{45} - r_{15}r_{43}) - r_{41}(r_{13}r_{25} - r_{15}r_{23})] \\ & - [r_{23}r_{45} - r_{25}r_{43}][r_{21}(r_{14}r_{35} - r_{15}r_{34}) - r_{31}(r_{14}r_{25} - r_{15}r_{24})] = 0 \,, \end{aligned} \right.$$

as the single consistency condition. If the intercorrelations of five variables satisfy (4.18), or the equivalent condition (4.17), then five communalities can be determined to make the rank of Δ_5 equal to two, i.e., the five variables can be described in terms of two common factors.

According to Table 4.2, the correlations among six variables must satisfy

---

* It is believed that this condition was first obtained by T. L. Kelley, *Crossroads in the Mind of Man*, p. 58; see also Ledermann, *op. cit.*

four independent conditions in order for the matrix Δ_6 to attain rank two. It will be convenient to make the following definition:

$$(4.19) \qquad \left| h_1^2 \quad r_{ab} \quad r_{cd} \right| = \begin{vmatrix} h_1^2 & r_{1b} & r_{1d} \\ r_{a1} & r_{ab} & r_{ad} \\ r_{c1} & r_{cb} & r_{cd} \end{vmatrix} ,$$

that is, a determinant is represented by the elements of the principal diagonal.

In order that Δ_6 be of rank two, every third-order minor must vanish; five such determinants are

$$\left| h_1^2 \quad r_{23} \quad r_{45} \right| = \left| h_1^2 \quad r_{23} \quad r_{46} \right| = \left| h_1^2 \quad r_{23} \quad r_{56} \right| = \left| h_1^2 \quad r_{24} \quad r_{56} \right|$$
$$= \left| h_1^2 \quad r_{34} \quad r_{56} \right| = 0 .$$

The solutions for h_1^2 from these five equations are as follows:

$$(4.20) \qquad \begin{cases} h_1^2 = \dfrac{r_{21} \left| r_{13} \quad r_{45} \right| - r_{41} \left| r_{13} \quad r_{25} \right|}{\left| r_{23} \quad r_{45} \right|} , \\[2ex] h_1^2 = \dfrac{r_{21} \left| r_{13} \quad r_{46} \right| - r_{41} \left| r_{13} \quad r_{26} \right|}{\left| r_{23} \quad r_{46} \right|} , \\[2ex] h_1^2 = \dfrac{r_{21} \left| r_{13} \quad r_{56} \right| - r_{51} \left| r_{13} \quad r_{26} \right|}{\left| r_{23} \quad r_{56} \right|} , \\[2ex] h_1^2 = \dfrac{r_{21} \left| r_{14} \quad r_{56} \right| - r_{51} \left| r_{14} \quad r_{26} \right|}{\left| r_{24} \quad r_{56} \right|} , \\[2ex] h_1^2 = \dfrac{r_{31} \left| r_{14} \quad r_{56} \right| - r_{51} \left| r_{14} \quad r_{36} \right|}{\left| r_{34} \quad r_{56} \right|} , \end{cases}$$

where

$$(4.21) \qquad \left| r_{ab} \quad r_{cd} \right| = \begin{vmatrix} r_{ab} & r_{ad} \\ r_{cb} & r_{cd} \end{vmatrix} = r_{ab} r_{cd} - r_{ad} r_{cb} .$$

Eliminating h_1^2 from the five equations (4.20), the four conditions which the correlations must satisfy are obtained. The equality of the right-hand members of equations (4.20) are then the necessary conditions for six variables to be describable in terms of two common factors.

This process can be continued for any number of variables. The positive entries for $m = 2$ in Table 4.2 give the number of conditions that must exist among the correlations for a set of n variables to be describable in terms of only two common factors. In general, the correlations among n variables must satisfy $(n^2 - 5n + 2)/2$ conditions in order that their matrix shall be of rank two. These conditions may be obtained by eliminating any communality h_e^2 from $(n^2 - 5n + 4)/2$ equations of the form

$$(4.22) \qquad h_e^2 = \frac{r_{ae}\begin{vmatrix} r_{eb} & r_{cd} \end{vmatrix} - r_{ce}\begin{vmatrix} r_{eb} & r_{ad} \end{vmatrix}}{\begin{vmatrix} r_{ab} & r_{cd} \end{vmatrix}}$$

$$\left(\begin{matrix} e, a, b, c, d = 1, 2, \ldots, n \\ e \neq a \neq b \neq c \neq d \end{matrix} \right).$$

It will be noted that many more conditions than the number indicated in Table 4.2 can be written for the intercorrelations of n variables by means of the foregoing procedure. Corresponding to any four indices in the denominator of (4.22) there is a third-order determinant of the form (4.19) which is to be set equal to zero for the calculation of a particular communality h_e^2. Out of a given set of n variables there are $\binom{n-1}{4} = (n-1)!/(n-5)!4!$ choices for the denominator, and each of these may be permuted in 4! ways. The total number of possible denominators, and hence, third-order determinants, for the calculation of the communalities would seem to be enormous. Fortunately, however, this number is considerably reduced owing to the symmetry of the correlation matrix and certain properties of second-order determinants.

Although there are 24 possible permutations of four indices, leading to as many determinants (4.21), it will now be shown that these 24 determinants have only two different numerical values (and their differences and negatives). By means of definition (4.21) the following two properties are immediately verified:

$$(4.23) \qquad \begin{vmatrix} ab & cd \end{vmatrix} = \begin{vmatrix} ba & dc \end{vmatrix},$$

$$(4.24) \qquad \begin{vmatrix} ab & cd \end{vmatrix} = - \begin{vmatrix} cb & ad \end{vmatrix},$$

where, for simplicity, only the indices of the correlation coefficients are written. Then the two values of (4.21) for any four indices a, b, c, d arise from the successive applications of (4.23) and (4.24), as follows:

$$(4.25) \qquad \begin{vmatrix} ab & cd \end{vmatrix} = \begin{vmatrix} ba & dc \end{vmatrix} = - \begin{vmatrix} da & bc \end{vmatrix} = - \begin{vmatrix} ad & cb \end{vmatrix} = \begin{vmatrix} cd & ab \end{vmatrix}$$
$$= \begin{vmatrix} dc & ba \end{vmatrix} = - \begin{vmatrix} bc & da \end{vmatrix} = - \begin{vmatrix} cb & ad \end{vmatrix},$$

$$(4.26) \qquad \begin{vmatrix} ab & dc \end{vmatrix} = \begin{vmatrix} ba & cd \end{vmatrix} = - \begin{vmatrix} ca & bd \end{vmatrix} = - \begin{vmatrix} ac & db \end{vmatrix} = \begin{vmatrix} dc & ab \end{vmatrix}$$
$$= \begin{vmatrix} cd & ba \end{vmatrix} = - \begin{vmatrix} bd & ca \end{vmatrix} = - \begin{vmatrix} db & ac \end{vmatrix}.$$

Any one of the remaining eight determinants, resulting from another permutation of the four indices, is a combination of two expressions, one from (4.25) and the other from (4.26). For example, $\begin{vmatrix} ac & bd \end{vmatrix} = \begin{vmatrix} ab & cd \end{vmatrix}$

$- |ab\ dc|$, which may be checked by writing these determinants in full and making use of the symmetric property of correlations.

The evaluations of a communality (4.22) which are based upon the denominators indicated in (4.25) are all equal.* These equalities are quite independent of the assumed rank of the correlation matrix. The investigator should employ thus only one of the equivalent denominators in (4.25). If he should employ all eight, and obtain eight identical evaluations of the communality, he would still have no assurance that the assumed rank of two for the correlation matrix is correct. The values of the communality employing the denominators in (4.26) are, again, all equal, but usually different from the value involving a denominator of (4.25). If one of the remaining eight permutations of four indices is employed, it can be shown that the resulting evaluation of the communality is a direct result of the preceding two evaluations.

To establish this property, consider the two evaluations of h_e^2 dependent upon the denominators of (4.25) and (4.26), respectively:

$$E = \frac{N}{D} = \frac{ae|eb\ \ cd| - ce|eb\ \ ad|}{|ab\ \ cd|},$$

$$\text{and} \qquad E' = \frac{N'}{D'} = \frac{ae|eb\ \ dc| - de|eb\ \ ac|}{|ab\ \ dc|},$$

where E and E' are used to represent the particular evaluations, and only the indices of the correlation coefficients are written for simplicity. Consider also the evaluation employing $|ac\ bd|$ in the denominator, namely,

$$E'' = \frac{N''}{D''} = \frac{ae|ec\ \ bd| - be|ec\ \ ad|}{|ac\ \ bd|}.$$

---

* The equality of the eight evaluations of a particular communality employing the denominators of (4.25) is indicated in the following manner. Let E be the evaluation of a communality h_e^2 based upon the first determinant of (4.25), namely,

$$E = \frac{r_{ae}|r_{eb}\ r_{cd}| - r_{ce}|r_{eb}\ r_{ad}|}{|r_{ab}\ r_{cd}|}.$$

The evaluation based upon the second determinant of (4.25) is

$$E' = \frac{r_{be}|r_{ea}\ r_{dc}| - r_{de}|r_{ea}\ r_{bc}|}{|r_{ba}\ r_{dc}|}$$

$$= \frac{r_{be}(r_{ea}r_{cd} - r_{ec}r_{da}) - r_{de}(r_{ea}r_{bc} - r_{ec}r_{ba})}{r_{ba}r_{dc} - r_{bc}r_{da}}$$

$$= \frac{r_{ea}(r_{be}r_{cd} - r_{de}r_{bc}) - r_{ec}(r_{be}r_{da} - r_{de}r_{ba})}{r_{ab}r_{cd} - r_{cb}r_{ad}},$$

which is evidently equal to E. As one further illustration consider the evaluation based

It was indicated before that $|ac\ bd| = |ab\ cd| - |ab\ dc|$, that is, $D'' = D - D'$. By expanding the determinants in the numerators, it follows that

$$N - N' = r_{ae}(r_{eb}r_{cd} - r_{cb}r_{ed}) - r_{ce}(r_{eb}r_{ad} - r_{ab}r_{ed})$$
$$- r_{ae}(r_{eb}r_{dc} - r_{db}r_{ec}) + r_{de}(r_{eb}r_{ac} - r_{ab}r_{ec})$$
$$= r_{ae}(r_{ec}r_{bd} - r_{bc}r_{ed}) - r_{be}(r_{ec}r_{ad} - r_{ac}r_{ed})$$
$$= ae|ec\ bd| - be|ec\ ad| = N''.$$

Hence the evaluation E'' can be expressed in terms of the other two evaluations as follows:

$$E'' = \frac{N''}{D''} = \frac{N - N'}{D - D'} = \frac{ED - E'D'}{D - D'}.$$

If the evaluations E and E' are reasonably close to the true value h_1^2, then E'' is also equal to this value, for, setting $E = E' = h_e^2$, it follows that

$$E'' = \frac{h_e^2(D - D')}{D - D'} = h_e^2.$$

The preceding discussion indicates that, of the twenty-four evaluations of a particular communality from the permutations of four variables selected for the denominator of (4.22), only two determinations need be considered. For a set of n variables there are then $2\binom{n-1}{4} = (n-1)!/12(n-5)!$ third-order determinants which must vanish in order that the rank of the correlation matrix shall be two. The number of conditions which arise upon equating the evaluations of a communality from these determinants is in excess of that indicated in Table 4.2 for $n > 5$. Although all these determinations of a particular communality must necessarily be equal (statistically) if the rank is two, these conditions are not all independent. The use of the large set of conditions furnishes an exact check on the rank. In practice, however, it will be found sufficiently accurate to equate a smaller number of evaluations of communality for an approximate check of the rank, and for subsequent approximation of the communalities of a set of variables. An illustration of this is given in **4.6**.

---

upon the last arrangement of the indices a, b, c, d in (4.25), that is,

$$E'' = \frac{r_{ce}|r_{eb}\ r_{ad}| - r_{ae}|r_{eb}\ r_{cd}|}{|r_{cb}\ r_{ad}|},$$

which, on applying (4.24) to the denominator, becomes

$$E'' = \frac{-[r_{ae}|r_{eb}\ r_{cd}| - r_{ce}|r_{eb}\ r_{ad}|]}{-|r_{ab}\ r_{cd}|} = E.$$

Similarly, any other evaluation employing the denominators of (4.25) can be shown to be equal to E.

4.5. *Conditions for m Common Factors*

In the general case, the correlation matrix Δ will be of rank m if every $(m + 1)$-order minor vanishes. By the selection of appropriate minors, a number of linear equations can be obtained for the solution of each of the communalities. Then, by eliminating the communality, there results the conditions that the correlations must satisfy in order for Δ to be of rank m. A typical equation involving h_1^2 linearly is

$$
D = \begin{vmatrix}
h_1^2 & r_{13} & r_{15} & \cdots & r_{1,2k-1} & \cdots & r_{1,2m+1} \\
r_{21} & r_{23} & r_{25} & \cdots & r_{2,2k-1} & \cdots & r_{2,2m+1} \\
r_{41} & r_{43} & r_{45} & \cdots & r_{4,2k-1} & \cdots & r_{4,2m+1} \\
\cdot & \cdot & \cdot & \cdots & \cdot & \cdots & \cdot \\
r_{2j,1} & r_{2j,3} & r_{2j,5} & \cdots & r_{2j,2k-1} & \cdots & r_{2j,2m+1} \\
\cdot & \cdot & \cdot & \cdots & \cdot & \cdots & \cdot \\
r_{2m,1} & r_{2m,3} & r_{2m,5} & \cdots & r_{2m,2k-1} & \cdots & r_{2m,2m+1}
\end{vmatrix} = 0 .
$$

It may be noted that the $(j + 1)$st row is given by the first index equal to $2j$ and the kth column by the second index equal to $2k - 1$. The determinant D is thus seen to contain $(m + 1)$ rows and $(m + 1)$ columns.

The determinant D may be expanded according to the elements of the first column, as follows:

$$
h_1^2 D_{11} - r_{21} D_{21} + r_{41} D_{41} + \ldots (-1)^i r_{2j,1} D_{2j,1} + \ldots (-1)^m r_{2m,1} D_{2m,1} = 0 ,
$$

where

$$
D_{11} = \text{minor of the element } h_1^2 ,
$$
$$
D_{jk} = \text{minor of the element } r_{jk} .
$$

The communality of the first variable is then given by

(4.27)
$$
h_1^2 = \frac{1}{D_{11}} \sum_{s=1}^{m} (-1)^{s-1} r_{2s,1} D_{2s,1} .
$$

This solution involves the correlations among the first $(2m + 1)$ variables, and, except for the first one, the correlations of an even-numbered variable are only with odd-numbered ones, and odd only with even. Other determinants than D, still employing only the first $(2m + 1)$ variables, may be equated to zero to yield linear equations in h_1^2 only. Then different variables may be introduced from the original set of n to obtain still other linear equations in h_1^2. Thus the requisite number of equations of the form (4.27) can be obtained, and from them, in turn, necessary restrictions on the correlations. The number of such independent conditions is given in Table 4.2. In the general case of n variables and m factors, the number of conditions is given by

$$\nu_m - n = \frac{(n - m)(n - m + 1)}{2} - n = \frac{n(n - 2m - 1)}{2} + \binom{m}{2},$$

so that there should be one more than this number of equations of the form (4.27). Actually many more equations of this form can be written, just as in the case of rank two. Again, however, it may be remarked that a good approximation can be obtained by employing the indicated number of expressions (4.27).

In the preceding analysis it has been tacitly assumed that

$$n \geqq 2m + 1 \, ,$$

so that a determinant of the type D, involving the correlations among $(2m + 1)$ variables, would be possible. If there were not this number of variables, then some other procedure would be necessary, for it would not be possible to obtain linear equations in only one communality. Perhaps the best procedure then would be to select $(m + 1)$-order determinants involving the smallest number of communalities to set equal to zero. From a sufficient number of such equations the communalities could be eliminated to produce the necessary restrictions on the correlations. In a practical problem this difficulty is not to be expected because the variables are so selected as to form clusters or groups, and hence n is usually many times the size of m.

4.6. *Determination of Communality*

Up to this point various conditions for a correlation matrix to have a given rank were set down. These conditions were obtained by equating a number of evaluations of a particular diagonal entry or communality. It is then evident that this procedure could be employed in determining the communalites if the rank were known. Although the rank of a correlation matrix cannot be obtained directly, it may be approximated by the number of groups of variables, determined by such methods as those of Chapter II. The number of such groups is approximately equal to the number of linearly independent factors, and these in turn determine the dimensionality of the common-factor space. Then the converse of Theorem 3.5 states that the rank of the correlation matrix is equal to the number of dimensions of the space containing the vectors representing the variables.

In an actual analysis the number of common factors (or the rank of the correlation matrix) may be assumed to be equal to the number of groups G_s. Then the methods of the preceding sections may be applied to check whether the correlations satisfy the necessary conditions for their matrix to be of the assumed rank. If the correlations satisfy these conditions, then the communalities are given by equations of the form (4.22) for rank two, or, in general, by (4.27) for rank m. As will be indicated, the order of procedure is to set down a number of evaluations of each communality for the assumed rank. The consistency of these values will serve as a check on the assumed rank, and their average may then be taken as the appropriate communality. Similar determinations would be required for each variable in the set. The assumed rank must check for all such determinations of the communalities.

Of course, the correlations need not satisfy the conditions for a given rank exactly with actual data because allowance must be made for chance errors. A sampling error formula for the general expression in the right-hand member of (4.27) is not known at the present time. The standard error of the simplest instance of this expression (the triad), however, is developed in **6.5.** When the rank of a matrix of correlations is assumed to be one, the true values of the various triads for the communality of any variable are equal. Thus by means of the standard error formula for triads, it is possible to determine whether the variations of the obtained values are attributable entirely to fluctuations in sampling. It is suggested that for rank one all possible triads be written in the calculation of a particular communality. If the variation among these values can reasonably be assigned to chance fluctuations, the mean value may be taken as the communality.

In the case of rank two, all possible expressions (4.22) for the determination of each communality could be considered. Before being averaged, however, those based upon insignificant denominators would need to be rejected. The variables yielding insignificant tetrads for the denominator of (4.22) can be identified when the design of the variables is known, and there are but two groups. In such a case each group of variables will approximate rank one, and the tetrads involving three variables of such a group will be insignificant. Knowing the combinations of variables which produce insignificant denominators, it is not necessary to consider the expressions (4.22) which involve them. The denominators should include two variables of each group, considerably reducing the total number of expressions for each communality.

When the rank of a correlation matrix is assumed, and the determination of the communalities is attempted, it may sometimes happen that some of the values exceed unity. Of course, such values of the communalities are not permitted, and they indicate that the assumption of the rank is inexact. Before the hypothesis of the specified rank is discarded, however, a number of evaluations of communality should be attempted. If, in general, several consistent values for each communality can be obtained, they should be averaged for the best determination of the communality, ignoring those values which exceed unity. The justification for this procedure lies in the fact that the observed correlations are themselves subject to error, and the values to be supplied in the diagonal of the correlation matrix to produce a specified rank can only be expected to satisfy this hypothesis approximately. The final check lies in the agreement of the reproduced correlations, from the solution employing these communalities, with the observed correlations.

TABLE 4.3

INTERCORRELATIONS OF EIGHT PHYSICAL VARIABLES
FOR 305 FIFTEEN-YEAR-OLD GIRLS

Variable	1	2	3	4	5	6	7	8
1. Height................								
2. Arm span............	.846							
3. Length of forearm......	.805	.881						
4. Length of lower leg.....	.859	.826	.801					
5. Weight...............	.473	.376	.380	.436				
6. Bitrochanteric diameter.	.398	.326	.319	.329	.762			
7. Chest girth...........	.301	.277	.237	.327	.730	.583		
8. Chest width..........	.382	.415	.345	.365	.629	.577	.539	

If the final residuals are insignificant, then the choice of the communalities is statistically sound.

An illustration of the calculation of the communalities when the design is known and the rank can be assumed to be two is furnished by the eight physical variables the correlations for which are given in Table 4.3.* The first four variables were selected as measures of "lankiness" and the latter four as measures of "stockiness." This design is substantiated by the method of B-coefficients. It is thus found that

$$B(1, 2, 3, 4) = 235 \,,$$
$$B(5, 6, 7, 8) = 179 \,.$$

These values clearly indicate that the two sets of variables form two distinct groups. Rank two can then be assumed and checked in the process of obtaining the communalities.

* Frances Mullen, "Factors in the Growth of Girls Seven to Seventeen Years of Age" (Ph.D. dissertation, Department of Education, University of Chicago), 1939.

Assuming rank two, the communality of any variable z_e can be obtained by averaging a number of evaluations of (4.22). The calculation of such expressions can be facilitated by organizing the work as in Table 4.4, where the communality for the first variable in the given set is determined.

TABLE 4.4

CALCULATION OF h_1^2

ab	cd	$r_{a1}\|r_{1b}\quad r_{cd}\| - r_{c1}\|r_{1b}\quad r_{ad}\|$	N	D	h_1^2
23	56	.846(.4622) − .473(−.0882)	.4327	.5474	.7905
23	57	.846(.4733) − .473(−.0422)	.4204	.5379	.7815
23	58	.846(.3612) − .473(−.0025)	.3068	.3964	.7739
23	67	.846(.3733) − .398(−.0422)	.3326	.4253	.7821
23	68	.846(.3426) − .398(−.0025)	.2908	.3760	.7735
23	78	.846(.3434) − .301(−.0025)	.2913	.3765	.7736
24	56	.846(.4810) − .473(−.0487)	.4300	.4873	.8823
24	57	.846(.4958) − .473(−.0107)	.4245	.4822	.8804
24	58	.846(.3738) − .473(.0410)	.2968	.3386	.8767
24	67	.846(.4018) − .398(−.0107)	.3442	.3904	.8816
24	68	.846(.3700) − .398(.0410)	.2967	.3401	.8724
24	78	.846(.3381) − .301(.0410)	.2737	.3095	.8843
34	56	.805(.4810) − .473(−.0448)	.4084	.4713	.8665
34	57	.805(.4958) − .473(−.0375)	.4169	.4814	.8659
34	58	.805(.3738) − .473(−.0096)	.3054	.3534	.8643
34	67	.805(.4018) − .398(−.0375)	.3384	.3890	.8699
34	68	.805(.3700) − .398(−.0096)	.3017	.3487	.8651
34	78	.805(.3381) − .301(−.0096)	.2751	.3189	.8625
Mean					.842

In the stub of the table are recorded the four indices a, b, c, d which determine the denominator D of (4.22), namely,

$$D = \begin{vmatrix} r_{ab} & r_{cd} \end{vmatrix}.$$

These indices are selected so that two are included from each group, and duplications which arise by certain permutations, as indicated in (4.25) and (4.26), are omitted. Thus an orderly arrangement can be obtained by considering all possible combinations of pairs of variables from the first group with every pair of variables from the second group. The variable for which the communality is being calculated must, of course, be omitted from such pairings. In Table 4.4 each pair of variables 23, 24, and 34 is considered along with each pair 56, 57, 58, 67, 68, and 78. Eighteen distinct values of the denominator, and hence the expression (4.22), are thus considered in Table 4.4. It is true that eighteen additional determinations could be made by interchanging the variables in only one of the pairs ab or cd. Since the computed values in Table 4.4 check the rank closely, it is highly improbable that the additional eighteen determinations would be inconsistent with the former, and hence they need not be calculated.

When the indices in the stub have been set down, it is suggested that the denominators in column D be computed. Some unnecessary work might be avoided by doing this first. For, if the original design of the variables was not accurate, three of the four variables might actually belong to one group (or measure a single factor), and the resulting D would then be very small. Such a combination of four variables would be rejected from the calculations, and no further work would be done in that row of the table.

After the denominators have been computed, cross out any that are insignificant, and then obtain the numerators of (4.22). For the communality of the first variable these numerators are

$$N = r_{a1} \begin{vmatrix} r_{1b} & r_{cd} \end{vmatrix} - r_{c1} \begin{vmatrix} r_{1b} & r_{ad} \end{vmatrix} .$$

In the tabular arrangement of the work it is well to record all the coefficients r_{a1} and r_{c1} before calculating the second-order determinants. It is also desirable to calculate all the second-order determinants of the first column, and then those in the second column, rather than the two in each row. With this procedure the successive second-order determinants can be calculated from Table 4.3 in an orderly fashion. By performing the indicated multiplications and combination of terms in each row, the numerators are obtained. These are then divided by the respective denominators to get the eighteen values of h_1^2. The consistency of these values, as shown below, indicates that the assumption of rank two was justified. The mean is then taken as the value of the communality.

It will be noted that many of the second-order determinants repeat themselves in Table 4.4. This is true also of the determinants involved in the calculation of the communalities for the other variables, and many of the determinants involved in one table occur again in a later table for another communality. Hence the work involved in the determination of additional communalities, after the first, decreases. The complete calculations for each of the eight communalities will not be produced here, but the eighteen evaluations for each of the variables are given in Table 4.5. The assumed rank of two is checked by the consistency of the values in the columns of Table 4.5. The mean values of the columns are then taken as the respective communalities.

No exact standard for judging the consistency of these values is available, but a basis for determining the maximum allowable variation from the mean value can be set down. The calculated communality, although a derived statistic, may be regarded as a variance, and the usual formula for the standard error of a variance applied to it. This formula is given by

$$(4.28) \qquad \sigma_{\sigma^2} = \sigma^2 \sqrt{\frac{2}{N}} \, .$$

As in the case of other formulas involving derived statistics, it is expected that the values obtained from (4.28) will be smaller than those which would arise from a true formula developed for the communality. Therefore, if the variations of a set of values for a communality from their mean can be shown to be insignificant by use of formula (4.28), they would also be in-

TABLE 4.5

DETERMINATION OF COMMUNALITIES FOR EIGHT
PHYSICAL VARIABLES

Trial	h_1^2	h_2^2	h_3^2	h_4^2	h_5^2	h_6^2	h_7^2	h_8^2
1.............	.7905	.9301	.8347	.8332	.9503	.6117	.5599	.4871
2.............	.7815	.9279	.8354	.8416	.9518	.6105	.5656	.4813
3.............	.7739	.9258	.8357	.8378	.9567	.6063	.5595	.4793
4.............	.7821	.9270	.8369	.8386	.9538	.6093	.5613	.4880
5.............	.7735	.9261	.8373	.8388	.9547	.6075	.5589	.4842
6.............	.7736	.9255	.8416	.8378	.9567	.6065	.5593	.4808
7.............	.8823	.8190	.7534	.8510	.8297	.7010	.6360	.4889
8.............	.8804	.8147	.7529	.8561	.8290	.7023	.6476	.4766
9.............	.8767	.8076	.7513	.8535	.8268	.7068	.6367	.4722
10.............	.8816	.8133	.7496	.8541	.8220	.7075	.6544	.4798
11.............	.8724	.8138	.7504	.8551	.8079	.7224	.6433	.4759
12.............	.8843	.8080	.7526	.8519	.8209	.7116	.6391	.4735
13.............	.8665	.9090	.8539	.7552	.8482	.6234	.5484	.5475
14.............	.8659	.9028	.8590	.7608	.8446	.6224	.5534	.5401
15.............	.8643	.8945	.8663	.7489	.8481	.6247	.5419	.5408
16.............	.8699	.9060	.8565	.7556	.8242	.6127	.5578	.5431
17.............	.8651	.9036	.8588	.7500	.8342	.6287	.5397	.5463
18.............	.8625	.8962	.8715	.7480	.8439	.6262	.5409	.5435
Communality.....	.842	.881	.817	.815	.872	.647	.584	.502
Standard error....	.068	.071	.066	.066	.071	.052	.047	.041

significant by the more accurate test. The standard errors for the eight communalities, as given by the above formula, are presented in Table 4.5. It will be observed that the maximum variation from the mean in any column does not exceed 1.5 times the standard error, clearly demonstrating the consistency of these values and justifying the assumed rank and the determinations of the communalities.

The preceding analysis is based upon a knowledge of the design of the variables in a given set. In case the variables are selected without a particular design, they might still be grouped from the nature of their correlations, and the same procedure applied in the calculation of the communalities. If such grouping of the variables is not feasible, then the suggested selection of variables (e.g., as in Table 4.4) may be modified.

Without knowledge of the grouping of variables, which guided the selection of the stub in Table 4.4, the indices might be selected on an arbitrary basis. One suggestion is to write a number of trials based upon variables selected with equal frequency from the whole set. An illustration of the stub of such a table for the calculation of h_1^2 from a total set of eight variables is presented in Table 4.6. The total number of distinct trials for the determination of any communality from a set of eight variables is

$$\frac{(n-1)!}{12(n-5)!} = \frac{7!}{12(3!)} = 70 ,$$

as indicated on page 76. The proposed Table 4.6 includes only special combinations of four variables, namely, four consecutive ones in the first seven trials and the corresponding four with the first pair interchanged in the last seven trials.

TABLE 4.6

STUB FOR VARIABLES WITHOUT DESIGN

Trial	ab	cd	Trial	ab	cd
1.........	23	45	8......	32	45
2.........	45	67	9......	54	67
3.........	67	82	10......	76	82
4.........	82	34	11......	28	34
5.........	34	56	12......	43	56
6.........	56	78	13......	65	78
7.........	78	23	14......	87	23

If the assumed rank of two is verified by the evaluations from a set of indices such as those in Table 4.6, then the communality would be accepted as the average of these evaluations. In checking the rank, and computing the communality, the evaluations based upon insignificant denominators must be rejected. Thus the actual number of evaluations retained for checking the rank and computing the communality may be smaller than that indicated in such a table. A more refined check on the rank could be obtained by employing additional evaluations.

The direct application of the foregoing method of computing communalities is practical when m is equal to one or two. For a larger number of factors the direct procedure becomes too cumbersome. The methods of this chapter, however, form the basis of analysis into any number of common factors (see Chap. VI).

4.7. *Illustration of Direct Solution*

For a small set of variables, when the communalities have been computed by the method of the preceding section, it may be possible to obtain a direct solution for the factor pattern. Such a solution is possible if, in addition to the knowledge of the communalities, a pattern plan is also postulated. This type of analysis will be illustrated with a set of six hypothetical variables.

Assume a matrix of intercorrelations of the six variables as follows:

$$\Delta = \begin{Vmatrix} & .72 & .75 & .49 & .42 & .28 \\ .72 & & .78 & .42 & .36 & .24 \\ .75 & .78 & & .35 & .30 & .20 \\ .49 & .42 & .35 & & .42 & .28 \\ .42 & .36 & .30 & .42 & & .24 \\ .28 & .24 & .20 & .28 & .24 & \end{Vmatrix} .$$

The problem is to formulate the pattern plan, determine the six communalities, and calculate the coefficients of the common factors.

In order to compute the communalities, the approximate rank of Δ is required. This rank may be determined indirectly from the number of groups of variables. Applying the method of B-coefficients, it is found that

$$B(1, 2, 3) = 221 ,$$
$$B(4, 5, 6) = 92 .$$

The variables 1, 2, 3 are thus seen to belong together while 4, 5, 6 do not belong together any more than to the preceding three variables. The following groups are consistent with this analysis:

$$G_0 = (1, 2, 3, 4, 5, 6) ,$$
$$G_1 = (1, 2, 3) ,$$

and so the rank of Δ may be assumed to be two. A plausible factor pattern plan,* which takes these facts into account, is given in Table 4.7, where uncorrelated factors are assumed for convenience.

Now the four necessary conditions which the correlations must satisfy in order that the six variables shall be describable in terms of two common factors are obtained by equating the right-hand members of equations (4.20).

---

* The pattern plan is plausible because the correlations among the variables 1, 2, 3 are higher than those among 4, 5, 6. Such a plan is consistent with the hypothesis that an extra factor should be postulated for a group of variables with high intercorrelations. This hypothesis is implicit in all current methods of factor analysis.

The value of each of the first three of these expressions is exactly .74, while the last two expressions are indeterminate.* The correlations satisfy the necessary conditions, and hence Δ is of rank two. The communalities are then given by equation (4.22), for $n = 6$, and the average of the various determinations of each communality may be taken. For the present hypothetical problem the different solutions for any communality yield the same value. The computed communalities are presented in Table 4.8.

TABLE 4.7

FACTOR PATTERN PLAN[a]

Variable	F_0	F_1
1............	a_{10}	a_{11}
2............	a_{20}	a_{21}
3............	a_{30}	a_{31}
4............	a_{40}	....
5............	a_{50}	....
6............	a_{60}	....

[a] A factor pattern will usually be presented in such a tabular form with the coefficients of the respective factors appearing in the columns headed by the factors.

TABLE 4.8

COMMUNALITIES OF SIX HYPOTHETICAL VARIABLES

Variable	1	2	3	4	5	6
h_j^2........	.74	.72	.89	.49	.36	.16

From the intercorrelations and communalities, all the coefficients of the factor pattern can be obtained. Since the last three variables involve only one common factor, each of their communalities is merely the square of the coefficient of this factor. Hence

$$h_4^2 = .49 = a_{40}^2 ,$$

or

$$a_{40} = .7 .$$

Similarly,

$$a_{50} = .6 \quad \text{and} \quad a_{60} = .4 .$$

* This is due to the fact that the tetrads formed from variables 4, 5, 6 and any one of 1, 2, or 3 vanish. As a consequence the minors in the numerators of these expressions also vanish. It is thus apparent that four such variables are describable in terms of only one common factor.

The coefficient a_{10} may be obtained by means of any one of the correlations r'_{14}, r'_{15}, or r'_{16}; for, by (2.22),

$$r'_{1k} = a_{10}a_{k0} \qquad\qquad (k = 4, 5, 6) .$$

A similar argument holds for the determination of a_{20} and a_{30}. Then, employing the mean of the three evaluations of any one of these coefficients, they are given by

$$a_{j0} = \frac{1}{3} \sum_{k=4}^{6} \frac{r_{jk}}{a_{k0}} \qquad\qquad (j = 1, 2, 3) ,$$

where the correlations from the factor pattern (the r'_{jk}) are replaced by the observed correlations in $\boldsymbol{\Delta}$. The tacit assumption is that the residuals are zero. The coefficients of F_0 for the first three variables have the following values:

$$a_{10} = .7 , \qquad a_{20} = .6 , \qquad a_{30} = .5 .$$

Since the coefficient a_{10} is known, the remaining coefficient a_{11} in the first equation of the pattern may be determined from h_1^2. For

$$h_1^2 = a_{10}^2 + a_{11}^2 ,$$

or

$$a_{11} = \sqrt{h_1^2 - a_{10}^2} = \sqrt{.74 - .49} = .5 .$$

Similarly, $a_{21} = .6$ and $a_{31} = .8$. The factor pattern thus computed from the correlations in $\boldsymbol{\Delta}$ is given in Table 4.9.

TABLE 4.9

FACTOR PATTERN FOR SIX
HYPOTHETICAL
VARIABLES

Variable	F_0	F_1
1...........	.7	.5
2...........	.6	.6
3...........	.5	.8
4...........	.7	....
5...........	.6	....
6...........	.4	....

It may readily be checked that the correlations reproduced from the pattern of Table 4.9 agree exactly with those given in **Δ**. Thus,

$$r'_{12} = .7(.6) + .5(.6) = .72 = r_{12}.$$

In ordinary practice, of course, some discrepancies between the original and reproduced correlations would be expected. The approximate agreement between these values is the essential requisite for the adoption of any factor solution, the form selected being somewhat arbitrary. This is illustrated in the present example by postulating the plan of solution of Table 4.7. A discussion of various preferred pattern plans which may be employed for a given set of data will be taken up in the following chapter.

CHAPTER V

PREFERRED TYPES OF ORTHOGONAL SOLUTIONS

5.1. *Introduction*

In the choice of a scientific hypothesis two possibilities immediately arise from the fact that the factors may be taken as correlated or uncorrelated. This leads to two distinct developments of the theory. In this and the next five chapters the common factors will be assumed to be uncorrelated, or geometrically the axes representing them will be taken as orthogonal. Then in Chapter XI the case of correlated, or oblique, factors will be discussed.

When it has been decided to describe a set of variables in terms of uncorrelated factors, the problem is not yet unique. There are still an infinite number of orthogonal reference systems in terms of which the variables may be described. The next problem is to select one of these frames of reference, on some rational basis, as a *preferred* system. Certain preferred types of orthogonal factor patterns will be discussed in this chapter, after a consideration of some basic standards for judging the satisfactoriness of form as a simple scientific description of the variables.

The extent to which each of these types of solution conforms to the basic statistical criteria will be discussed in detail. It is shown that by the introduction or elimination of one or more of these standards it is possible to pass from one preferred form to another. Thus it is hoped that some unification of factorial methods will be achieved.

In this chapter only schematic, or formal, solutions of the preferred types are presented. Although the algebraic equations of the various factor patterns are exhibited, the formulas for the computation of the coefficients are not given here. The special analytical methods employed in obtaining numerical solutions of the preferred types will be developed and illustrated in detail in later chapters.

5.2. *Some Standards for Judging Preferred Patterns*

In order to limit the infinitude of possible factor solutions that can be obtained in describing a given matrix of correlations, a set of restrictions must be imposed to obtain some preferred reference system. To this end, a list of statistical standards is presented which is based partially upon those found useful in previous investigations. Some of these standards are analytical in character, while others are of a geometric nature. Inasmuch as both these types of standards are designed to produce simple forms of solution, certain of these standards are somewhat related. They are listed here separately, however, because they support one another and simplify the selection of preferred solutions. By presenting such a broad list of criteria, the assumptions underlying each type of preferred solution can be exhibited explicitly.

1. AGREEMENT WITH ASSUMED COMPOSITION OF VARIABLES

The composition of variables postulated in Chapter II was based on three types of observation, namely, that correlations are found among variables of a set, that potential linkages may also occur among variables in the set with others not included, and that all measurement is subject to error. These considerations led to the fundamental equations (2.8) involving common, specific, and unreliable factors. All forms of solution should obviously conform to the factorial composition of the statistical variables postulated in such linear equations.

2. PARSIMONY

According to the principle of parsimony common to all branches of science, a law or description should be simpler than the data upon which it is based. This may be illustrated in the fitting of a theoretical curve to a series of observations. The number of constants in such a function should be much smaller than the number of observations in order to give a simple and useful interpretation of the latter. Similarly in a factor problem the functional description of the variables should be much simpler than the original data.

a) *Number of common factors.*—In agreement with this principle the total number of common factors should be considerably smaller than the number of descriptive variables comprising the original set.

b) *Complexity.*—It is also desirable that this principle of parsimony be applied to individual variables. In the linear description of each variable the complexity should be as small as possible.

3. UNCORRELATED FACTORS

The first stage in any factorial analysis must involve a choice of correlated or uncorrelated factors. In the assumed composition of variables there is no restriction as to whether or not the factors shall be correlated. The observed correlations are fitted equally well by solutions involving factors of either type. Because of the indeterminacy of factorial solutions, investigators have found it convenient to start with an orthogonal solution. This form may then be retained or else rotated to some preferred orthogonal or oblique solution.

The advantages of a solution involving uncorrelated factors arise from convenience of initial solution and subsequent interpretation of factors. As just indicated, an orthogonal solution is the fundamental form from which others may be derived. In some instances, however, such a solution may conform to a preferred type without further transformation. If uncorrelated factors are selected for the final solution, there is a decided clarity of interpretation, especially in the description of individuals in terms of factors. Such descriptions are clearer and more economical than if expressed in terms of interrelated factors.

4. RELATIVE CONTRIBUTIONS OF FACTORS

Another standard which may be useful in the selection of a particular type of solution is based upon the relative contributions of factors. As defined in **2.3**, the contribution of a factor is given by the sum of the squares of its coefficients for all the variables. Three useful types of relationships between the contributions of a set of factors follow:

a) Decreasing contributions.—In this case the various factors contribute successively smaller amounts to the total communality.

b) Level contributions.—A second choice is one in which each factor contributes approximately an equal amount to the total communality.

c) One large and remaining level contributions.—The third type of relationship is that in which one factor contributes a large amount, while the remaining factors contribute a much less but fairly uniform amount to the total communality.

It can be shown that the contribution of a factor is related to its statistical significance. This has been demonstrated both by theoretical treatment and by empirical evidence.

5. GEOMETRIC FIT: VECTOR REPRESENTATION

As pointed out in Chapter III, the geometric interpretation of the factor problem frequently adds clarity to the analytical method. This is especially true in formulating a set of standards leading to several distinct types of preferred patterns. When such distinctions have been made in geometric terms, the corresponding analytical properties of the factor patterns are explained. The following geometric criteria furnished the bases for several scientifically desirable factor patterns.

a) Linear fit.—An obvious justification for postulating common factors is that the variables in a particular investigation usually are correlated. Furthermore, certain subsets of variables may show generally higher intercorrelations among themselves than with the remaining variables of the total set. Group factors corresponding to each cluster of this type may then be assumed. In a sense, then, a group factor may be regarded as a sort of average or the common element of the variables of such a subset.

It has been shown in **3.7** and **3.8** that the variables may be regarded as vectors with a common origin and that the correlations between variables are given by the cosines of the angles between such vectors in the N-space, or by the scalar products of the projected vectors in the common-factor space. A group of variables yielding a cluster of high intercorrelations is thus encompassed by a "cone" with a relatively small generating angle. If a *reference axis* or *vector* of the common-factor space is chosen in the midst of this cone, all variables in the group will correlate high with it. To a factor common to a group of variables, there thus corresponds a reference vector. The degree of linear fit is measured by the compactness of the "cone" representing the particular group of variables, or the extent to which the vectors of these variables approach the axis of reference. By selecting a number of such reference axes, each one passing through a cone of vectors, the whole configuration may finally be well fitted.

The standard of linear fit, together with that of uncorrelated factors, usually can be met only roughly in the case of positive correlations among the variables. It is evident that a closer linear fit can be obtained by permitting the factors to be correlated, as will be shown in Chapter XI.

b) Planar fit.—The type of geometric fit just described may also be interpreted as a planar fit. Each plane is defined by two of the reference axes, or by the end points of the two reference vectors and the origin. Good geometric fit is then indicated by the proximity of the vectors representing the variables in the common-factor space to such planes.

A subset of variables may be well represented by vectors in a reference plane of the common-factor space, even though they do not form two distinct clusters. In this case the vectors present a fan-shaped configuration by means of which the reference plane is defined. The two reference axes in this plane can be selected with much greater freedom than when the axes are restricted to the clusters of vectors.

The equivalence of the geometric and algebraic interpretation of a statistical variable will now be pointed out. As shown in Chapter II, a variable may be considered as a linear function of, say, m common factors. Geometrically, this means that the vector representing the variable lies in an m-space, which is defined by the m reference axes representing the factors. Thus if a vector lies in a plane, it is describable in terms of two reference vectors, and hence in the algebraic description of the variable only two common factors appear. Of course, other variables of the set might involve these or other factors.

c) Hyperplanar fit.—In the two preceding standards one-spaces and two-spaces were the bases for determining the adequacy of geometric fit. This idea can be extended to higher spaces. By hyperplanar fit in a space of m

dimensions is meant that each vector representing a variable in the common-factor space lies in an $(m - 1)$, or smaller, space.

When a set of variables satisfies this standard, the complexity of any one of them is less than the total number of common factors. This does not appear as a very stringent criterion at first sight, because it is satisfied if each variable is of complexity $(m - 1)$ for m common factors. The strength of this standard, however, lies in the fact that the hyperplane is the largest permissible space containing each variable. In other words, it is hoped that there will always be smaller reference spaces which contain certain subgroups of variables. Thus the complexities of the variables are reduced below $(m - 1)$. In particular, a vector which lies on a reference axis is contained in that one-space, and the variable it represents has a complexity of one. Similarly, if a vector lies in a reference plane, the variable is of complexity two. This analogy of the smallest reference space in which a vector is contained and the complexity of the variable can be extended to any degree.

It is evident that the two preceding geometric standards may be considered as special cases of hyperplanar fit. For, if a set of variables satisfies the criterion of linear fit, or planar fit, it certainly conforms to hyperplanar fit. The converse, of course, is not true generally. Hence the ideal to be aimed for is to reduce the hyperplanar fit to a geometric fit of as small a number of dimensions as possible, the limit being linear fit.

6. GEOMETRIC FIT: POINT REPRESENTATION

In **3.7** two alternative geometric representations of a set of variables were presented. By employing the vector representation, three standards were immediately evident which will lead to as many types of preferred factor patterns. Now, by considering the point representation, another standard evolves. It will be recalled that in this representation there is one point for each of the N individuals, referred to a system of n reference axes—one for each variable. The points which are plotted in this n-space are contained in a common-factor space of only m dimensions.* The loci of the swarm of points of uniform frequency density are, more or less, concentric, similar, and similarly situated m-dimensional ellipsoids, being exactly so for a normally distributed population.† It then seems natural to take the

* According to Theorem 3.2, the N points, $(z_{11}, z_{21}, \ldots, z_{n1})$, $(z_{12}, z_{22}, \ldots, z_{n2})$, $\ldots$, $(z_{1N}, z_{2N}, \ldots, z_{nN})$, whose coordinates are the elements in the columns of the matrix $\|z_{ji}\|$, are all contained in a linear m-space, where m is the rank of this matrix. Then the argument of **3.8** indicates that the common-factor space (containing the N points) is of m dimensions, where m is the rank of the correlation matrix, with communalities in the diagonal.

† G. Udny Yule and M. G. Kendall, *An Introduction to the Theory of Statistics*, 1937, Chap. XII.

principal axes of these ellipsoids as the fundamental reference axes. This standard, which is called *ellipsoidal fit*, leads to another preferred type of factor pattern.*

From a statistical point of view several of the preferred patterns may fit a matrix of observed correlations equally well. The ultimate choice of type of factor pattern must then rest, in part, upon the nature of the variables and the utility of the solution in the particular field of investigation.

5.3. *Algebraic Solution of Any Symmetric Matrix*

Before describing the various preferred types of factor patterns, a solution of special mathematical and historical interest will first be exhibited. This solution is obtainable by means of a general algebraic procedure for factoring any symmetric matrix, known as "completing the square." The method was applied specifically to a correlation matrix by McMahon[†] before 1923. In the early stages of factor analysis one writer[‡] developed the *solid staircase* method, while another[§] also treated this type of solution under the title *diagonal method*.

The n variables may be described in terms of n (or possibly fewer) new uncorrelated factors, by means of the above methods, in the following form:

$$(5.1) \quad \begin{cases} z_1 = a_{11}F_1, \\ z_2 = a_{21}F_1 + a_{22}F_2, \\ z_3 = a_{31}F_1 + a_{32}F_2 + a_{33}F_3, \\ \quad . \quad . \quad . \quad . \quad . \quad . \quad . \\ z_n = a_{n1}F_1 + a_{n2}F_2 + a_{n3}F_3 + \ldots + a_{nn}F_n. \end{cases}$$

It is evident that a great many variations of this particular form of solution are possible, since any one of the variables may be selected as involving only one factor. A solution of the form (5.1) is therefore undesirable, since it is not definitive enough.

The preferred types of solution that are presented in the remainder of this chapter are well defined inasmuch as they conform closely to certain of the standards discussed in **5.2**. By adhering to the assumptions underlying any one of the preferred types of pattern, a single solution may be obtained from a given set of correlations.

* The application of higher-dimensional ellipsoids in the field of factor analysis was proposed by Truman L. Kelley at a meeting of the Unitary Traits Committee in 1933.

† James McMahon, "Hyperspherical Goniometry; and Its Application to Correlation Theory for n Variables," *Biometrika*, 1923.

‡ K. J. Holzinger, *Preliminary Report on Spearman-Holzinger Unitary Trait Study*, No. 5.

§ L. L. Thurstone, *The Vectors of Mind*, 1935, pp. 78–81.

5.4. *Uni-factor Pattern*

The first of the preferred patterns to be discussed may be regarded as an ideal, since it is highly improbable that it will be attained with actual data. This, as well as all the other preferred types, is in agreement with the assumed composition of statistical variables. Another property which will hold true for all solutions in this chapter is that the factors are uncorrelated. The additional assumptions, which distinguish the particular pattern under discussion, are those of best geometric fit and minimum complexity. In the vector representation of variables the best geometric fit is attained when the projected vectors (into the common-factor space) of a group of variables lie close to a reference axis. When the vectors lie exactly on such axes, each variable then measures but a single factor. Of course, variables of distinct groups measure different factors.

Such an ideal solution, which satisfies the standard of linear fit and hence minimum complexity, will be called a *uni-factor* pattern. This type of pattern will now be discussed in detail. Let there be n variables and m group factors ($m \leq n$) such that p_1 variables are expressible as linear functions of only the first factor F_1, p_2 other variables are expressible as linear functions of the second factor F_2, and so forth, to the remaining p_m variables which are expressible as linear functions of only the last factor F_m. The n variables may be subdivided into m groups $G_1, G_2, \ldots, G_m$ according to the factor involved in each variable, so that $n = (p_1 + p_2 + \ldots + p_m)$. Then, if the variables are numbered consecutively from 1 to n, such a uni-factor pattern (omitting unique factors) may be written as follows:*

$$(5.2) \quad \begin{cases} z_1 = a_{11}F_1, \\ z_2 = a_{21}F_1, \\ \quad \cdot \quad \cdot \quad \cdot \quad \cdot \\ z_{p_1} = a_{p_1 1}F_1, \\ z_{p_1+1} = \qquad\qquad a_{(p_1+1)2}F_2, \\ \quad \cdot \quad \cdot \quad \cdot \quad \cdot \quad \cdot \quad \cdot \quad \cdot \\ z_{p_1+p_2} = \qquad\qquad a_{(p_1+p_2)2}F_2, \\ \quad \cdot \quad \cdot \quad \cdot \quad \cdot \quad \cdot \quad \cdot \quad \cdot \\ z_{n-p_m+1} = \qquad\qquad\qquad\qquad a_{(n-p_m+1)m}F_m, \\ z_n = \qquad\qquad\qquad\qquad a_{nm}F_m. \end{cases}$$

* A simplification in notation is employed in this and all succeeding factor patterns. Since the linear expressions are approximations to observed variables, they should be denoted by z_i' in accordance with (2.4). Also when unique factors are omitted, the variables may be considered as projected into the common-factor space and thus be represented by z_i''. For simplicity, however, all primes are dropped, and it is understood that any linear expression stands for an approximation to the indicated variable.

It is assumed in this pattern, and the two succeeding ones, that the coefficients of the factors are positive. The contributions of the factors are evidently dependent on the number of variables in the subgroups which measure the respective factors. When these subgroups are fairly equal, the contributions tend to be uniform. The uni-factor pattern may therefore be said to satisfy standard 4*b* of section **5.2.**

A simple schematic representation of a uni-factor pattern is given in Table 5.1. The vertical lines represent the coefficients of the respective factors. Such a diagram then indicates clearly the mutually exclusive character of the subgroups of variables.

TABLE 5.1
UNI-FACTOR PATTERN SCHEME

Variable	F_1	F_2	F_3	...	F_m
1........					
2........					
3........					
.					
.					
.					
.					
.					
.					
.					
n........					

To distinguish between variables of different groups, the standard set-theory notations* can be adapted to the present needs. The primary definitions follow:

(5.3)

a) $e \epsilon G_s$ means e is a variable in the group G_s.

b) $(z_j; j \epsilon G_s, s = 1, 2, \ldots, m)$ denotes the *system* of elements z_j for all values of j in groups G_s, where the range of s is indicated. The elements of the system are first designated, followed by a semicolon, and all the properties on the elements are to the right of the semicolon.

c) $\Sigma(z_{ji}; i = 1, 2, \ldots, N)$ means the sum of all the elements in the system $(z_{ji}; i = 1, 2, \ldots, N)$. The index j is fixed, the summation extending over i. This sum is equivalent to the more conventional form $\sum_{i=1}^{N} z_{ji}$.

* See, for example, L. R. Wilcox, "Modularity in the Theory of Lattices," *Annals of Mathematics*, 1939.

It will be found that these definitions* aid in clarity and ultimate simplicity in describing much of the following theory.

Since the factors are always assumed to be in standard form, the correlation coefficient between any two variables $j \epsilon G_s$ and $k \epsilon G_t$ is reproduced by means of pattern (5.2) as follows:†

(5.4)
$$
\begin{cases}
r'_{jk} = \dfrac{1}{N} \Sigma(z_{ji} z_{ki}; \ i = 1, 2, \ldots, N) \\[2mm]
\quad = \dfrac{1}{N} \Sigma(a_{js} F_{si} a_{kt} F_{ti}; \ i = 1, 2, \ldots, N) \\[2mm]
\quad = a_{js} a_{kt} r_{F_s F_t} .
\end{cases}
$$

When the two variables belong to different groups, the reproduced correlation becomes

(5.5)
$$ r'_{jk} = 0 \qquad (j \epsilon G_s, \ k \epsilon G_t, \ s \neq t), $$

since the factors are uncorrelated; whereas, if the variables are in the same group,

(5.6)
$$ r'_{jk} = a_{js} a_{ks} \qquad (j, k \epsilon G_s) . $$

From formulas (5.5) and (5.6), it is seen that a factor pattern of type (5.2) can only reproduce a set of correlations of the form shown in Figure 5.1. The plus signs in the small triangles represent positive correlations among variables within groups, and the zeros in the rectangles represent lack of correlation between variables in different groups. It is unlikely that such a picture of intercorrelations of variables would be obtained in practice, and hence a pattern of type (5.2) has been termed "ideal." To the extent to which a matrix of observed correlations approaches the above form, its solution may be considered as approaching the uni-factor pattern.

The only practical instance in which a solution conforms to the uni-factor

---

* To illustrate the definitions given in (5.3), consider a set of ten variables ($z_1, z_2, \ldots, z_{10}$), grouped as follows:

$$ G_1 = (1, 2, 3, 4, 5), \quad G_2 = (6, 7, 8), \quad G_3 = (9, 10) . $$

An instance of (a) is $7 \epsilon G_2$, which means that variable 7 is included in group G_2. The system of elements ($z_j; \ j \epsilon G_s, \ s = 1, 3$) is the set of variables ($z_1, z_2, z_3, z_4, z_5, z_9, z_{10}$). The sum of N values of variable 4, which may be taken as an example of (c), is

$$ \Sigma(z_{4i}; \ i = 1, 2, \ldots, N) . $$

† Pattern (5.2) could be written explicitly for the individual values of the variables, as was done in eq. (2.5). Actually, that is the form implied in the development of (5.4).

form is the classical "Two-factor" pattern.* This solution is called "Two-factor" by Spearman because two types of factors—general and unique—are involved. From the point of view of complexity, however, this solution is a uni-factor one, since each variable involves just one common factor (the same one). To illustrate a "Two-factor" pattern, suppose that four vari-

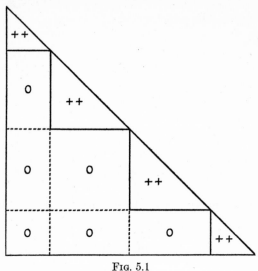

Fig. 5.1

ables satisfy the tetrad conditions (4.6) for the existence of just one common factor. Then the pattern may be written in the form:

$$(5.7) \quad \begin{cases} z_1 = a_{10}F_0 + a_1U_1, \\ z_2 = a_{20}F_0 \qquad\qquad + a_2U_2, \\ z_3 = a_{30}F_0 \qquad\qquad\qquad + a_3U_3, \\ z_4 = a_{40}F_0 \qquad\qquad\qquad\qquad + a_4U_4. \end{cases}$$

It will be noted that this pattern is a special case of (5.2), namely, for only one factor. The correlations of a set of variables leading to a "Two-factor" pattern correspond to those in one triangle of Figure 5.1, which satisfy the general conditions (4.13) for one general factor.

5.5. *Bi-factor Pattern*

The next type of factor solution to be discussed is a modification of the preceding one. As already noted, a uni-factor pattern can only be produced from a matrix of correlations of the form indicated in Figure 5.1, and which is highly improbable of attainment. In a practical case, when a set of rele-

* Charles Spearman, *The Abilities of Man*, 1927.

vant variables is employed to study the common attributes of a group of individuals, it is to be expected that the correlations between subgroups of such variables will be positive throughout rather than zero. Still higher correlations will usually be found for the variables within subgroups of the entire set. Such a matrix of correlations is indicated schematically in Figure 5.2. The need for modifying the uni-factor type of pattern when dealing with observed data is thus apparent.

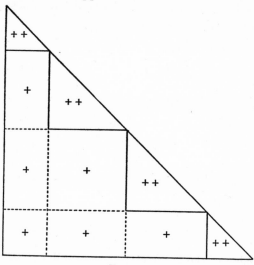

FIG. 5.2

If, in addition to the distinct group factors postulated in the uni-factor pattern, a general factor is also included, the positive correlations throughout the observed matrix can be accounted for. This modification of the uni-factor pattern is tantamount to substituting planar for linear geometric fit. When the vectors of a group of variables lie in a reference plane, each variable measures just two factors. If, furthermore, the vectors lie only in the reference planes formed by a general-factor (F_0) axis and one group-factor axis (none in the planes of two group factors), the configuration can be described as a *pencil of planes* through the F_0 axis.* A solution satisfying standards 1, 2, 3, 4c, and planar fit, as here described, will be called a *bi-factor* pattern.†

* In ordinary space geometry a pencil of planes refers to the totality of planes through a line, i.e., all the planes linearly dependent on two distinct planes through the line. In the present setting, however, a pencil of planes in a space of $(m + 1)$ dimensions will refer to all the planes through a line which are mutually orthogonal. It is clearly seen that there are m such planes in the pencil through the F_0 axis.

† The bi-factor pattern actually becomes a uni-factor pattern when the factors are correlated, as will be shown in **11.3**.

The formal presentation of the bi-factor pattern will now be given. Let the n variables be expressible as linear functions of $(m + 1)$ common factors as follows: every variable involves a general factor F_0, and, in addition, p_1 variables involve the first group factor F_1, p_2 other variables involve the second group factor F_2, and so on to the remaining p_m variables which involve the last group factor F_m. The n variables may be rearranged according to the groups $G_1, G_2, \ldots, G_m$, and numbered consecutively from 1 to n. Then, employing the notation of the preceding section, the bi-factor pattern, omitting unique factors, may be written in the form

$$(5.8) \quad \begin{cases} z_1 = a_{10}F_0 + a_{11}F_1, \\ z_2 = a_{20}F_0 + a_{21}F_1, \\ \quad \cdot \quad \cdot \quad \cdot \quad \cdot \quad \cdot \quad \cdot \\ z_{p_1} = a_{p_10}F_0 + a_{p_11}F_1, \\ z_{p_1+1} = a_{(p_1+1)0}F_0 \quad\quad + a_{(p_1+1)2}F_2, \\ \quad \cdot \quad \cdot \quad \cdot \quad \cdot \quad \cdot \quad \cdot \quad \cdot \quad \cdot \\ z_{p_1+p_2} = a_{(p_1+p_2)0}F_0 \quad\quad + a_{(p_1+p_2)2}F_2, \\ \quad \cdot \quad \cdot \quad \cdot \quad \cdot \quad \cdot \quad \cdot \quad \cdot \quad \cdot \\ z_{n-p_m+1} = a_{(n-p_m+1)0}F_0 \quad\quad\quad\quad\quad\quad + a_{(n-p_m+1)m}F_m, \\ \quad \cdot \quad \cdot \quad \cdot \quad \cdot \quad \cdot \quad \cdot \quad \cdot \quad \cdot \quad \cdot \\ z_n = a_{n0}F_0 \quad\quad\quad\quad\quad\quad\quad + a_{nm}F_m. \end{cases}$$

A schematic plan of the bi-factor pattern, similar to that given for the uni-factor pattern, is presented in Table 5.2. It is apparent from this dia-

TABLE 5.2

BI-FACTOR PATTERN SCHEME

Variable	F_0	F_1	F_2	F_3	$\cdots$	F_m
1........						
2........						
3........						
n........						

gram that each of the group factors overlaps with the general factor but not with any of the others.

The correlation between any two variables $j \epsilon G_s$ and $k \epsilon G_t$ may be reproduced by means of a bi-factor pattern as follows:

$$(5.9) \quad \begin{cases} r'_{jk} = \dfrac{1}{N} \Sigma (z_{ji} z_{ki} \; ; \; i = 1, 2, \ldots, N), \\[2mm] \qquad = \dfrac{1}{N} \Sigma ([a_{j0} F_{0i} + a_{js} F_{si}][a_{k0} F_{0i} + a_{kt} F_{ti}] \; ; \; i = 1, 2, \ldots, N), \\[2mm] \qquad = a_{j0} a_{k0} + a_{j0} a_{kt} r_{F_0 F_t} + a_{js} a_{k0} r_{F_s F_0} + a_{js} a_{kt} r_{F_s F_t}, \\[2mm] \qquad = a_{j0} a_{k0} + a_{js} a_{kt} r_{F_s F_t}, \end{cases}$$

where the last equality follows from the fact that the general factor is uncorrelated with the group factors. If the two variables are in different groups, then

$$(5.10) \qquad\qquad r'_{jk} = a_{j0} a_{k0} \qquad\qquad (j \epsilon G_s, \; k \epsilon G_t, \; s \neq t),$$

but, if they are in the same group, their reproduced correlation becomes

$$(5.11) \qquad\qquad r'_{jk} = a_{j0} a_{k0} + a_{js} a_{ks} \qquad\qquad (j, k \epsilon G_s).$$

From equation (5.10) it is evident that the relatively small correlations between variables of different groups are produced through the general factor F_0. These correlations appear in the rectangles of a correlation matrix as in Figure 5.2. The higher correlations between variables within a group are reproduced by formula (5.11), which involves the general and one group factor. Such correlations are represented in the triangles of Figure 5.2.

The form of the bi-factor pattern was conceived* as a direct extension of Spearman's "Two-factor" solution in the case of sets of variables which do not meet the assumptions underlying the latter solution. For a specialized set of variables the "Two-factor" pattern, i.e., one general factor, may be sufficient to reproduce the correlations. With a complex set of variables, however, the criteria for a single general factor may not be satisfied, and group factors may be required. The bi-factor solution makes allowance for both general and group factors.

5.6. *Multiple-Factor Pattern*

An alternative solution to the bi-factor pattern which accounts for a table of essentially positive correlations, but which does not involve a general factor, will be called a *multiple-factor* pattern.* In this solution the next stage of geometric fit, viz., hyperplanar, is employed. Analytically, this means that a number of "overlapping" group factors must be postulated in order to account for the generally positive correlations among a set of variables, as exhibited in Figure 5.2. These factors are called "overlapping" to distinguish them from the distinct group factors which are employed in the pattern (5.2). The term "overlapping" indicates that several factors appear in the description of a variable. Thus, in the bi-factor pattern the group factors overlap with the general factor, whereas in the multiple-factor pattern the group factors overlap among themselves. Overlapping thus implies a complexity of two or more. By sacrificing the general factor of a bi-factor pattern, a higher complexity than two will usually be required in a multiple-factor pattern. It is for this reason that the prefix "multiple" is employed.

A multiple-factor pattern satisfies standards 1, 2, 3, 4b, and 5c. The standards of parsimony and hyperplanar fit may be stated in analytical terms. In conformity with these standards, it is desirable that the complexities of the variables in a multiple-factor pattern be as small as possible; and, in spite of the necessary overlapping of factors, it is also desirable that there be as many zero coefficients in the columns as possible.† If these conditions are satisfied, then the factors can be identified by means of the groups of variables with appreciable coefficients.

For a given table of correlations there should be a unique multiple-factor pattern with a large number of zero coefficients. However, the particular configuration of zeros and overlap of group factors will usually vary for different sets of variables. Hence no general mathematical formulation of the multiple-factor pattern is possible apart from a given matrix of correlations. Therefore, no schematic plan for this type of solution is presented. An illus-

---

* Although a multiple-factor pattern is here formulated as one of the preferred types, in actual practice it must be derived by rotation from some preliminary solution. One such preliminary pattern, known as the centroid pattern, will be described in detail in Chap. VIII.

† Such a configuration, with correlated or uncorrelated factors, has been called a *simple structure* by Thurstone (*op. cit.*, Chap. VI) when the following conditions are satisfied:

1. Each row of the factor structure V (see 2.4) should have at least one zero
2. Each column of V should have at least m zeros (m being the total number of common factors)
3. For every pair of columns of V there should be at least m variables whose entries vanish in one column but not in the other

With special reference to psychology, Thurstone has called the factors determined by hyperplanar fit "primary abilities."

tration of a possible form of a multiple-factor pattern, however, is given for a special case of twelve variables and four factors:

$$(5.12) \quad \begin{cases} z_1 = a_{11}F_1 + a_{12}F_2 + a_{13}F_3 , \\ z_2 = a_{21}F_1 \qquad\qquad\qquad + a_{24}F_4 , \\ z_3 = a_{31}F_1 + a_{32}F_2 + a_{33}F_3 , \\ z_4 = a_{41}F_1 \qquad\qquad\qquad + a_{44}F_4 , \\ z_5 = \qquad\quad a_{52}F_2 + a_{53}F_3 + a_{54}F_4 , \\ z_6 = a_{61}F_1 + a_{62}F_2 , \\ z_7 = \qquad\quad a_{72}F_2 + a_{73}F_3 + a_{74}F_4 , \\ z_8 = a_{81}F_1 + a_{82}F_2 , \\ z_9 = \qquad\quad a_{92}F_2 + a_{93}F_3 + a_{94}F_4 , \\ z_{10} = a_{10,1}F_1 \qquad + a_{10,3}F_3 , \\ z_{11} = a_{11,1}F_1 \qquad + a_{11,3}F_3 , \\ z_{12} = \qquad\quad a_{12,2}F_2 + a_{12,3}F_3 + a_{12,4}F_4 . \end{cases}$$

As in the case of the uni-factor pattern, the contributions of these factors are approximately level. From such a pattern, it is obvious that the correlations are reproduced by the general formula (2.22). Every pair of variables is linked by overlapping group factors and thus yields a positive correlation. A given matrix of correlations, of the form in Figure 5.2, can thus be reproduced by a multiple-factor pattern.

Although the three preferred types of patterns are formally distinct, with actual data the resulting solution may be a combination of them to a certain extent. Thus a solution may be of the bi-factor form but have some overlap of group factors and, to this extent, resemble a multiple-factor solution. Likewise a pattern of the multiple-factor type may have a factor appearing essentially in all variables and thus resemble the bi-factor form. Either the bi-factor or the multiple-factor types may involve several variables which approximate unit complexity and thus partially approach the ideal uni-factor form.

5.7. *Principal-Factor Pattern*

The preferred types of factor patterns exhibited thus far are of a special kind, that is, they require that all factor coefficients be positive, and the multiple-factor pattern furthermore precludes a general factor. If a matrix of correlations is observed to be in the form of Figure 5.1, there is no doubt but that a uni-factor solution is most meaningful. On the other hand, when a table of correlations appears as in Figure 5.2, there is no assurance, from the statistics alone, that a bi-factor or multiple-factor solution will afford the most useful interpretation of the variables. The nature of the data may then aid in the selection of a particular form of representation. It is conceivable that certain sets of variables may be better interpreted in terms of factors, the coefficients of which are not restricted to be positive.

A factor for which several of the coefficients are positive and others are negative will be called a bipolar factor.* Such a factor may appear in all variables of a set or only in a subgroup of them. A bipolar factor is not essentially different from any other but is merely one for which several of the variables have significant negative projections. Such variables may be regarded as measuring the negative aspect of the usual type of factor. Thus, if a number of variables identified with "fear" are represented by positive projections, variables with negative projections might be interpreted as measuring "courage." It would appear simpler, however, to regard the factor merely as "fear," and the opposing set of variables as measures of "negative fear." Of course, the signs of all the coefficients of the factor may be changed without altering the adequacy of the solution. Such reversal in the foregoing example would lead to the interpretation of the factor as "courage," and the subgroup of variables with negative coefficients would be regarded as measuring "negative courage." In the illustrations of the text a single name for a bipolar factor will be employed. This is consistent with representing any factor by a single continuum.

The preferred type of pattern now to be discussed involves bipolar factors which are present in all variables of the set. In addition to these bipolar factors, there is also a general factor with positive coefficients throughout. Such a solution which satisfies standards 1, 2a, 3, 4a, and 6 is called a *principal-factor* pattern.†

The criterion of ellipsoidal fit determines the essential nature of the reference system. For then the factors are represented geometrically by the principal axes of the ellipsoids described in standard 6. The corresponding analytic standard is given by 4a, since the factors contribute decreasing amounts to the total communality. Thus the first factor is one with reference to which the individuals of the sample show the greatest possible variability. The remaining factors contribute successively smaller variances.

* This term was introduced by Cyril Burt in "The Factorial Analysis of Emotional Traits," *Character and Personality*. In the present text, however, the term is used in a more general sense.

† Harold Hotelling devised a solution of this form but factored the total unit variance or the reliability of each variable instead of the (estimate of) communality (cf. "Analysis of a Complex of Statistical Variables into Principal Components," *Journal of Educational Psychology*, 1933).

A principal-factor pattern, in which the unique factors have again been omitted, may be exhibited as follows:

$$(5.13) \quad \begin{cases} z_1 = a_{11}F_1 + a_{12}F_2 + a_{13}F_3 + \ldots + a_{1m}F_m\,, \\ z_2 = a_{21}F_1 + a_{22}F_2 + a_{23}F_3 + \ldots + a_{2m}F_m\,, \\ z_3 = a_{31}F_1 + a_{32}F_2 + a_{33}F_3 + \ldots + a_{3m}F_m\,, \\ \cdot \quad \cdot \quad \cdot \quad \cdot \quad \cdot \quad \cdot \quad \cdot \quad \cdots \quad \cdots \\ z_n = a_{n1}F_1 + a_{n2}F_2 + a_{n3}F_3 + \ldots + a_{nm}F_m\,. \end{cases}$$

In such a pattern the complexity of each variable is equal to the total number of common factors. The first factor is an ordinary general factor whose coefficients a_{j1} $(j = 1, 2, \ldots, n)$ are all positive when the solution is based upon a table of positive correlations. On the other hand, approximately half the coefficients of each of the remaining factors are negative, that is, $F_2, F_3, \ldots, F_m$ are bipolar factors.

Obviously a pattern of type (5.13) can reproduce a general table of correlations like those exhibited in Figure 5.2. The solution is thus perfectly satisfactory from a statistical point of view. Although a principal-factor pattern may be more complex than the other preferred types, it may sometimes furnish a more convenient representation of a particular set of variables.

Since the uni-factor, bi-factor, and multiple-factor patterns involve only positive coefficients, they can reproduce a table of positive correlations only. In actual analysis, therefore, these types are adapted only to sets of variables which are positively correlated or to sets which can be put in that form. If there are a few insignificant negative correlations, the preceding types of solutions can be obtained. If a variable has significant negative correlations with all the rest, its scale may be reversed, thereby changing the signs of the correlations. One such example is that in which a measure of stupidity is changed to that of intelligence by changing the sign of the scale. By this procedure of "reflection of variables" a matrix of essentially positive correlations might be obtained.

If, after such sign-changing, significant negative and positive correlations appear for some of the variables, the first three preferred types would not be applicable. Since the principal-factor pattern is not restricted to positive coefficients, it can reproduce negative as well as positive correlations. This type of solution may then be applied to any matrix of correlations. An example of a principal-factor solution based upon positive and negative correlations is given in **7.5**. In this solution all factors, including the first, are of the bipolar form.

5.8. *Summary of Preferred Patterns*

It will be noted that the names "uni-factor," "bi-factor," and "multiple-factor" indicate the complexities of the variables in the respective patterns. Thus in the uni-factor pattern each variable is of complexity one, while in the bi-factor pattern each variable is of complexity two. In the multiple-factor pattern the complexities of the variables may differ greatly, but no variable involves all the factors. As already indicated, the principal-factor pattern takes its name from the property of the reference system rather than from the complexities of the variables, which are generally equal to m for m common factors. In recapitulation the various assumptions and properties of the four preferred types of factor patterns are given in Table 5.3.

TABLE 5.3

ASSUMPTIONS AND PROPERTIES OF PREFERRED PATTERNS

Type of Pattern	Assumptions (Enumerated in **5.2**)	Number of Common Factors	Complexity of Each Variable	Distinguishing Characteristics
Uni-factor..........	1, 2a, 2b, 3, 4b, 5a	m	1	Distinct group factors
Bi-factor............	1, 2a, 2b, 3, 4c, 5b	m or $m+1$	2	One general *plus* group factors
Multiple-factor.......	1, 2a, 2b, 3, 4b, 5c	m	$< m$	Overlapping group factors
Principal-factor.......	1, 2a, 3, 4a, 6	m	m	One general *plus* bipolar factors

From the above discussion it is apparent that the uni-factor pattern is the ideal sought in all factor analysis. The remaining preferred types meet various standards for acceptable solutions, but these criteria do not furnish the complete basis for a choice of form. This choice will also depend upon the nature of the variables and the theories or laws in a particular field of application. Thus, if an investigator considers the variables to be of the "bipolar" type, the principle-factor form would be appropriate. A simple example of such a set of variables, in the field of biology, is given by standing height, sitting height, and length of forearm as opposed to weight, chest girth, and chest width. If a general factor were denied by a theory in a particular field, then the multiple-factor type would be consistent; but, if the general factor were accepted in such a theory, then the bi-factor form would be suitable. Such contrasting theories now exist in the field of psychological abilities, but a theory including a general factor is commonly accepted for physical traits in biology. According to another theory, an analysis might be desired in which the factors appear in the order of their importance. This type of importance is indicated by the decreasing contributions of successive factors of the principal-factor solution. It is thus evident that general scientific, as well as statistical, standards in any field of investigation must be employed in the selection of a preferred pattern.

It will be shown in Part III that, once estimates of communalities have been made for a given solution, the latter may be converted into any other form desired by a suitable transformation, and all such solutions will fit the correlations equally well. Preference for a given form must thus depend upon statistical standards, such as those discussed in this chapter as well as criteria apart from the statistics. Examples of such criteria are Spearman's psychological theory of a general factor generalized to the bi-factor form and Thurstone's contrasting theory of primary abilities in which the general factor is not included.

In psychology, or any other field, an investigator is free to postulate a theory and show that it is compatible with experimental evidence. It is possible, however, that another investigator may postulate an alternative theory also compatible with such evidence. The mathematical expressions (the patterns) of these theories may be formally different because the standards employed in the two cases would not be the same. Inasmuch as both theories are consistent with empirical evidence, neither should be used as a basis for judging the appropriateness, or inappropriateness, of the other. This type of conditioned thinking has been used in factor analysis, however, leading to much confusion as to the ultimate form of solution to be adopted.

In the application of factor analysis to psychology it has been argued that one form of solution is incorrect because it is inconsistent with another form. In particular, the principal-factor form of solution has been rejected on the grounds that it depends upon the nature of the test battery, while another form of solution has been accepted because it is argued that the latter is invariant for the battery. It should be apparent, however, that all solutions are dependent on the particular set of variables analyzed, and any argument for choice of solution cannot logically depend upon such assumed invariance.

The form of any factor solution, ultimately selected, depends upon the following features: (a) the group of individuals measured; (b) the set of variables and all their intercorrelations; (c) statistical standards, such as those in the present chapter; and (d) outside criteria from the particular field of investigation. Like all other statistics, factor analysis is obviously dependent upon the particular sample of individuals, and generalizations may be made by conventional methods. It is also apparent that factor analysis is a correlational analysis and, therefore, is dependent upon all the variables producing the correlations. If additional variables are added to a given set, the table of correlations, as a whole, will usually change. Inasmuch as any factor solution is based upon all the intercorrelations, it will vary as the set of variables is changed. Practically, of course, the addition of only a few variables may not change the resulting solution appreciably.

The dependence of a factor solution upon the groups and the variables is analogous to the dependence of a multiple regression equation upon the sample and the particular variables used for estimation. Statistical standards and criteria from a given field are introduced so as to obtain a determinate solution in harmony with a postulated theory.

The above considerations should be clearly evident if factor analysis is viewed as a statistical method yielding solutions which are convertible from one to another. Because of their statistical nature, factor solutions will, in general, not be invariant, and because of their convertibility a preference of form can be made only upon employing appropriate outside criteria. In factor analysis, as in all empirical sciences, several equally satisfactory laws may be usefully employed, although they may be formally quite different.*

In the field of psychology attempts have been made to formulate invariant solutions. The theory underlying such invariant factors involves the arbitrary specification of the four aspects upon which factor analysis depends. Thus by fixing the population and the set of variables, and agreeing upon the form of solution, a fundamental set of factors may be obtained. Then all other variables in the given field may be expressed in terms of these factors.

After the methods of solution for various types of factor patterns have been presented, the above points will be discussed in connection with the choice of form of solution for practical problems (see Chap. XIII). The problem of invariance, or stability of solutions, will again be considered and illustrated with actual data.

---

* A somewhat analogous situation arises in that branch of physics known as hydrodynamics. A clear discussion of this problem is given by Horace Lamb as follows: "The equations of motion of a fluid have been obtained in two different forms, corresponding to the two ways in which the problem of determining the motion of a fluid mass, acted on by given forces and subject to given conditions, may be viewed. We may either regard as the object of our investigations a knowledge of the velocity, the pressure, and the density, at all points of space occupied by the fluid, for all instants; or we may seek to determine the history of every particle" (*Hydrodynamics*, p. 2).

The equations obtained according to these two approaches are called the "Eulerian" and the "Lagrangian" forms of the hydrokinetic equations. In like manner, it has been the custom in factor analysis to label a particular form of factor solution after the man who has done most toward its development.

PART II

DIRECT ORTHOGONAL SOLUTIONS

CHAPTER VI

THE BI-FACTOR SOLUTION AND SAMPLING FORMULAS

6.1. *Introduction*

The foundations and formal groundwork for factor analysis have been laid in the preceding chapters. Now the analytical methods that may be employed in the solution of a practical problem will be developed in detail. In the present chapter the method of obtaining a bi-factor pattern for a set of variables will be discussed.

To pave the way for a bi-factor analysis, the complete solution of Spearman's "Two-factor" pattern is given; first, in the classical manner in **6.2**, and then by a revised method. The assumptions underlying either method of solution are examined in detail so that the validity of a "Two-factor" pattern can be clearly judged. In **6.4** the solution for a bi-factor pattern is developed. The plan of Chapter V is adopted, and the methods of **6.2** and **6.3** are adjusted, to this more complex situation. When the simple plan (5.8) cannot be met by a particular set of variables, certain modifications must be made. Such revisions and verification of the simple bi-factor pattern are considered in **6.9**.

To aid in the judgment of the adequacy of any factor solution, certain sampling error formulas are necessary. The first of these—for the standard error of a general-factor coefficient—is developed in **6.5**. Then a formula for the standard error of a residual is worked out for the case of any number of factors. This formula, however, involves the standard errors of the pattern coefficients. Additional sampling error formulas, based upon further approximations, are presented in **6.7**. Then, to facilitate the computation in an actual problem, tables of their values are given in Appendix H.

To illustrate the analytical methods of this chapter several numerical examples are employed. A set of five physical variables is used to clarify some of the ideas in connection with the sampling error formulas. The battery of twenty-four psychological tests, which has been introduced in Chapter II, is employed in **6.10**, where the bi-factor solution is exhibited. The complete outline for the computation of this pattern is given in Appendix C. It is believed that the procedure for calculation will be useful for reference purposes after the reader has become acquainted with the logical basis of the method, and it was therefore separated from the text and put in the appendix.

111

6.2. *Spearman's "Two-Factor" Solution*

According to Spearman's fundamental theorem,* the necessary and sufficient conditions for a set of n variables to be describable in terms of just one general factor and n unique factors are the vanishing of all tetrads.† The relationships between the tetrad conditions and the more parsimonious triads have been discussed in **4.3**. The "Two-factor" type of pattern may be written as follows:

$$(6.1) \qquad z_j = a_{j0}F_0 + a_jU_j \qquad (j = 1, 2, \ldots, n),$$

where F_0 is the general factor and the U_j are the n unique factors, and again, as in the case of (2.4), the prime on z_j has been dropped for simplicity. When the correlations r_{jk} $(j, k = 1, 2, \ldots, n)$ satisfy the tetrad conditions, or the equivalent conditions (4.13), the pattern (6.1) may be assumed and the coefficients a_{j0} and a_j have to be determined. In the present section formulas will be developed for the computation of the a_{j0} under the assumption that the residuals

$$\bar{r}_{jk} = r_{jk} - r'_{jk}$$

vanish. Then, in the following section, formulas for the a_{j0} will be obtained merely on the assumption that the conditions (4.13) are satisfied statistically, i.e., within errors of sampling.

The correlations reproduced from the pattern (6.1) are given by

$$r'_{jk} = a_{j0}a_{k0},$$

and, under the assumption that the residuals vanish, the observed correlations may be written

$$(6.2) \qquad r_{jk} = r'_{jk} = a_{j0}a_{k0}.$$

In the remainder of this section the reproduced correlations will be replaced by observed correlations. Upon multiplying equation (6.2) by the square of the general-factor coefficient for any variable z_e, this equation becomes

$$(6.3) \qquad a_{e0}^2 r_{jk} = a_{e0}^2 a_{j0}a_{k0} = (a_{e0}a_{j0})(a_{e0}a_{k0}) = r_{ej}r_{ek},$$

and, summing over the correlations, there results

$$(6.4) \qquad a_{e0}^2 \sum_{j<k=1}^{n} r_{jk} = \sum_{j<k=1}^{n} r_{ej}r_{ek} \qquad \begin{pmatrix} e \text{ is fixed} \\ j, k \neq e \end{pmatrix}.$$

* Spearman's theorem was deduced specifically for psychological tests, but it is applicable to any set of statistical variables.

† Formulas for the sampling errors of tetrad differences are developed by Spearman and Holzinger, "Note on the Sampling Error of Tetrad Differences," *British Journal of Psychology*, 1925.

As in **2.7,** the symbol $\sum_{j<k=1}^{n} r_{jk}$ stands for the sum of all the correlations r_{jk}, where j and k each range over the variables $1, 2, \ldots, n$ but subject to the restriction that j is always less than k. In a matrix of correlations, this sum is merely the total of all the entries above (or below) the principal diagonal.

Since there is only one common factor, the coefficient of this factor for any variable is merely the square root of the communality of the variable. Hence formula (6.4) may be written explicitly for the square of the coefficient, or the communality, of any variable z_e, as follows:

$$(6.5) \qquad a_{e0}^2 = h_e^2 = \frac{\Sigma(r_{ej}r_{ek}; \; j, k = 1, 2, \ldots, n, \; j, k \neq e, \; j < k)}{\Sigma(r_{jk}; \; j, k = 1, 2, \ldots, n, \; j, k \neq e, \; j < k)}.$$

It will be observed that the diagonal elements of the correlation matrix do not enter into formula (6.5). In fact, the formula yields values of the communalities, which theoretically are the diagonal elements preserving the unit rank of the matrix. When the conditions (4.13), which are applied to observed correlations, are satisfied, a single factor is postulated. The computed diagonal elements must also satisfy these conditions in order that the rank of the complete correlation matrix be unity.

It may be illuminating to write out formula (6.5) in detail for a particular case. Thus for n variables, the square of the first coefficient is

$$(6.6) \quad \begin{cases} a_{10}^2 = \\ \dfrac{r_{12}r_{13} + r_{12}r_{14} + \ldots + r_{12}r_{1n} + r_{13}r_{14} + \ldots + r_{13}r_{1n} + \ldots + r_{1,n-1}r_{1n}}{r_{23} \; + \; r_{24} \; + \ldots + \; r_{2n} \; + \; r_{34} \; + \ldots + \; r_{3n} \; + \ldots + \; r_{n-1,n}}. \end{cases}$$

For purposes of computation, formula (6.5) may be expressed as follows:[*]

$$(6.7) \qquad a_{e0}^2 = h_e^2 = \frac{\left(\sum_{j=1}^{n} r_{ej}\right)^2 - \sum_{j=1}^{n} r_{ej}^2}{2\left(\sum_{j<k=1}^{n} r_{jk} - \sum_{j=1}^{n} r_{ej}\right)} \qquad \binom{e \text{ is fixed}}{j \neq e}.$$

[*] In the set-theory notations formula (6.7) would be written as follows:

$$a_{e0}^2 = h_{e0}^2 = \frac{[\Sigma(r_{ej}; \; j = 1, \ldots, n, \; j \neq e)]^2 - \Sigma(r_{ej}; \; j = 1, \ldots, n, \; j \neq e)^2}{2[\Sigma(r_{jk}; \; j, k = 1, \ldots, n, \; j < k) - \Sigma(r_{ej}; \; j = 1, \ldots, n, \; j \neq e)]}.$$

The adaptability of this formula to machine calculation will be clear from the following restatements of the terms in the formula. Let $\mathbf{R}$ be the matrix of correlations with the elements in the principal diagonal omitted, then

$$\sum_{j=1}^{n} r_{ej} \text{ is the sum of the correlations in column } e \text{ of } \mathbf{R},$$

$$\sum_{j=1}^{n} r_{ej}^2 \text{ is the sum of squares of the correlations in column } e,$$

$$\sum_{j<k=1}^{n} r_{jk} \text{ is the sum of all the correlations below the diagonal.}$$

After the communalities, and hence the coefficients of the general factor, have been obtained, the unique variances can be determined. As pointed out in **2.3,** the uniqueness for variable e is given by

$$a_e^2 = 1 - h_e^2 .$$

If, in addition, the reliability coefficients of the variables are known, the uniqueness may be split into unreliability and specificity by means of formulas (2.11) and (2.12).

6.3. *Computation of a "Two-Factor" Pattern by the Method of Triads*

The method of analysis that will now be described may be employed in place of the procedure of the last section. If the conditions for one common factor are satisfied by the correlations among n variables, the pattern (6.1) may again be assumed. It will become evident that the conditions to be checked for a general factor are actually included in the computation of the coefficients of that factor and therefore involve no superfluous calculations. If one suspects that a general factor will account for the intercorrelations, he may proceed to the calculation of a "Two-factor" pattern, and in the course of this analysis he may determine the adequacy of such a hypothesis.

The grouping of variables by means of B-coefficients may lead the investigator to the hypothesis of just one factor. When the correlations among n variables indicate the sufficiency of just one common factor, then the communality of any variable z_e is given by any one of the following $\nu = \binom{n-1}{2}$ triads:

(6.8)
$$t_{jk} = \frac{r_{ej} r_{ek}}{r_{jk}} \qquad \left(\begin{array}{l} e \text{ is fixed} \\ j, k = 1, 2, \ldots, n \\ j < k, \ j, k \neq e \end{array} \right).$$

Each triad is subject to a small sampling error, so that the ν numbers, $t_{12}, t_{13}, \ldots, t_{n-1,n}$ (e omitted), are generally distinct. The most representative number h_e^2, in the least-square sense, is that which makes the quantity $\Sigma((t_{jk} - h_e^2)^2;\ j,\ k = 1,\ 2,\ \ldots,\ n,\ j < k,\ j,\ k \neq e)$ a minimum. The minimum value is given by the arithmetic mean of the set of numbers t_{jk}, that is,

$$(6.9)\quad \begin{cases} h_e^2 = \dfrac{1}{\nu}\, \Sigma(t_{jk};\ j,\ k = 1,\ 2,\ \ldots,\ n,\ j < k,\ j,\ k \neq e) \\[2mm] = \dfrac{1}{\nu}\, \Sigma\left(\dfrac{r_{ej}r_{ek}}{r_{jk}};\ j,\ k = 1,\ 2,\ \ldots,\ n,\ j < k,\ j,\ k \neq e\right). \end{cases}$$

In determining the communality of a variable, therefore, the mean of all possible triads is used. Since there is only one common factor, formula (6.9) also gives the square of the coefficient of that factor for any variable z_e.

The basic assumption which validates formula (6.9), or formula (6.7), is that the set of variables can be described in terms of just one common factor. In addition, formula (6.7) was deduced under the assumption that the residuals were zero. On the other hand, the conditions for just one common factor are the equality of all the triads for any variable; so that, strictly speaking, all the triads in (6.9) should be equal. The essential difference between the method of **6.2** and this section is that in the former case the additional assumption is made explicitly in the derivation of the formulas, whereas in the latter case no assumptions are made aside from the basic one. Of course, the conditions for one general factor are expected to be met only within errors of sampling. The method of this section involves the computation of individual triads, which may be inspected for statistical equality. In the following sections sampling error formulas will be developed which may be of use in this connection.

There is one further assumption which must be made for the practical problem. When the solution for the communality h_e^2 is made by either formula (6.7) or (6.9), it is tacitly assumed that

$$(6.10)\qquad \frac{r_{ej}r_{ek}}{r_{jk}} \leqq 1 \qquad \begin{pmatrix} e \text{ is fixed} \\ j,\ k = 1,\ 2,\ \ldots,\ n \\ j < k,\ j,\ k \neq e \end{pmatrix}.$$

Furthermore, for any statistical variable $h_e^2 \leqq r_{eE}$, so that

$$(6.11)\qquad \frac{r_{ej}r_{ek}}{r_{jk}} \leqq r_{eE},$$

where r_{eE} is the reliability coefficient of variable z_e. These assumptions will usually be satisfied in practical problems, but if a particular triad exceeds unity it should be dropped from the evaluation of the communality.

6.4. *The Bi-factor Method*

The "Two-factor" pattern is very limited in its application because it implies that the rank of the matrix of correlations is unity. Such a simple relationship among the correlations is not ordinarily to be expected for a large set of variables. The method of analysis as given in **6.2** and **6.3** is very useful, however, in the more general bi-factor form of solution. A bi-factor pattern of the type (5.8), or one with slight modifications, can be obtained for any matrix of positive correlations by applying the preceding methods.

The procedure is to select appropriate variables out of the total set, which taken alone have a matrix of correlations of rank one, and then to apply the analysis for variables involving only one common factor. This procedure is justified by Theorem 3.5, which states that the dimension of the common-factor space is equal to the rank of the correlation matrix. The common-factor space in the new situation refers, of course, only to the space containing the specified variables. Now these variables are selected from the pattern plan to involve only one common factor, and so the rank of their matrix of correlations must be one.

The complete development of a bi-factor pattern will now be given. Suppose a set of n variables has been shown to be divisible into m groups G_s $(s = 1, 2, \ldots, m)$ by the method of B-coefficients. If the m groups involve $p_1, p_2, \ldots, p_m$ variables, respectively, the bi-factor type of solution can be written as in (5.8). For convenience the pattern* is repeated here:

$$(6.12) \quad \left\{ \begin{aligned}
z_1 &= a_{10}F_0 + a_{11}F_1 \\
z_2 &= a_{20}F_0 + a_{21}F_1 \\
&\quad \cdot \quad \cdot \quad \cdot \quad \cdot \quad \cdot \\
z_{p_1} &= a_{p_10}F_0 + a_{p_11}F_1 \\
z_{p_1+1} &= a_{(p_1+1)0}F_0 \qquad + a_{(p_1+1)2}F_2 \\
&\quad \cdot \quad \cdot \quad \cdot \quad \cdot \quad \cdot \quad \cdot \quad \cdot \\
z_{p_1+p_2} &= a_{(p_1+p_2)0}F_0 \qquad + a_{(p_1+p_2)2}F_2 \\
&\quad \cdot \quad \cdot \quad \cdot \quad \cdot \quad \cdot \quad \cdot \quad \cdot \\
z_{n-p_m+1} &= a_{(n-p_m+1)0}F_0 \qquad\qquad\qquad + a_{(n-p_m+1)m}F_m \\
&\quad \cdot \quad \cdot \quad \cdot \quad \cdot \quad \cdot \quad \cdot \quad \cdot \quad \cdot \\
z_n &= a_{n0}F_0 \qquad\qquad\qquad\qquad + a_{nm}F_m .
\end{aligned} \right.$$

The problem now is to determine values for the coefficients in pattern (6.12) which will reproduce the original correlations, within errors of sampling.

---

* See n. *, p. 95.

The computation of the coefficients falls into two parts: first, the general-factor coefficients, then, the group-factor coefficients.

Before developing the methods of obtaining the factor coefficients, the geometric interpretation of the bi-factor plan will be briefly reviewed. The common-factor space which is used to describe the n variables in (6.12) is clearly of $(m + 1)$ dimensions, there being that many factors or axes. It may be possible, perhaps, to describe the variables in a space of only m dimensions, but the complexity of each variable would then be greater. There is a great deal of geometrical elegance and statistical simplicity in describing the variables in the form (6.12). Although the total common-factor space is of $(m + 1)$ dimensions, each vector representing a variable lies in a plane, that is, each variable measures only the general and one group factor. The total configuration is described as a pencil of planes through the F_0 axis.* When no variable measures more than one group factor, there are no points in the planes formed by pairs of group-factor axes.† This geometric interpretation of the bi-factor configuration gave the clue for further analysis into correlated factors, which will be presented in Chapter XI.

The general-factor coefficients of a bi-factor pattern can be obtained by the method of **6.2,** applied to appropriate subsets of variables. Any one of the triples (e, j, k) of the system $((e, j, k); e \epsilon G_u, j \epsilon G_s, k \epsilon G_t, u \neq s \neq t, u, s, t = 1, 2, \ldots, m)$ involves only one common factor. Hence, assuming that the residuals vanish and replacing correlations from the pattern by observed correlations, there results

$$r_{jk} = a_{j0}a_{k0} \qquad (j \epsilon G_s, k \epsilon G_t, s \neq t)$$

according to (5.10). Then, multiplying both sides of this equation by a_{e0}^2, and reapplying this equation, the following expression arises:

$$(6.13) \qquad a_{e0}^2 r_{jk} = a_{e0}^2 a_{j0} a_{k0} = (a_{e0}a_{j0})(a_{e0}a_{k0}) = r_{ej}r_{ek}.$$

Formula (6.13) gives the value of a_{e0}^2 as computed from the correlations with particular variables j and k. To obtain a more reliable evaluation of any general-factor coefficient, sum both sides of (6.13) for all values‡ of j and k

---

* Cf. **5.5.**

† An exception occurs when a variable measures a single group factor and not even the general factor. In this case the vector representing the variable actually lies on the group-factor reference axis, and hence in the plane of this axis and each of the other group-factor axes.

‡ If j and k are merely restricted to be in different groups, and the variables range over all groups, each correlation would appear twice, since $r_{jk} = r_{kj}$. To avoid this, the indices j and k are permitted to range over all groups, namely, $j \epsilon G_s$ and $k \epsilon G_t$ for $s, t = 1, 2, \ldots, m$, but under the condition $s < t$.

which, together with e, preserve the property of involving only one common factor. For any $e \epsilon G_u$ it follows that

$$(6.14) \quad a_{e0}^2 = \frac{\Sigma(r_{ej}r_{ek}; \, j\epsilon G_s, \, k\epsilon G_t, \, s < t, \, s, t \neq u, \, s, t = 1, 2, \ldots, m)}{\Sigma(r_{jk}; \, j\epsilon G_s, \, k\epsilon G_t, \, s < t, \, s, t \neq u, \, s, t = 1, 2, \ldots, m)}.$$

This formula gives the square of the general-factor coefficient for any variable z_e.

To illustrate the application of formula (6.14) and to clarify the notation, a concrete algebraic example will be considered. Let there be fourteen variables which, according to the B-coefficient technique, group as follows:

$$G_1 = (1, 2, 3), \qquad G_3 = (8, 9, 10, 11),$$
$$G_2 = (4, 5, 6, 7), \qquad G_4 = (12, 13, 14).$$

Then the bi-factor plan may be formulated as in Table 6.1. The general-

TABLE 6.1

BI-FACTOR PATTERN PLAN FOR FOURTEEN
HYPOTHETICAL VARIABLES

Variable	F_0	F_1	F_2	F_3	F_4
1.........	a_{10}	a_{11}	......	......	......
2.........	a_{20}	a_{21}	......	......	......
3.........	a_{30}	a_{31}	......	......	......
4.........	a_{40}	......	a_{42}	......	......
5.........	a_{50}	......	a_{52}	......	......
6.........	a_{60}	......	a_{62}	......	......
7.........	a_{70}	......	a_{72}	......	......
8.........	a_{80}	......	......	a_{83}	......
9.........	a_{90}	......	......	a_{93}	......
10.........	$a_{10,\,0}$	......	......	$a_{10,\,3}$	......
11.........	$a_{11,\,0}$	......	......	$a_{11,\,3}$	......
12.........	$a_{12,\,0}$	......	......	......	$a_{12,\,4}$
13.........	$a_{13,\,0}$	......	......	......	$a_{13,\,4}$
14.........	$a_{14,\,0}$	......	......	......	$a_{14,\,4}$

factor coefficients can be computed by means of formula (6.14). For example, the first coefficient is given by

$$a_{10}^2 = \frac{\Sigma(r_{1j}r_{1k}; \, j\epsilon G_s, \, k\epsilon G_t, \, s < t, \, s, t = 2, 3, 4)}{\Sigma(r_{jk}; \, j\epsilon G_s, \, k\epsilon G_t, \, s < t, \, s, t = 2, 3, 4)} = \frac{N}{D},$$

where N and D have been used to denote the numerator and denominator, respectively. As it stands, this formula involves the sum of forty correlations in the denominator and the sum of the same number of paired products of correlations in the numerator. The denominator may be written in the more conventional (and longer) form, namely,

$$D = \sum_{j=4}^{7}\sum_{k=8}^{14}r_{jk} + \sum_{j=8}^{11}\sum_{k=12}^{14}r_{jk}\,.$$

After some factoring (algebraically), the numerator may be written as follows:

$$N = \Sigma(r_{1j}; j\epsilon G_2)\Sigma(r_{1k}; k\epsilon G_s, s = 3, 4) + \Sigma(r_{1j}; j\epsilon G_3)\Sigma(r_{1k}; k\epsilon G_4)\,,$$

or more explicitly in the form

$$N = (r_{14} + r_{15} + r_{16} + r_{17})(r_{18} + r_{19} + r_{1,10} + r_{1,11} + r_{1,12} + r_{1,13}$$
$$+ r_{1,14}) + (r_{18} + r_{19} + r_{1,10} + r_{1,11})(r_{1,12} + r_{1,13} + r_{1,14}).$$

From the values of N and D, the coefficient a_{10} is readily obtained.

The correlations which are involved in the calculation of a_{10}^2 may be represented schematically as in Figure 6.1. The numerator consists of the sum

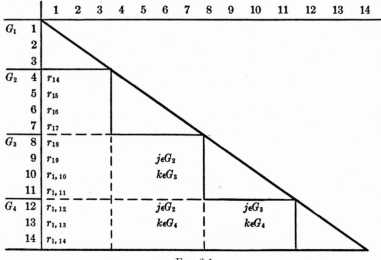

FIG. 6.1

of appropriate products of correlations appearing in the first column, while the correlations entering into the denominator are merely indicated by the blocks showing the locations of the variables j and k. The arrangement of work for routine calculation of a numerical problem is described in Appendix C.

An important extension of formula (6.14) should be noted. If the pattern plan of a set of variables is of the bi-factor form, but includes a number of variables which measure only the general and no group factors, additional terms can be included in formula (6.14). For any two such variables, together with any other variable e, will involve only one common factor. The summations in (6.14) should extend to all such variables j, k; the only restriction being $j < k$ so that no correlation should be used more than once. There seems to be no reason for unnecessarily complicating formula (6.14) to cope with this case, it being clear how the formula is extended.

After the general-factor coefficients are computed there remains the problem of determining the group-factor coefficients. The first step is to obtain the residual correlations with the general factor removed, or the *general-factor residuals* as they will be called hereafter. These are defined by

$$(6.15) \qquad\qquad \dot{r}_{jk} = r_{jk} - a_{j0}a_{k0} \qquad (j, k = 1, 2, \ldots, n) .$$

In general, the table of these residual correlations will be of the form shown in Figure 5.1, the values in the rectangles being approximately equal to zero. The standard error of a residual correlation will be developed in a later section, so that the significance of any entry in this table can be verified.

In the residual-factor space, the n variables can be described by a uni-factor pattern, i.e., the bi-factor pattern may be considered as a uni-factor pattern with a general factor superimposed. The residual correlations (6.15) for each group of variables, taken alone, should have a matrix of rank one and hence measure only one common factor. Either of the methods of **6.2** or **6.3** can now be used for the calculation of the group-factor coefficients. Since there will usually be a relatively small number of variables in each group, it seems more advisable to use the method of triads of **6.3**. By this procedure the group-factor coefficient for any variable $e \epsilon G_s$ is given by

$$(6.16) \qquad a_{es}^2 = \frac{1}{\binom{p_s - 1}{2}} \sum \left(\frac{\dot{r}_{ej}\dot{r}_{ek}}{\dot{r}_{jk}} \ ; \ j, k \epsilon G_s, \ j < k, \ j, k \neq e \right) ,$$

where, it will be recalled, p_s is the number of variables in the group G_s. This formula, of course, agrees perfectly with (6.9) when the general-factor residuals are considered as the observed correlations and p_s is taken to be the total number of variables under consideration.

It may be enlightening to apply formula (6.16) in the evaluation of one group-factor coefficient of Table 6.1. Thus, the coefficient of F_2 for the fourth variable is given by

$$a_{42}^2 = \frac{1}{\binom{3}{2}} \sum \left(\frac{\dot{r}_{4j}\dot{r}_{4k}}{\dot{r}_{jk}} ; \; j, \, k \epsilon G_2, \;\; j < k, \;\; j, \, k \neq 4 \right)$$

$$= \frac{1}{3} \left(\frac{\dot{r}_{45}\dot{r}_{46}}{\dot{r}_{56}} + \frac{\dot{r}_{45}\dot{r}_{47}}{\dot{r}_{57}} + \frac{\dot{r}_{46}\dot{r}_{47}}{\dot{r}_{67}} \right).$$

The complete determination of a bi-factor pattern (6.12) has been shown to be possible by means of the formulas (6.14) and (6.16). When all the coefficients have been computed, the *final residuals* can be obtained. These are the residuals after all factors have been removed and may be written as follows:

(6.17) $$\bar{r}_{jk} = r_{jk} - r'_{jk} = \dot{r}_{jk} - a_{js}a_{ks} .$$

If the variables j and k do not belong to the same group, then $\bar{r}_{jk} = \dot{r}_{jk}$. The general-factor residuals for variables from different groups, being the final residuals, must not be significantly different from zero. At the same time, the general-factor residuals for variables within a group must be significantly positive in order for an additional factor to be postulated among them. Sampling error formulas for the residuals are given later.

When it is found that certain residuals between variables of different groups are significant, it may be necessary to modify the bi-factor plan slightly. The same is true if certain general-factor residuals within a group are practically zero. Some of these modifications will be illustrated later, after the sampling errors are considered.

The method of analysis of this section is adaptable to any matrix of positive correlations and yields a very parsimonious solution. The variables are probably described in the simplest manner and with complete rigor and statistical soundness. Furthermore, with the aid of the sampling error formulas which are developed in the next three sections, the investigator can tell to what degree to factor a set of variables, i.e., determine the number of factors that are necessary to reproduce the observed correlations within errors of sampling. To aid the reader in applying this method of factorization, a complete outline is presented in Appendix C. There the detailed numerical calculations are exhibited on the battery of twenty-four psychological tests which has been used before. The calculations of the factor coefficients, by means of formulas (6.14) and (6.16), have been put in a routine form.

6.5. *Standard Error of a Factor Coefficient*

The coefficients in a factor pattern, that is, the correlations of the variables with the factors, may vary from sample to sample. Here the term "sample" must include the variables as well as the group of individuals. Inasmuch as factor analysis is essentially a correlational analysis, the entire table of correlations is subject to sampling error due to the sampling of individuals and variables from their respective populations. It is evident, then, that any formula for the sampling error of a factor coefficient must be a function of the number of variables and the number of observations of each variable.

In this section the standard error of a general-factor coefficient will be developed. It will be assumed that the coefficient is obtained by the method of triads. This assumption is made for the sake of logical rigor because, as will be seen, the standard error formula depends upon the triads. Practically, however, the formula will also be applicable to coefficients obtained by the method of **6.2,** since such a coefficient differs very little from one evaluated by the method of triads. In addition, the standard error formula will be applied to group-factor coefficients after some justification for this is made.

As a first step, it is necessary to determine the standard error of an individual triad. Proceeding in the classical manner by taking logarithms of both sides of (6.8), there arises

$$\log t_{jk} = \log r_{ej} + \log r_{ek} - \log r_{jk} .$$

Then, differentiating this expression, it becomes

$$(6.18) \qquad \frac{dt}{t} = \frac{da}{a} + \frac{db}{b} - \frac{dc}{c} ,$$

where, for simplicity, the following substitutions have been made:

$$(6.19) \qquad t = t_{jk} , \qquad a = r_{ej} , \qquad b = r_{ek} , \qquad c = r_{jk} .$$

Squaring the expression (6.18) and taking the mean value over the population gives

$$(6.20) \qquad \frac{\sigma_t^2}{t^2} = \frac{\sigma_a^2}{a^2} + \frac{\sigma_b^2}{b^2} + \frac{\sigma_c^2}{c^2} + 2\left(\frac{\sigma_a \sigma_b}{ab} r_{ab} - \frac{\sigma_a \sigma_c}{ac} r_{ac} - \frac{\sigma_b \sigma_c}{bc} r_{bc} \right) .$$

The purpose now is to reduce formula (6.20) to an expression in the original correlations a, b, and c. This is accomplished by means of, first, the well-known formula for the standard error of a correlation coefficient, namely,

$$(6.21) \qquad \sigma_a^2 = \frac{(1 - a^2)^2}{N},$$

where N is the number of observations in the sample; and, second, the Pearson-Filon equations for the correlation between correlation coefficients. The form of these equations for the case where an index is repeated on the two correlations may be written*

$$(6.22) \qquad r_{ab} = c - \frac{ab(1 - a^2 - b^2 - c^2 + 2abc)}{2(1 - a^2)(1 - b^2)}.$$

In the derivation of these formulas it is assumed that the variables are distributed normally in the population. Substituting expressions of the type (6.21) and (6.22) for the σ's and r's in (6.20), this equation becomes

$$N\sigma_t^2 = t^2 \left\{ \left(\frac{1 - a^2}{a}\right)^2 + \left(\frac{1 - b^2}{b}\right)^2 + \left(\frac{1 - c^2}{c}\right)^2 + \frac{2c(1 - a^2)(1 - b^2)}{ab} \right.$$
$$- \frac{2b(1 - a^2)(1 - c^2)}{ac} + \frac{2a(1 - b^2)(1 - c^2)}{bc}$$
$$\left. + (1 - a^2 - b^2 - c^2 + 2abc) \right\}.$$

By algebraic reductions this expression can be put in the form

$$(6.23) \quad N\sigma_t^2 = 2\frac{ab}{c} + \frac{a^2}{c^2} + \frac{b^2}{c^2} - 2\frac{ab^3}{c^3} - 2\frac{a^3b}{c^3} + \frac{a^2b^2}{c^4} - 5\frac{a^2b^2}{c^2} + 4\frac{a^3b^3}{c^3}.$$

This formula gives the standard error of a particular triad. Formula (6.23) may also be written as follows:

$$(6.24) \quad N\sigma_t^2 = t\left[t(1 - 2t)\left(\frac{1}{a^2} + \frac{1}{b^2}\right) + \frac{t}{c^2} + 2(1 - t)(1 - 2t) + t \right],$$

which is a simple form for computation.

In the above development only the variation in the sample of individuals was considered. When the sampling error of a communality or a factor

* Karl Pearson and L. N. G. Filon, "On the Probable Errors of Frequency Constants and on the Influence of Random Selection on Variation and Correlation," *Phil. Trans. Roy. Soc.*, 1898, p. 263.

coefficient is desired, however, the variation in the sample of variables must be taken into account. Inasmuch as no method for dealing with the simultaneous variation of individuals and variables is known, approximative methods are used. The general procedure, in making allowance for the variation of variables, is to employ averaging methods.

In obtaining the standard error of a communality, all variables will be considered by taking the mean of all possible triads. In the case of only one common factor, of course, each coefficient is merely the square root of the communality, that is, $a_{e0} = \sqrt{h_e^2}$ $(e = 1, 2, \ldots, n)$. Hence the standard error of the coefficient can be readily deduced from the standard error of the communality by means of the formula*

$$(6.25) \qquad \sigma_{a_{e0}}^2 = \frac{1}{4h_e^2}\, \sigma_{h_e^2}^2 .$$

According to the foregoing argument for developing an approximate formula for $\sigma_{a_{e0}}$, it would be necessary to obtain the mean value of (6.24) for all possible triads and then apply (6.25). It appears to be somewhat simpler, however, to obtain the standard error of a particular evaluation of a coefficient by means of (6.24) and then to take the mean value over all possible evaluations. Thus the value of the coefficient from the triad t is $\sqrt{t}$, and

$$(6.26) \qquad \sigma_{\sqrt{t}}^2 = \frac{1}{4t}\, \sigma_t^2 .$$

The formula for $\sigma_{\sqrt{t}}^2$ in terms of the original correlations then becomes

$$(6.27) \quad 4N\sigma_{\sqrt{t}}^2 = 2 + \frac{a}{bc} + \frac{b}{ac} - 2\left(\frac{a}{c}\right)^2 - 2\left(\frac{b}{c}\right)^2 + \frac{ab}{c^3} - 5\frac{ab}{c} + 4\left(\frac{ab}{c}\right)^2 .$$

There now remains the problem to take the mean value of (6.27) over all possible triads.

The terms in the right-hand member of (6.27) group themselves into five distinct types of nonlinear functions of two or three of the correlations a, b, c. The means of such functions can, in general, only be expressed in terms of the means, standard deviations, and correlations of the original variables (i.e., the correlations a, b, c) to a first approximation. The implicit assumption is that the deviations are small compared with the means of

---

* For the general theorem relating the standard error of a function to the standard errors of its variables see Appen. **B.7.**

these variables. Designating the mean over ν values by a bar, the means of the various types of functions in (6.27) may then be tabulated as follows:[*]

$$(6.28) \quad \begin{cases} \overline{\left(\dfrac{ab}{c}\right)} = \dfrac{\bar{a}\bar{b}}{\bar{c}}\left(1 + \dfrac{\sigma_a\sigma_b r_{ab}}{\bar{a}\bar{b}} - \dfrac{\sigma_a\sigma_c r_{ac}}{\bar{a}\bar{c}} - \dfrac{\sigma_b\sigma_c r_{bc}}{\bar{b}\bar{c}} + \dfrac{\sigma_c^2}{\bar{c}^2}\right), \\[2mm] \overline{\left(\dfrac{a}{c}\right)^2} = \dfrac{\bar{a}^2}{\bar{c}^2}\left(1 + \dfrac{\sigma_a}{\bar{a}^2} - \dfrac{4\sigma_a\sigma_c r_{ac}}{\bar{a}\bar{c}} + \dfrac{3\sigma_c^2}{\bar{c}^2}\right), \\[2mm] \overline{\left(\dfrac{ab}{c}\right)^2} = \dfrac{\bar{a}^2\bar{b}^2}{\bar{c}^2}\left(1 + \dfrac{\sigma_a^2}{\bar{a}^2} + \dfrac{4\sigma_a\sigma_b r_{ab}}{\bar{a}\bar{b}} + \dfrac{\sigma_b^2}{\bar{b}^2} - \dfrac{4\sigma_a\sigma_c r_{ac}}{\bar{a}\bar{c}} - \dfrac{4\sigma_b\sigma_c r_{bc}}{\bar{b}\bar{c}} + \dfrac{3\sigma_c^2}{\bar{c}^2}\right), \\[2mm] \overline{\left(\dfrac{a}{bc}\right)} = \dfrac{\bar{a}}{\bar{b}\bar{c}}\left(1 - \dfrac{\sigma_a\sigma_b r_{ab}}{\bar{a}\bar{b}} + \dfrac{\sigma_b^2}{\bar{b}^2} - \dfrac{\sigma_a\sigma_c r_{ac}}{\bar{a}\bar{c}} + \dfrac{\sigma_b\sigma_c r_{bc}}{\bar{b}\bar{c}} + \dfrac{\sigma_c^2}{\bar{c}^2}\right), \\[2mm] \overline{\left(\dfrac{ab}{c^3}\right)} = \dfrac{\bar{a}\bar{b}}{\bar{c}^3}\left(1 + \dfrac{\sigma_a\sigma_b r_{ab}}{\bar{a}\bar{b}} - \dfrac{3\sigma_a\sigma_c r_{ac}}{\bar{a}\bar{c}} - \dfrac{3\sigma_b\sigma_c r_{bc}}{\bar{b}\bar{c}} + \dfrac{6\sigma_c^2}{\bar{c}^2}\right), \end{cases}$$

where the standard deviations and correlations are over the observed ν values of the original correlations. In the derivation of these formulas it is assumed that the ratio of the deviation of a, b, or c from its respective mean to that mean is so small that third- and higher-degree powers can be neglected.

The mean value of $\sigma_{\sqrt{t}}^2$ over all possible triads will be written $\overline{\sigma_{a_{e0}}^2}$ to indicate the passage from an individual evaluation of a factor coefficient to the final value based on all ν triads. Then, substituting the values from (6.28), and other expressions like these, for the mean values of the ratios in (6.27) gives

$$(6.29) \quad \begin{aligned} 4N\overline{\sigma_{a_{e0}}^2} = &\left\{2 + \frac{\bar{a}}{\bar{b}\bar{c}} + \frac{\bar{b}}{\bar{a}\bar{c}} - \frac{2\bar{a}^2}{\bar{c}^2} - \frac{2\bar{b}^2}{\bar{c}^2} + \frac{\bar{a}\bar{b}}{\bar{c}^3} - \frac{5\bar{a}\bar{b}}{\bar{c}} + \frac{4\bar{a}^2\bar{b}^2}{\bar{c}^2}\right\} \\ &+ \left\{\frac{\sigma_a^2}{\bar{a}^2}\left(\frac{\bar{b}}{\bar{a}\bar{c}} - \frac{2\bar{a}^2}{\bar{c}^2} + \frac{4\bar{a}^2\bar{b}^2}{\bar{c}^2}\right) + \frac{\sigma_b^2}{\bar{b}^2}\left(\frac{\bar{a}}{\bar{b}\bar{c}} - \frac{2\bar{b}^2}{\bar{c}^2} + \frac{4\bar{a}^2\bar{b}^2}{\bar{c}^2}\right)\right. \\ &+ \frac{\sigma_c^2}{\bar{c}^2}\left(\frac{\bar{a}}{\bar{b}\bar{c}} + \frac{\bar{b}}{\bar{a}\bar{c}} - \frac{6\bar{a}^2}{\bar{c}^2} - \frac{6\bar{b}^2}{\bar{c}^2} + \frac{6\bar{a}\bar{b}}{\bar{c}^3} - \frac{5\bar{a}\bar{b}}{\bar{c}} + \frac{12\bar{a}^2\bar{b}^2}{\bar{c}^2}\right) \\ &- \frac{\sigma_a\sigma_b r_{ab}}{\bar{a}\bar{b}}\left(\frac{\bar{a}}{\bar{b}\bar{c}} + \frac{\bar{b}}{\bar{a}\bar{c}} - \frac{\bar{a}\bar{b}}{\bar{c}^3} + \frac{5\bar{a}\bar{b}}{\bar{c}} - \frac{16\bar{a}^2\bar{b}^2}{\bar{c}^2}\right) \\ &- \frac{\sigma_a\sigma_c r_{ac}}{\bar{a}\bar{c}}\left(\frac{\bar{a}}{\bar{b}\bar{c}} - \frac{\bar{b}}{\bar{a}\bar{c}} - \frac{8\bar{a}^2}{\bar{c}^2} + \frac{3\bar{a}\bar{b}}{\bar{c}^3} - \frac{5\bar{a}\bar{b}}{\bar{c}} + \frac{16\bar{a}^2\bar{b}^2}{\bar{c}^2}\right) \\ &+ \left.\frac{\sigma_b\sigma_c r_{bc}}{\bar{b}\bar{c}}\left(\frac{\bar{a}}{\bar{b}\bar{c}} - \frac{\bar{b}}{\bar{a}\bar{c}} + \frac{8\bar{b}^2}{\bar{c}^2} - \frac{3\bar{a}\bar{b}}{\bar{c}^3} + \frac{5\bar{a}\bar{b}}{\bar{c}} - \frac{16\bar{a}^2\bar{b}^2}{\bar{c}^2}\right)\right\}. \end{aligned}$$

[*] For the method of deriving these formulas see Appen. **B.8.**

Formula (6.29) gives the complete expression for $\overline{\sigma^2_{a_{e_0}}}$ to the degree of approximation indicated by (6.28). The complete formula, however, seems to be too long for practical purposes. It has been checked empirically that the first bracket gives a very good approximation to the complete expression. The indication seems to be that the second bracket contributes a small positive quantity to the right-hand member. If the function of the correlations in the entire right-hand member is designated by $f(r)$ and that in the first bracket by $\phi(r)$, then the preceding observations may be stated as follows:

$$f(r) > \phi(r) ,$$

or

(6.30) $$f(r) = \phi(r) + \delta^2 ,$$

where δ^2 is a small positive quantity.

Now the desired standard error is $\overline{\sigma}_{a_{e_0}}$, so that it is necessary to express $\overline{\sigma^2_{a_{e_0}}}$ in terms of $\overline{\sigma}^2_{a_{e_0}}$. It is a well-known fact that

$$\overline{\sigma^2} \geqq \overline{\sigma}^2 ,$$

where the standard deviations are for any variables. The last expression may also be put in the form

(6.31) $$\overline{\sigma^2} = \overline{\sigma}^2 + \epsilon^2 ,$$

where ϵ^2 is a small positive quantity. Making the substitutions (6.30) and (6.31) in (6.29), there arises

(6.32) $$\overline{\sigma}^2_{a_{e_0}} + \epsilon^2 = \frac{\phi(r)}{4N} + \frac{\delta^2}{4N} .$$

The errors tend to compensate for one another, and the final formula is taken to be

(6.33) $$\overline{\sigma}^2_{a_{e_0}} = \frac{1}{4N} \phi(r) .$$

Written out fully, and dropping the scoring over the σ, this formula becomes

(6.34) $$\sigma^2_{a_{e_0}} = \frac{1}{4N} \left(2 + \frac{\bar{a}}{\bar{b}\bar{c}} + \frac{\bar{b}}{\bar{a}\bar{c}} - \frac{2\bar{a}^2}{\bar{c}^2} - \frac{2\bar{b}^2}{\bar{c}^2} + \frac{\bar{a}\bar{b}}{\bar{c}^3} - \frac{5\bar{a}\bar{b}}{\bar{c}} + \frac{4\bar{a}^2\bar{b}^2}{\bar{c}^2} \right) .$$

This represents the best approximation to the required formula for the standard error of a general-factor coefficient.

To clarify the meaning of the terms in (6.34), suppose the number of variables in the set to be five and that the standard error of the first coefficient of the general factor is required. The coefficient is denoted by a_{10} and is evaluated from $\nu = \binom{5-1}{2} = 6$ different triads. Its solution, according to (6.9), is given by

$$a_{10}^2 = h_1^2 = \frac{1}{6} \sum \left(\frac{r_{1j}r_{1k}}{r_{jk}} ; \; j, k = 2, 3, 4, 5, \; j < k \right).$$

The parameters defined in (6.19) are, for this case,

$$t = t_{jk}, \qquad a = r_{1j}, \qquad b = r_{1k}, \qquad c = r_{jk}$$

$$(j, k = 2, 3, 4, 5, \; j < k).$$

The meaning of the terms in (6.34) will then be evident from Table 6.2.

TABLE 6.2

jk	$a = r_{1j}$	$b = r_{1k}$	$c = r_{jk}$	$t_{jk} = \dfrac{ab}{c}$
23.......	r_{12}	r_{13}	r_{23}	t_{23}
24.......	r_{12}	r_{14}	r_{24}	t_{24}
25.......	r_{12}	r_{15}	r_{25}	t_{25}
34.......	r_{13}	r_{14}	r_{34}	t_{34}
35.......	r_{13}	r_{15}	r_{35}	t_{35}
45.......	r_{14}	r_{15}	r_{45}	t_{45}
Mean..	$\bar{a}$	$\bar{b}$	$\bar{c}$	a_{10}^2

Here all the correlations leading to the averages $\bar{a}$, $\bar{b}$, $\bar{c}$ are written down for clarity. In an actual problem, however, considerable time can be saved by omitting these three columns. The stub, giving the indices, should be retained to keep track of the variables, but this can be followed immediately by the column of triads. The appropriate correlations for computing $\bar{a}$, $\bar{b}$, $\bar{c}$, and the individual triads can be read off directly from the matrix of correlations. A numerical example, illustrating the computation of (6.34), will be given later.

Before leaving the present discussion, it may be well to point out another application of the standard error formula (6.34). This formula was developed on the assumption that the general-factor coefficients were computed by means of formula (6.9), i.e., the method of triads. As already remarked, formula (6.34) applies equally well when the general-factor coefficients are computed by the classical method indicated in **6.2**. Now it would be very convenient if this standard error formula also applied to group-factor coefficients. Such coefficients are obtained by the method of triads, as may be seen from formula (6.16). The essential distinction between (6.9) and (6.16) is that every correlation in the former is replaced by a general-factor residual in the latter. When the development of the standard error of a group-factor coefficient was attempted, employing triads of general-factor residuals, a very unwieldy formula resulted. A very good approximation to the standard error of a group-factor coefficient, however, is given by formula (6.34) in which the observed correlations are replaced by general-factor residuals.

6.6. *Standard Error of a Residual*

It will be recalled that a residual is defined by $\bar{r}_{jk} = r_{jk} - r'_{jk}$, where r_{jk} is an observed correlation and r'_{jk} is the corresponding correlation reproduced from a factor pattern. For the case of just one common factor $r'_{jk} = a_{j0}a_{k0}$ and $\bar{r}_{jk} = r_{jk} - a_{j0}a_{k0}$. The total differential for $\bar{r}_{jk}$ is

$$d\bar{r}_{jk} = dr_{jk} - a_{j0}da_{k0} - a_{k0}da_{j0},$$

which, upon squaring and taking the mean value over the population, gives

$$(6.35) \quad \begin{cases} \sigma^2_{\bar{r}_{jk}} = \sigma^2_{r_{jk}} + a^2_{j0}\sigma^2_{a_{k0}} + a^2_{k0}\sigma^2_{a_{j0}} + 2[a_{j0}a_{k0}\sigma_{a_{j0}}\sigma_{a_{k0}}r_{a_{j0}a_{k0}} \\ \qquad\qquad - a_{j0}\sigma_{r_{jk}}\sigma_{a_{k0}}r_{r_{jk}a_{k0}} - a_{k0}\sigma_{r_{jk}}\sigma_{a_{j0}}r_{r_{jk}a_{j0}}]. \end{cases}$$

At the present time no formulas are known which express the correlations in the bracket in terms of the original variables, a_{j0}, a_{k0}, and r_{jk}. Hence the following expression

$$(6.36) \qquad \sigma_{\bar{r}_{jk}} = \sqrt{\sigma^2_{r_{jk}} + a^2_{j0}\sigma^2_{a_{k0}} + a^2_{k0}\sigma^2_{a_{j0}}}$$

is the best approximation to the standard error of a residual, for one factor removed. The standard errors involved in formula (6.36) may be computed by means of (6.21) and (6.34).

When two variables, z_j and z_k, involve two uncorrelated common factors, F_0 and F_1, their residual correlation is given by

$$(6.37) \qquad \bar{r}_{jk} = r_{jk} - a_{j0}a_{k0} - a_{j1}a_{k1}.$$

The result of differentiating and squaring the expression (6.37) and then taking the mean for the population is

$$(6.38) \quad \begin{cases} \sigma^2_{\bar{r}_{jk}} = \sigma^2_{r_{jk}} + a^2_{j0}\sigma^2_{a_{k0}} + a^2_{k0}\sigma^2_{a_{j0}} + a^2_{j1}\sigma^2_{a_{k1}} + a^2_{k1}\sigma^2_{a_{j1}} \\ \qquad + 2(a_{j0}a_{k0}\sigma_{k0}\sigma_{j0}r_{a_{k0}a_{j0}} + a_{j0}a_{j1}\sigma_{a_{k0}}\sigma_{a_{k1}}r_{a_{k0}a_{k1}} \\ \qquad + a_{j0}a_{k1}\sigma_{a_{k0}}\sigma_{a_{j1}}r_{a_{k0}a_{j1}} + a_{k0}a_{j1}\sigma_{a_{j0}}\sigma_{a_{k1}}r_{a_{j0}a_{k1}} \\ \qquad + a_{k0}a_{k1}\sigma_{a_{j0}}\sigma_{a_{j1}}r_{a_{j0}a_{j1}} + a_{j1}a_{k1}\sigma_{a_{k1}}\sigma_{a_{j1}}r_{a_{k1}a_{j1}} \\ \qquad - a_{j0}\sigma_{r_{jk}}\sigma_{a_{k0}}r_{r_{jk}a_{k0}} - a_{k0}\sigma_{r_{jk}}\sigma_{a_{j0}}r_{r_{jk}a_{j0}} \\ \qquad - a_{j1}\sigma_{r_{jk}}\sigma_{a_{k1}}r_{r_{jk}a_{k1}} - a_{k1}\sigma_{r_{jk}}\sigma_{a_{j1}}r_{r_{jk}a_{j1}}). \end{cases}$$

The best approximation for the standard error of the residual (6.37) is given by

$$(6.39) \qquad \sigma^2_{\bar{r}_{jk}} = \sigma^2_{r_{jk}} + a^2_{j0}\sigma^2_{a_{k0}} + a^2_{k0}\sigma^2_{a_{j0}} + a^2_{j1}\sigma^2_{a_{k1}} + a^2_{k1}\sigma^2_{a_{j1}} \,.$$

The foregoing results can easily be extended to the general case. If two variables have a general and m group factors in common, they may be described as follows:

$$z_j = a_{j0}F_0 + a_{j1}F_1 + a_{j2}F_2 + \ldots + a_{jm}F_m \,,$$
$$z_k = a_{k0}F_0 + a_{k1}F_1 + a_{k2}F_2 + \ldots + a_{km}F_m \,.$$

The final residual correlation is

$$(6.40) \qquad \bar{r}_{jk} = r_{jk} - \sum_{s=0}^{m} a_{js}a_{ks} \,.$$

Then, as before, it can be shown that a good approximation to the standard error of this residual is given by

$$(6.41) \qquad \sigma^2_{\bar{r}_{jk}} = \sigma^2_{r_{jk}} + \sum_{s=0}^{m} (a^2_{js}\sigma^2_{a_{ks}} + a^2_{ks}\sigma^2_{a_{js}}) \,.$$

Ostensibly, formula (6.41) gives the standard error of any residual after any number of factors have been removed, without any restrictions as to the type of factor pattern or method of computation of the coefficients. Such restrictions are implied, however, in the practical application of this formula. The formula involves the standard errors of the factor coefficients, which are not known for any type pattern but the two-factor and bi-factor. After further approximations, in the next section, a formula for the standard error of a residual will be obtained which does not involve the standard errors of the coefficients explicitly. In that form the formula may be applied as an approximation to other types of factor solutions, for which the sampling errors of the coefficients are not known.

6.7. *Further Approximations to the Sampling Error Formulas*

Other approximations to the sampling errors of a factor coefficient or a residual may be obtained by means of additional arbitrary, but reasonable, assumptions. For example, if a set of correlations is more or less homogeneous, one may assume a constant value for any one of the correlations. Thus the correlations used in the evaluation of any factor coefficient may be set equal to their mean value, say ρ, yielding $a_{e0}^2 = \rho$. Under this hypothesis, formula (6.34) for the standard error of a coefficient reduces to

$$(6.42) \qquad \sigma_a^2 = \frac{1}{4N}\left(\frac{3}{\rho} - 2 - 5\rho + 4\rho^2\right),$$

which applies to any coefficient. The index a should not be confused with that defined in (6.19). Since this formula applies to all a_{e0} ($e = 1, 2, \ldots, n$), the subscripts have been dropped.

Then, employing the value (6.42) for the standard error of a coefficient in (6.36) but letting the other elements retain their individual identities, that formula becomes

$$(6.43) \qquad \sigma_{\bar{r}_{jk}}^2 = \frac{(1 - r_{jk}^2)^2}{N} + \frac{a_{j0}^2 + a_{k0}^2}{4N}\left(\frac{3}{\rho} - 2 - 5\rho + 4\rho^2\right).$$

For a rough estimate of the standard error of any residual, with one factor removed, an even simpler formula can be used. In place of the individual correlation r_{jk} the average correlation ρ can be used, and, setting $a_{j0}^2 = a_{k0}^2 = \rho$, formula (6.43) reduces to

$$(6.44) \qquad \sigma_{\bar{r}}^2 = \frac{(1 - \rho)^2(5 + 8\rho + 2\rho^2)}{2N},$$

where the indices have been dropped from the residual correlation because this formula applies to any residual.

Approximate formulas for the standard error of a residual, with two or more factors removed, can be obtained similarly. Substituting (6.42) for $\sigma_{a_{j0}}^2$, $\sigma_{a_{k0}}^2$, and similar expressions for $\sigma_{a_{j1}}^2$, $\sigma_{a_{k1}}^2$, into (6.39), and setting $r_{jk} = \rho$, $a_{j0}^2 = a_{k0}^2 = \rho$, and $a_{j1}^2 = a_{k1}^2 = \rho_1$,

$$(6.45) \quad \sigma_{\bar{r}}^2 = \frac{(1 - \rho)^2(5 + 8\rho + 2\rho^2)}{2N} + \frac{\rho_1}{2N}\left(\frac{3}{\rho_1} - 2 - 5\rho_1 + 4\rho_1^2\right),$$

where

ρ = average correlation used in computing F_0 coefficients,

ρ_1 = average residual correlation used in computing F_1 coefficients.

In general, the standard error of a residual with $(m + 1)$ factors removed is given by

$$(6.46) \quad \sigma_{\bar{r}}^2 = \frac{(1 - \rho)^2(5 + 8\rho + 2\rho^2)}{2N} + \frac{1}{N}\sum_{s=1}^{m}\left(\tfrac{3}{2} - \rho_s - \tfrac{5}{2}\rho_s^2 + 2\rho_s^3\right),$$

where ρ_s is the average residual correlation used in computing the F_s coefficients.

Any one of the formulas (6.42) to (6.46) must be used with great caution and with a full realization of the underlying assumptions. Most important of all, one must check whether the assumption of setting all observed correlations equal to their mean is a tenable one. This assumption, of course, is over and above those assumptions made to get more or less practical formulas like (6.34) and (6.41). Fortunately, the general direction of the discrepancies in using any of the approximate sampling error formulas is fairly well known. It has been verified empirically that at each stage of approximation the values obtained for the sampling errors generally become smaller. As has already been pointed out, the standard error of a coefficient as given by (6.34) is usually smaller than that given by (6.29). Again, if (6.34) is approximated by (6.42) the value generally becomes a little smaller. As a consequence of this, the standard error of a residual according to formula (6.46) is generally somewhat smaller than that obtained by formula (6.41), unless the original correlation is much larger than the average employed in the former formula. By knowing the general direction of the discrepancies in the approximations, the investigator can make due allowance in setting a level of significance.*

With the foregoing limitations clearly in mind, it may still be very desirable to use formula (6.42) and the various formulas for the standard error of a residual. For this purpose some of these formulas have been put in tabular form and are presented in Appendix H. The standard error of a coefficient for an average correlation from $\rho = .10$ to $\rho = .75$ and for samples from $N = 20$ to $N = 500$ is presented in Table H.1. For the same range of values of ρ and N Table H.2 gives the standard error of a residual for one factor removed. Only one supplementary table is necessary, and, with very little computation, any value of (6.46) can be obtained. Table H.3 gives the values of

$$\left(\tfrac{3}{2} - \rho_s - \tfrac{5}{2}\rho_s^2 + 2\rho_s^3\right) .$$

Thus, in general, the standard error of a residual with $(m + 1)$ factors removed is obtained as follows: square the entry in Table H.2, for the particular ρ and N, and add to this $1/N$ times the sum of the m entries of Table H.3, corresponding to the m values of ρ_s; then the square root of this sum is the required standard error of the residual.

* For example, if a particular residual is just twice its standard error (as given by one of the approximate formulas), it can safely be said that this residual is probably insignificantly different from zero. The argument is that the standard error is probably a little larger, and the ratio a little less, than two. For such investigation, then, the level of significance should be taken to be at least three times the standard error.

The statistical tables of Appendix H, or the more exact formulas of **6.5** and **6.6**, may be used in determining the standard error of a factor coefficient or a residual correlation when such statistics refer to a bi-factor solution. For other types of factor solutions, which were presented formally in Chapter V and which will be described further in later chapters, the sampling error formulas do not apply. Since no sampling error formulas are known for other types of solutions, the formulas which have been developed for the bi-factor solution may be used, in such cases, as first approximations.

6.8. *Interpretation of Standard Errors*

The statement that a statistical constant (e.g., a factor coefficient or residual) has a value $\tilde{x}$ with a standard error σ_x means that, if the constant be determined many times from random samples of relevant material, the observed value x obtained in a sample will differ in absolute value from $\tilde{x}$ by less than σ_x in approximately 68 per cent of the number of samples. This conclusion is based on the assumption that the sampled values of x are distributed in accord with the normal law; the value σ_x ceases to have the same significance if the distribution is not normal.

The equation of the normal distribution of x may be put in the form

$$(6.47) \qquad y = \frac{1}{\sqrt{2\pi}\sigma} e^{-\frac{1}{2}\left(\frac{x}{\sigma}\right)^2},$$

where the origin is at the mean and the total area under the curve is unity. The values of $z = x/\sigma$, or the number of standard deviations from the mean, are called deviates, and $\frac{1}{2}a$ will be used to denote the *area* from the mean to such a deviate. Then

$$(6.48) \qquad \tfrac{1}{2}a = \frac{1}{\sqrt{2\pi}\sigma} \int_0^{\frac{x}{\sigma}} e^{-\frac{1}{2}\left(\frac{x}{\sigma}\right)^2} dx = \frac{1}{\sqrt{2\pi}} \int_0^z e^{-\frac{z^2}{2}} dz.$$

The area $\frac{1}{2}a$ gives the frequency of occurrence, or the probability of occurrence, in the range from the mean to x/σ. Table H.4 gives this total frequency, or probability integral, for values of x/σ from 0 to 4 in intervals of .02.

Frequently the question is to determine what fraction of the total population has a larger deviation than $\pm x/\sigma$; or, in other words, what is the probability that a statistical constant so distributed, and chosen at random, will exceed a given deviation in absolute value. This probability is given by the areas in the tail pieces beyond $\pm x/\sigma$, which may be written

$$(6.49) \qquad P = 1 - a.$$

If the probability of exceeding $+x/\sigma$ is required, it is, of course, given by $\frac{1}{2}P$.

The problem of greatest interest is to determine the significance of statistics obtained from a given sample. A statistic is an appropriate function of the values of a variable given by a sample and used to estimate the corresponding population parameter, which is a hypothetical quantity helping to specify the mathematical form of distribution in the universe. Now an observed variance s^2 may be used as an estimate of the parameter σ^2 of the distribution of x, or, better still, the mean value of s^2 from repeated samples may be employed. The variance σ^2 refers to deviations from $\tilde{x}$, whereas any s^2 refers to deviations from an x obtained in a particular sample. The value $\tilde{x}$ may be considered as an arbitrary origin for a given sample, and the sum of the squares of deviates from this arbitrary point will generally be greater than the sum of the squares of deviates from the mean of the sample (by the least-square property of the arithmetic mean). Hence it is to be anticipated that the mean of the values of s^2 will be less than σ^2. The extent of this inequality is given by*

$$E(s^2) = \frac{N-1}{N}\,\sigma^2\,,$$

where E has been used to denote the expected value from repeated samples. It is advisable, especially when dealing with small samples, to use the *unbiased estimate* of the population parameter, which is defined by

$$\dot{\sigma}^2 = \frac{N}{N-1}\,s^2\,.$$

If N is large, the coefficient in the right-hand member approaches unity, and it is not invalid, to any appreciable extent, to use s in place of the unbiased estimate.

When the "true" value of a parameter $\tilde{x}$ is known, and when the distribution of this statistic in successive samples follows the normal law, the probability of obtaining a deviation from the "true" value less than any given multiple k of the standard error of the parameter in question is given by the area under the normal curve *inside* the range $\tilde{x} \pm k\sigma_x$. For example, if the observed value of a general-factor residual (say, $x = .255$) and its standard error ($\sigma_x = .117$) where the "true" values, then, referring to Table H.4 for the area, $\frac{1}{2}a = .3413$ corresponding to one deviate, it may be concluded that the probability is $a = .6826$ that in further samples from rele-

---

* See Dunham Jackson, "Mathematical Principles in the Theory of Small Samples," *American Mathematical Monthly*, 1935, pp. 344–64.

vant material the value of the residual obtained will be within the range
.255 ± .117. Similarly, it may be argued that the probability is $a = .9544$,
or that in about 95 per cent of the samples the value obtained will be within
the range .255 ± 2(.117). These results may be stated in another manner.
Under the same assumptions the residual obtained will differ from .255 by
more than .117 in absolute value (i.e., it will lie *outside* the range of .138
to .372) in 32 per cent of the cases; and it will differ from .255 by more than
.234 = 2(.117) units in only 5 per cent of the cases. These are the percent-
ages (to the nearest integer) of the total area under the normal curve outside
of the respective ranges $\pm \sigma$ and $\pm 2\sigma$. Obviously, the greater the range
adopted, the less likely it is that the sampled value will fall outside of it.

When only the standard error, but not the parameter, is accurately
known, the table of the probability integral may still be used to answer the
question whether the observed parameter differs significantly from any
given hypothetical value. This is usually the more important question.
Thus, in the present illustration, it is not so important to know how close
the value .255 is to the "true" value of the residual, but whether the observed value is significantly different from zero. Assuming that the standard error .117 is the true value of that parameter, it is found that the deviation 0–.255 is 2.18 times the standard error. The area under the normal
curve to the left and to the right of the range ±2.18 is

$$P = 1 - a = 1 - 2(.4854) = .0292 ,$$

where $\frac{1}{2}a = .4854$ is obtained from Table H.4 for the ratio .255/.117 =
2.18. This means that if the residual be determined many times from random samples of relevant material, for which the true value of the residual
is zero, the value .255 would be exceeded in absolute value in 2.92 per cent
of the cases. Even more important, however, is to test the hypothesis that
the value obtained for the residual is significantly *positive*. In this case only
the area to the right of 2.18σ should be computed. The corresponding
probability is

$$\tfrac{1}{2}P = \tfrac{1}{2}(.0292) = .0146 ,$$

which means that in sampling the residual, from an assumed true value of
zero, the value .255 would be exceeded positively in only 1.46 per cent of
the time. Consequently, one may conclude that the true value of the residual is different from zero or, for the second hypothesis, that the residual .255
is significantly positive.* By the same procedure the significance of the de-
parture of the residual from any other hypothetical value could be tested.

* Of course, if there is sufficient evidence, on other than pure statistical grounds, for
the validity of the hypothesis that the true value is zero, then it would not be rejected.
One might argue, however, that the particular sample was a very unusual one.

In drawing conclusions, the investigator may be more or less exacting in the smallness of the probability that he would require. "It is usual and convenient for experimenters to take 5 per cent as a standard level of significance, in the sense that they are prepared to ignore all results which fail to reach this standard, and, by this means, to eliminate from further discussion the greater part of the fluctuations which chance causes have introduced into their experimental results."* With this standard for the level of significance, an investigator would attribute to "pure chance" results having probabilities up to 1 in 20. In the preceding example the odds against the conclusions on a pure random sampling chance are .9708 to .0292 or 33 to 1 in the first case, and .9854 to .0146 or 67 to 1 in the second case. It is thus seen that the conclusions were drawn in accordance with common practice.

Although the foregoing procedure cannot, strictly speaking, be applied to parameters of factor analysis because the standard errors are not accurately known, it may be used when N is large. In factor analysis the samples are usually large, and for this reason it is suggested that the ratio of the deviation (of an observed statistic from an assumed value) to the standard error be referred to a normal probability scale. It should be emphasized that, when the "true" value of the parameter is taken to be zero and the preceding test is applied, there are really two hypotheses being tested: first, that zero is the true value and, second, that the parent distribution from which the sample is drawn is a normal one. An extremely high value of the ratio might then suggest either that zero is not the "true" value of the parameter or that the distribution is not normal.† The conclusion would be that the observed value of the parameter is significantly different from zero or that the assumption of a normal parent population was unjustified.

To guard against drawing erroneous conclusions, the investigator must supplement his purely statistical tests of significance with all the theoretical and factual knowledge at his disposal. Thus, the general-factor residuals among a set of variables, which were shown to belong together by the B-coefficients, may all turn out to be positive but not very significantly different from zero according to the purely statistical tests of significance. In this case, although it might be argued that the residuals are insignificantly different from zero (with perhaps probabilities of only up to 1 in 20 against pure random sampling chance), such a hypothesis would be rejected. The very consistency in positive values would lead the investigator to doubt that every one of these residuals was really a sampling fluctuation

---

* R. A. Fisher, *The Design of Experiments*, 1935, pp. 15–16.

† The assumption of normality is made, for convenience, in practically all sampling problems.

from zero, always in the same direction! A group factor would be postulated in such a case, and the final residuals for this set of variables would be expected to vary positively and negatively around zero.

The standard errors derived in this chapter must be used with great caution in drawing probable inferences, for they are, at best, only approximations to the true values. Furthermore, the tests of significance imply a normal parent population from which the sample is drawn. The form of distribution of a triad, a factor coefficient, or a residual in successive samples is not known; for, even if the correlations were normally distributed, the same could not be said, a priori, of these nonlinear functions of the correlations. It is evident, then, that the standard errors of factor analysis do not have the same heuristic properties that they are presumed to have in the natural sciences. The standard errors enable the investigator to answer the question, "If the observations constituting the sample are drawn at random from a normally distributed universe, and if the true value of the parameter is $\bar{x}$, what are the odds against the observed value x having arisen as a result of the fluctuations of sampling?" In this role the standard errors become one of the measures of goodness of fit and, as such, are extremely useful and often indispensable.

6.9. *Verification and Modification of the Bi-factor Pattern*

The sampling error formulas may be employed for the same purposes as such formulas are used in other branches of statistics. Thus, the significance of any factor coefficient or residual may be tested. Again, if two factor patterns, based upon two samples of individuals, are obtained, the difference between any two factor weights may be tested for significance. Some other applications of the sampling error formulas suggest themselves for factor analysis. Formula (6.24), for the standard error of a triad, may be used to justify the conditions for one common factor. This formula may also be applied at the second stage of analysis, i.e., when the general factor has been removed and a certain set of general-factor residuals are considered as measuring one group factor.

The refined check for one common factor among a set of correlations may be obviated, however, by employing the B-coefficients, dropping all triads which exceed unity, and observing the table of intercorrelations for insignificant correlations for an entire row and column. If several variables apparently form a group, but the set of general-factor residuals for that group includes a row and column of insignificant values, the variable with these residuals should be dropped from the group and should not be used to measure that group factor. Such a variable then measures only the general factor, and its residuals with all other variables are then final residuals. On the other hand, if some of the final residuals turn out to be significantly different from zero, further factorization is indicated. Variables producing such residuals have a factor in common, and the pattern plan must be modified to include these changes. If a new factor is indicated for a subset of variables, then the preceding group-factor coefficients for these variables must be modified, for the hypothesis that these variables had involved only that one group factor is then invalidated. In computing the common-factor variance, beyond the general factor, the variables must be assumed to have a correlation matrix of rank two rather than rank one. The important thing is to formulate the new pattern plan; once this is done, the actual computation of the factor coefficients is a simple matter. First, triads are selected so that no two variables measure more than one common factor. Then formula (6.9), with the appropriate triads, may be used to calculate the coefficients. If the overlapping between variables is so great that appropriate triads cannot be selected, then a formula of type (4.22) may be used and the coefficients determined as in **4.7**.

The procedures for modification suggested in the last paragraph may seem to be somewhat subjective. Nevertheless, it can be done very quickly and checked by the more exact sampling error formulas. The significance of a coefficient or residual may be determined from the statistical tables in Appendix H; or, in particular instances, formulas (6.34) and (6.41) can be applied. Not only particular residuals but the arrangement of the entire set for a variable, or several variables, may give a clue for modification of the factor pattern. For example, if there is one large residual while all others are insignificant for a given variable, a *doublet* (factor through only two variables) may be postulated between the two variables producing that residual.

It should be noted from Table 4.2 that, when only two variables are assumed to measure a factor, their communalities can have an infinite number of solutions, so that it requires at least three variables to determine the factor weights uniquely. The two variables may therefore be considered as indicating a potential factor, which might have appeared if more measures of that factor were present. In determining the doublet weights for the given variables, one standard deviation of the residual may be arbitrarily selected as chance error and the remainder divided equally between the two variables. Thus, if the one large general-factor residual is between z_j and z_k, and the doublet is denoted by D_1 and its coefficients by d_{j1}, d_{k1}, then

$$(6.50) \qquad\qquad d_{j1} = d_{k1} = \sqrt{r_{jk} - \sigma_r} \,.$$

For the example of the last section, if the significant residual $\hat{r}_{jk} = .255$ conformed to the conditions for postulating a doublet, the coefficients of variables j and k for this doublet would be

$$d_{j1} = d_{k1} = \sqrt{.255 - .117} = \sqrt{.138} = .371 \,.$$

The final residual would be $\bar{r}_{jk} = .117$, which, of course, is insignificantly different from zero.

Special attention should be paid to the analysis after the general factor has been removed. Slight modifications in the grouping of variables and new factors between several variables will not change the general-factor coefficients very much. Each of the general-factor coefficients is based on a large number of correlations so that a few changes in the pattern plan have little effect on them. A few discordant triads in the calculation of a group-factor coefficient, however, may greatly affect its value. For this reason, no triad should be used which exceeds unity. Also, no triad should be used which involves insignificant general-factor residuals. One other method might be used in the verification of variables measuring a group factor. The method of B-coefficients may be applied to general-factor residuals for purposes of verifying the elimination of certain doubtful variables from the original group. The B-coefficients for combinations of two or three variables, including the doubtful one, may be calculated and their magnitude inspected for the degree of belonging together.

The preceding discussion is mainly concerned with modifications of the bi-factor pattern when the residuals seem to indicate that higher complexities are required for some variables. By verifying the significance of particular factor coefficients, the complexity of a variable may be reduced. Thus one or two general-factor coefficients might be of the order of their standard errors and in further sampling they might be zero. In the modified bi-factor pattern these variables would be dropped from measuring the general factor. Hence the final solution would not involve a general factor. The blankness in a bi-factor pattern can similarly be justified by means of the standard error of a factor coefficient, for, if a coefficient were computed wherever there is a blank, its value would be insignificantly different from zero.

An illustration of one type of modification will now be given. Table 6.3 contains the observed intercorrelations of five physical variables, taken from a total set of seventeen and based upon $N = 305$ fifteen-year-old girls.* The complete analysis of the seventeen variables is of no concern

* These data are taken from Frances Mullen, "Factors in the Growth of Girls Seven to Seventeen Years of Age," 1939.

here, the particular portion having been selected to illustrate a point. A complete bi-factor solution will be exhibited in the next section. The present example of five variables is introduced to clarify some of the preceding ideas on the application of sampling error formulas and modification of a bi-factor solution.

TABLE 6.3

INTERCORRELATIONS OF FIVE PHYSICAL VARIABLES

Variable	1	2	3	4	5
1. Height..........					
2. Span of arms......	.846				
3. Length of forearm..	.805	.881			
4. Length of lower leg.	.859	.826	.801		
5. Sitting height.....	.740	.497	.494	.451	

In the total set of seventeen variables the five variables of Table 6.3 were found to belong together by the method of B-coefficients. The bi-factor pattern plan was then assumed to contain a general physical (or growth) factor, say F_0, and a group factor, say F_1, through these five variables. The general-factor coefficients were calculated by the method outlined in Appendix C, and for the given five variables these coefficients are $a_{10} = .691$, $a_{20} = .591$, $a_{30} = .581$, $a_{40} = .598$, and $a_{50} = .674$. The general-factor residual correlations among the five variables are presented in Table 6.4.

TABLE 6.4

GENERAL FACTOR RESIDUALS AMONG
FIVE VARIABLES

Variable	1	2	3	4	5
1.........					
2.........	.438				
3.........	.404	.538			
4.........	.446	.473	.454		
5.........	.274	.099	.102	.048	

The immediate problem is to determine whether the original hypothesis that the five tests measure a single group factor is warranted from the nature of the residual correlations in Table 6.4. A general inspection of Table 6.4 seems to indicate that variable 5 does not exactly fall in line with the other four. It seems quite likely that variable 5 has additional linkage with variable 1, beyond the general factor, but that no further linkage with the other three variables is necessary. In other words, the general-factor residuals of 5 with 2, 3, and 4 might very well be final residuals. This conclusion will be checked by various methods in order to exhibit the procedures for modification of the pattern plan.

First, the method of B-coefficients will be applied to the general-factor residuals to verify the elimination of the doubtful variable 5 from the original group. The B-coefficients for combinations of 5 with the other variables are presented in Table 6.5, where the notation employed is that of Chapter II. The value $B(1, 5) = 107$ indicates that the variables 1 and 5 belong together to just about the same extent to which they belong with the other three variables. All the remaining B-coefficients of 5 with the other variables are under 100 and clearly indicate that 5 does not belong in the group.

TABLE 6.5

B-COEFFICIENTS BASED ON GENERAL-FACTOR RESIDUALS

u	p	S	$200(n-p)$	T	$(p-1)T$	$B(u) = \dfrac{200(n-p)S}{(p-1)T}$
(1, 5)	2	.274	600	1.537	1.537	107
(2, 5)	2	.099	600	1.873	1.873	32
(3, 5)	2	.102	600	1.817	1.817	34
(4, 5)	2	.048	600	1.848	1.848	16
(1, 2, 5)	3	.811	400	2.011	4.022	81
(1, 3, 5)	3	.780	400	2.023	4.046	77
(1, 4, 5)	3	.768	400	1.970	3.940	78
(2, 3, 5)	3	.739	400	2.091	4.182	71
(2, 4, 5)	3	.620	400	2.252	4.504	55
(3, 4, 5)	3	.604	400	2.234	4.468	54
(2, 3, 4, 5)	4	1.714	200	1.562	4.686	73
(1, 2, 3, 4)	4	2.753	200	.523	1.569	164

The last entry, $B(1, 2, 3, 4) = 164$, is included in Table 6.5 for contrast. There is no doubt that variables 1, 2, 3, and 4 belong together, while variable 5 probably does not belong with this set.

The modification of the pattern plan implied by the preceding analysis is to drop variable 5 from measuring the group factor F_1. The entries in the last row of Table 6.4 would then be final residuals. Now the final residuals must be zero except for errors of sampling, so that these residuals should be tested for significance. For purposes of comparison, the standard errors of these residuals have been computed by formula (6.36) and also from Table H.2 and are listed in Table 6.6 together with the ratios of the residuals to their standard errors and the probabilities that, in random sampling, the observed deviations of the residuals from zero would be exceeded in absolute value. The probabilities that the observed residuals would be exceeded in the positive direction only are just one-half the respective probabilities given in the table.

In applying formula (6.36), the standard errors of the general-factor coefficients are required. For the present example the approximate value $\sigma_a =$

.066 from Table H.1, corresponding to an average correlation $\rho = .355^*$ and $N = 305$, was employed. Another numerical comparison of standard errors, in which the standard error of a coefficient is computed by means of (6.34), will be given in the following section. The two sets of standard errors in Table 6.6 are very little different.

The probability P for the residual $\dot{r}_{15} = .274$ is zero to four decimal places and clearly indicates that in sampling, assuming a true value of zero, the observed value would be exceeded in less than 1 per cent of the cases. It

TABLE 6.6

STANDARD ERRORS OF RESIDUALS

VARIABLE	RESIDU-AL	BY FORMULA (6.36)			FROM TABLE H.2		
j	$\dot{r}_{j5}$	$\sigma_{\dot{r}}$	$\dot{r}/\sigma_{\dot{r}}$	$P = 1-a$	$\sigma_{\dot{r}}$	$\dot{r}/\sigma_{\dot{r}}$	$P = 1-a$
1	.274	.069	3.97	.0000	.074	3.70	.0002
2	.099	.073	1.36	.1738	.074	1.34	.1802
3	.102	.073	1.40	.1616	.074	1.38	.1676
4	.048	.075	0.64	.5222	.074	0.65	.5092

may then be safely concluded that the true value of this residual is different from zero. The probabilities for the remaining three residuals are each greater than .05, the standard level of significance recommended in the last section, and so the deviations of these observed values from zero may be attributed to chance errors. In other words, the odds against the residuals being different from zero by "pure chance" are all less than 20 to 1; therefore, the conclusion that the true values are zero is acceptable.

Now the nature of the factor pattern plan of the five variables which was conjectured earlier from an inspection of Table 6.4 has been verified by the more objective statistical procedures. In accordance with these findings, the new pattern plan may be formulated as in Table 6.7.

TABLE 6.7

NEW PATTERN PLAN FOR
FIVE VARIABLES

Variable	F_0	F_1	D_1
1	a_{10}	a_{11}	d_{11}
2	a_{20}	a_{21}	......
3	a_{30}	a_{31}	......
4	a_{40}	a_{41}	......
5	a_{50}	......	d_{51}

* Computed from the intercorrelations of all 17 variables; see *ibid.*, Table 9.

The coefficients a_{e1} ($e = 1, 2, 3, 4$) may now be computed by means of formula (6.16), which reduces to

$$a_{e1}^2 = \frac{1}{3} \sum \left(\frac{\dot{r}_{ej}\dot{r}_{ek}}{\dot{r}_{jk}} \; ; \; j, k = 1, 2, 3, 4, \quad j < k, \quad j, k \neq e \right)$$

for the present case. They are as follows:

$$a_{11} = \sqrt{\tfrac{1}{3}(.32891 + .41300 + .39688)} = \sqrt{.37960} = .616 \,,$$
$$a_{21} = \sqrt{\tfrac{1}{3}(.58328 + .46452 + .56052)} = \sqrt{.53611} = .732 \,,$$
$$a_{31} = \sqrt{\tfrac{1}{3}(.49624 + .41125 + .51639)} = \sqrt{.47463} = .689 \,,$$
$$a_{41} = \sqrt{\tfrac{1}{3}(.48164 + .50120 + .39915)} = \sqrt{.46066} = .679 \,.$$

It is evident that the triads involved in the calculation of any one of these coefficients are sufficiently constant so that the conditions (4.13) for one common factor are satisfied by the intercorrelations of the first four variables in Table 6.4. The hypothesis of the single factor F_1 through these four variables is then quite adequate.

There remains the calculation of the doublet coefficients in the plan of Table 6.7. If, as indicated earlier in this section, one standard deviation is allowed for chance error and the remainder of the residual correlation .274 is divided equally between variables 1 and 5, then the communality of variable 1 exceeds unity, implying an imaginary unique factor. To circumvent this difficulty, allow only one-tenth of the total variance of variable 1 to the doublet D_1, making its coefficient $d_{11} = .316$. This arbitrary procedure is permissible as one of the infinite variety of ways in which the coefficients of a doublet can be assigned. The other coefficient then becomes

$$d_{51} = \frac{.274 - .069}{.316} = .649 \,.$$

The final factor pattern, for the given five variables, may now be written as follows:

$$z_1 = .691F_0 + .616F_1 + .316D_1$$
$$z_2 = .591F_0 + .732F_1$$
$$z_3 = .581F_0 + .689F_1$$
$$z_4 = .598F_0 + .679F_1$$
$$z_5 = .674F_0 \qquad\qquad + .649D_1$$

where, as usual, the unique factors have been omitted and the variables have been designated by z's without double primes.* All the final residuals, with the factors F_0, F_1, and the doublet D_1 removed, are insignificant so that no further factorization is required. The modification of the original bi-factor plan exhibited in the present example is, perhaps, one of most frequent occurrence. The analysis is simple and direct and was given in such detail here merely to bring out and clarify various procedures. In practice, the investigator would come to a conclusion as to the nature of the new pattern plan much more quickly: he might, at times, apply the B-coefficient technique; at other times, the tests of significance; while still more often, he might be able to formulate the new pattern plan simply by inspection of the general-factor residuals.

6.10. *Bi-factor Solution for Twenty-four Psychological Variables*

To round out the ideas of this chapter, a complete bi-factor solution for the data of **2.8** will be presented. The details of the straightforward analysis are given in outline form in Appendix C, while some of the refined techniques of modification and tests of significance will be discussed in this section. For purposes of reference, and to avoid repetition, the complete final factor pattern is given in Table 6.8. The manner in which the factor coefficients were obtained will be explained in the sequel.

In the outline of calculations of Appendix C the order of analysis is described in detail, beginning with the grouping of tests from the original matrix of correlations. This leads to step 17 in which the general-factor coefficients are calculated, and these are the values in column B_0 of Table 6.8. The next stage of analysis involves the elimination of the general factor, yielding residuals from which the group-factor coefficients are calculated. The coefficients of B_1, B_2, and B_3 are computed in steps 21 to 23. It is evident from Table C.6 that the general-factor residuals among the tests of G_5 are insignificantly different from zero and so may be considered as final residuals, obviating the original hypothesis of a group factor for these tests.† This leaves the group G_4 to be analyzed.

---

* See n. *, p. 95.

† With this modification of the original pattern plan, it is evident that there are additional terms which can be included in formula (6.14) for the calculation of any one of the general-factor coefficients. These additional terms arise because the tests of G_5 measure only the general factor and no group factor. Thus any two of the Tests 20 to 24, together with any other test of the battery, involve only one common factor. Since each general-factor coefficient is based on a large number of correlations, however, the addition of a few more terms into the average of more than a hundred terms will not change its value much. For this reason it is not necessary to recalculate the general-factor coefficients.

From an inspection of the general-factor residuals among the tests of G_4 it would appear that Tests 14 to 19 do not measure a single common factor. Instead, it would seem that 17, 18, and 19 belong together; 14, 15, 16, and 17 involve another factor; and the residuals for 14, 15, and 16 with 18 and 19 might be final residuals. These changes will now be justified.

TABLE 6.8

BI-FACTOR PATTERN FOR TWENTY-FOUR PSYCHOLOGICAL TESTS[a]

Test[b] j	General Deduction B_0	Spatial Relations B_1	Verbal B_2	Perceptual Speed B_3	Recognition B_4	Associative Memory B_5	Doublet D_1	Unique U_j
1	.589	.484	......	......	......	......	......	.647
2	.357	.285	......	......	......	......	......	.889
3	.401	.479	......	......	......	......	......	.781
4	.463	.317	......	......	......	......	......	.828
5	.582	......	.574	......	......	......	......	.576
6	.575	......	.559	......	......	......	......	.597
7	.534	......	.708	......	......	......	......	.463
8	.624	......	.375	......	......	......	......	.686
9	.560	......	.628	......	......	......	......	.540
10	.388	......	......	.594	......	......	.371	.599
11	.521	......	......	.478	......	......	......	.707
12	.404	......	......	.642	......	......	......	.652
13	.576	......	......	.438	......	......	......	.690
14	.388	......	......	......	.545	......	......	.743
15	.351	......	......	......	.476	......	......	.806
16	.496	......	......	......	.353	......	......	.793
17	.422	......	......	......	.361	.493	......	.670
18	.515	......	......	......	......	.468	......	.718
19	.442	......	......	......	......	.278	......	.853
20	.644	......	......	......	......	......	......	.765
21	.645	......	......	......	......	......	......	.764
22	.644	......	......	......	......	......	......	.765
23	.734	......	......	......	......	......	......	.679
24	.712	......	......	......	......	......	.371	.596
Contribution of factor	6.874	0.645	1.678	1.185	0.779	0.539	0.275	......

[a] This solution differs slightly, in the group factors, from the one given by Holzinger and Swineford, *A Study in Factor Analysis*, p. 33, since it was computed independently and the refined statistical techniques were employed here.

[b] The names and brief descriptions of the tests appear in Appen. **B.1**.

From step 24 in Appendix C it is evident that the general-factor residuals among the Tests 14 to 19 do not form a matrix of rank one. It will next be shown that the residuals for Tests 14, 15, 16 with 18 and 19 are insignificantly different from zero. The largest of these six residuals is $\dot{r}_{15,18} = .153$; if this can be shown to deviate from zero by chance errors of sampling, then the others would certainly be accepted as such. To make this statistical test, the standard error of the residual is required. This can be obtained from Table H.2 of Appendix H for $N = 145$ and $\rho = .30^*$ by linear interpolation giving $\sigma_{\hat{r}} = .113$. The ratio of the residual to its standard error is

$$\frac{\hat{r}}{\sigma_{\hat{r}}} = \frac{.153}{.113} = 1.35 ,$$

for which the probability $P = .1770$, obtained by linear interpolation from Table H.4. This result means that in sampling, assuming a true value of zero, the value .153 would be exceeded in absolute value in 17.70 per cent of the cases, or that the observed value is not significantly different from zero. Stated another way, the odds against the true value of the residual being different from zero by "pure chance" is only .8230 to .1770 or 4.65 to 1, so that it is quite likely that the deviation from zero is due to random sampling. Since the largest of the six residuals is insignificantly different from zero, it may safely be assumed that all six are insignificant. Hence no linkage beyond the general factor is required between any one of the Tests 14, 15, 16 with 18 and 19.

The modification of the original hypothesis for the tests of G_4 now clearly points to a factor for Tests 14, 15, 16, and 17, and another factor for Tests 17, 18, and 19. This conclusion is also corroborated by the B-coefficients for these two subsets of tests, namely,

$$B(14, 15, 16, 17) = 202 \quad \text{and} \quad B(17, 18, 19) = 177 ,$$

where the entire set of general-factor residuals for the six tests was employed. The new pattern plan may then be written as in Table 6.9.

TABLE 6.9

NEW PATTERN PLAN FOR
SIX VARIABLES

Test	B_0	B_4	B_5
14........	$a_{14,0}$	$a_{14,4}$	....
15........	$a_{15,0}$	$a_{15,4}$	....
16........	$a_{16,0}$	$a_{16,4}$	....
17........	$a_{17,0}$	$a_{17,4}$	$a_{17,5}$
18........	$a_{18,0}$	....	$a_{18,5}$
19........	$a_{19,0}$	....	$a_{19,5}$

* The average correlation is obtained from the entire set of raw correlations of Table 2.2 by summing all the column sums and dividing by twice the number of different correlations. In symbols, this is

$$\rho = \frac{1}{2\binom{24}{2}} \Sigma(r_{jk}; \, j, k = 1, 2, \ldots, 24, \, j \neq k) = \frac{166.298}{552} = .301 .$$

According to the revised plan, the general-factor residuals for Tests 14 to 19 are assumed to form a matrix of rank two. Now the direct method of analysis, as exhibited in **4.7**, may be employed for this case; or else appropriate tests may be selected, from the total set of six, which taken alone have a correlation matrix of rank one, and then the method of triads may be applied. The solution by the method of triads is given in Appendix C and the coefficients recorded in columns B_4 and B_5 of Table 6.8. For comparison, the solution has also been obtained by applying formula (4.22) and the procedure of **4.7**. The coefficients obtained by the latter method are listed in Table 6.10 under B_4' and B_5' to distinguish them from the values obtained by the former method. A comparison of the two sets of coefficients

TABLE 6.10

COMPARISON OF TWO SETS OF B_4 AND B_5 COEFFICIENTS

Test	B_4	B_4'	$B_4 - B_4'$	B_5	B_5'	$B_5 - B_5'$
14	.545	.601	$-.056$	....	....	....
15	.476	.481	$-.005$	....	....	....
16	.353	.347	.006	....	....	....
17	.361	.335	.026	.493	.513	$-.020$
18	....	....	....	.468	.556	$-.088$
19	....	....	....	.278	.257	.021

is also given in this table. The differences are obviously insignificant, and, because the values are obtained more easily by the method of triads, these are used in the final pattern.

The original correlations are now accounted for by means of the general factor and five group factors except for one* large residual, $\dot{r}_{10,24} = .255$. To test this residual for significance, its standard error is required and will be computed by means of formula (6.36) and compared with the value from Table H.2. A similar comparison was made in Table 6.6, but in using formula (6.36) the standard errors of the coefficients were obtained from Table H.1. Now formula (6.34) will be used to get the standard errors of the factor coefficients, thus illustrating the computation by means of this formula.

* There is one other large general-factor residual, namely, $\dot{r}_{3,10} = -.231$. But there would be no point in applying statistical tests of significance to this value, for the facts of the problem clearly indicate that this value must be insignificant. The original correlation was only $r_{3,10} = -.075$, and it is due to replacing this value by zero in the calculation of the general-factor coefficients that the residual for these tests is increased negatively.

First the standard error of $a_{10,0}$ will be calculated. It will be recalled that there are $n = 24$ variables and that there are

$$p_1 = 4, \qquad p_2 = 5, \qquad p_3 = 4, \qquad p_4 = 6, \qquad p_5 = 5$$

variables in the respective groups G_1 to G_5. Now $10\epsilon G_3$ so that the system $((10, j, k); j\epsilon G_s, k\epsilon G_t, s < t, s, t = 1, 2, 4, 5)$ may be used in evaluating $a_{10,0}$. The number of triads which can be set down from such triples is easily found to be

$$\nu = p_1(p_2 + p_4 + p_5) + p_2(p_4 + p_5) + p_4(p_5),$$
$$= 4(16) + 5(11) + 6(5) = 149.$$

The component parts of triads formed from such sets, designated by $a = r_{10,j}$, $b = r_{10,k}$, $c = r_{jk}$ according to (6.19), must be averaged over the ν values. It is necessary to write out neither the individual values of a, b, and c, as was done in Table 6.2, nor even the indices and triads for the present example because the coefficients have already been computed in Appendix C and the necessary sums of correlations can be picked out of Tables C.1 and C.2. Thus,

$$\bar{a} = \frac{1}{\nu}[(p_2 + p_4 + p_5)\Sigma(r_{10,j}; j\epsilon G_1) + (p_4 + p_5)\Sigma(r_{10,j}; j\epsilon G_2) + p_5\Sigma(r_{10,j}; j\epsilon G_4)]$$

$$= \frac{1}{149}[16(.272) + 11(1.215) + 5(1.246)]$$

$$= \frac{23.947}{149} = .1607,$$

where the appropriate sums of correlations for Test 10 with the tests of groups G_1, G_2, and G_4 are obtained from row 10 of Table C.1. Similarly,

$$\bar{b} = \frac{1}{\nu}[p_1\Sigma(r_{10,k}; k\epsilon G_2) + (p_1 + p_2)\Sigma(r_{10,k}; k\epsilon G_4) + (p_1 + p_2 + p_4)\Sigma(r_{10,k}; k\epsilon G_5)]$$

$$= \frac{1}{149}[4(1.215) + 9(1.246) + 15(1.531)]$$

$$= \frac{39.039}{149} = .2620.$$

The correlations $c = r_{jk}$ are precisely those involved in the denominator of formula (6.14) for the evaluation of a factor coefficient. Hence, employing the denominator for $10\epsilon G_3$ from Table C.2,

$$\bar{c} = \frac{42.348}{149} = .2842.$$

Now, substituting the values of $\bar{a}$, $\bar{b}$, and $\bar{c}$ into formula (6.34), the standard error of the coefficient $a_{10,0}$ becomes

$$\sigma^2_{a_{10,0}} = \frac{1}{4(145)} (2 + 2.15821 + 5.73668 - .63945 - 1.69974 + 1.83415$$
$$- .74073 + .08779)$$
$$= \frac{8.73691}{580} = .01506 ,$$

and

$$\sigma_{a_{10,0}} = .123 .$$

Before the standard error of the residual $\dot{r}_{10,24}$ can be calculated by formula (6.36), the standard error of $a_{24,0}$ must also be obtained. Proceeding as before, there are

$$\nu = p_1(p_2 + p_3 + p_4) + p_2(p_3 + p_4) + p_3(p_4)$$
$$= 4(15) + 5(10) + 4(6) = 134$$

sets from which triads may be formed in evaluating the general-factor coefficient for $24\epsilon G_5$. The average of the correlations $a = r_{24,j}$ is given by

$$\bar{a} = \frac{1}{\nu} [(p_2 + p_3 + p_4)\Sigma(r_{24,j}; j\epsilon G_1) + (p_3 + p_4)\Sigma(r_{24,j}; j\epsilon G_2)$$
$$+ p_4\Sigma(r_{24,j}; j\epsilon G_3)] = .3393 ,$$

where the sums are obtained from row 24 of Table C.1. In like manner, the average of the correlations $b = r_{24,k}$ is given by

$$\bar{b} = \frac{1}{\nu} [p_1\Sigma(r_{24,k}; k\epsilon G_2) + (p_1 + p_2)\Sigma(r_{24,k}; k\epsilon G_3)$$
$$+ (p_1 + p_2 + p_3)\Sigma(r_{24,k}; k\epsilon G_4)] = .3561 .$$

From Table C.2, the denominator for any test of G_5 is 31.455, so that

$$\bar{c} = \frac{31.455}{134} = .2347 .$$

The square of the standard error of the coefficient $a_{24,0}$ then becomes

$$\sigma^2_{a_{24,0}} =$$
$$\frac{2 + 4.05973 + 4.47171 - 4.17994 - 4.60413 + 9.34599 - 2.57403 + 1.06010}{4(145)}$$
$$= .01652 ,$$

and

$$\sigma_{a_{24,0}} = .129 .$$

Now the preceding values for the squares of the standard errors of the factor coefficients may be substituted into formula (6.36), giving

$$\sigma^2_{\tilde{r}_{10,24}} = \frac{(1 - .531^2)^2}{145} + .15036(.01652) + .50705(.01506) ,$$

where the first term is the square of the standard error of $r_{10,24} = .531$ as given by (6.21). The standard error of the required residual is then

$$\sigma_{\tilde{r}_{10,24}} = \sqrt{.01368} = .117 .$$

Previously, on page 145, the value for the standard error of any general-factor residual, according to Table H.2, was shown to be $\sigma_{\tilde{r}} = .113$. There appears to be a remarkably close agreement between the value obtained by means of formula (6.36) and that from Table H.2, just as in the case of the example of the last section.

The significance of the residual $\tilde{r}_{10,24} = .255$ can now be tested, knowing that its standard error is .117. As a matter of fact, these figures formed the basis of the illustrations in **6.8**, where it was shown that the residual .255 was significantly different from zero. Since all other residuals, with the general and the group factors removed, for Tests 10 and 24 are insignificant, a doublet may be postulated between these tests. Again, in **6.9**, the doublet weights were shown to be

$$d_{10,1} = d_{24,1} = .371 .$$

This completes the analysis into common factors.

It may be noted that there are no insignificant values in Table 6.8. A rough estimate of the standard error for any one of the coefficients may be taken from Table H.1 for $N = 145$ and $\rho = .30$, namely, $\sigma_a = .109$. The smallest coefficient is .278, which is 2.55 times this standard error, while any one of the other coefficients is more than three times its standard error. Hence every coefficient in the final factor pattern is definitely significant.

The unique-factor coefficients can readily be obtained by applying the formula

$$a_j = \sqrt{1 - h_j^2} ,$$

where h_j^2 is the communality of test z_j. The communality and uniqueness of each test are given in Table 6.11, while the square root of the uniqueness is entered in Table 6.8 as the coefficient of its unique factor. Table 6.11 also contains the unreliability and the specificity so that the apportionment of the unit variance of each test can be seen at a glance. In addition, the index of completeness of factorization is also given for each test. This shows the percentage of the reliability variance accounted for by the common factors.

The index H_j may be used as one standard for the adequacy of a factorial solution. The analysis of psychological tests into common factors should not be carried to the point where real specific factors disappear. In the pres-

TABLE 6.11

APPORTIONMENT OF TEST VARIANCES

Test j	Communality h_j^2	Reliability r_{jJ}	Uniqueness $a_j^2 = 1 - h_j^2$	Unreliability $c_j^2 = 1 - r_{jJ}$	Specificity $b_j^2 = a_j^2 - c_j^2$	Index of Factorization $H_j = 100 \dfrac{h_j^2}{r_{jJ}}$
1	.581	.756	.419	.244	.175	76.9
2	.209	.568	.791	.432	.359	36.7
3	.390	.544	.610	.456	.154	71.7
4	.315	.922	.685	.078	.607	34.1
5	.668	.808	.332	.192	.140	82.7
6	.643	.651	.357	.349	.008	98.8
7	.786	.754	.214	.246	−.032	104.2
8	.530	.680	.470	.320	.150	77.9
9	.708	.870	.292	.130	.162	81.4
10	.503[a]	.952	.497	.048	.449	52.8
11	.500	.712	.500	.288	.212	70.2
12	.575	.937	.425	.063	.362	61.4
13	.524	.889	.476	.111	.365	58.9
14	.448	.648	.552	.352	.200	69.1
15	.350	.507	.650	.493	.157	69.0
16	.371	.600	.629	.400	.229	61.8
17	.551	.725	.449	.275	.174	76.0
18	.484	.610	.516	.390	.126	79.4
19	.273	.569	.727	.431	.296	47.9
20	.415	.649	.585	.351	.234	63.9
21	.416	.784	.584	.216	.368	53.1
22	.415	.787	.585	.213	.372	52.7
23	.539	.931	.461	.069	.392	57.9
24	.507[b]	.836	.493	.164	.329	60.6

[a] The communality with the doublet D_1 included is .641.

[b] The communality with the doublet D_1 included is .645.

ent example, there is one value of H_j exceeding 100 per cent, and which is probably due to chance. The preceding checks, and the one to follow, indicate that the factorization has not been carried too far, so that this discrepancy may be attributed to chance errors in the reliability coefficient. Only when several values are greater than 100 per cent, for high reliability coefficients, should the factorization be changed.*

* An example where even this crude test would indicate that the factorization has been carried too far is available in Thurstone, *Primary Mental Abilities*, where the communalities for seven tests appreciably exceed the reliabilities.

As a final check on the adequacy of the factor pattern, the criterion of **2.5** will be applied. This requires the standard deviation of the series of final residuals to be less than, or equal to, the standard error of a zero correlation for a sample of $N = 145$. The frequency distribution of the final residuals (of Table C.6) is presented in Table C.12. The mean and standard deviation for the residuals are also given in this table. Now the standard error of a zero correlation is

$$\sigma_{r=0} = \frac{1}{\sqrt{145}} = .0830 .$$

Evidently the required inequality is satisfied, and the factor pattern may be regarded as acceptable.

Various standards for adequacy of factorization, or "when to stop factoring," should yield the same result for a particular problem if they are to be equally valid. Of course, if one of the criteria is more crude than the others, less emphasis should be placed on the changes which it may indicate. For the present example this would mean that, if the difference between the standard deviation of the final residuals and that of a zero correlation were considered too large,* the pattern would still not be revised because the more exact tests by means of the sampling error formulas indicate that the factor pattern is a valid description of the original variables. As a matter of fact, the difference $.0175 = .0830 - .0655$ usually would be considered insignificant, so that this check also indicates that the factorization has been carried to the proper stage. The important thing to note is that one cannot merely "turn a crank" and come out with a valid solution, although according to some crude, cover-all standard it may be deemed acceptable. The experimenter should use all the theoretical and factual knowledge at his disposal at each stage of the analysis to produce the best solution from the given techniques and data.

Before leaving the present example, a word about the naming of factors may be in order. It will be recalled that the fundamental purpose of factor analysis is to comprehend a large class of phenomena (the values of a set of variables) in terms of a small number of concepts (the factors); and for the present time, at least, this description is taken to be a linear function of the factors. In a mathematical or physical theory it may be sufficient to know that twenty-four variables can be described linearly in terms of only six new hypothetical ones—that is usually quite an accomplishment, and it is of little concern as to what the six new variables are called. But in the biological and social sciences—psychology, for example—it is usually demanded

---

* The standard is only a rough one, and the *permissible* difference is not known.

that these new variables be named in order that the solution can be given a more "practical interpretation."

The coefficients of a factor pattern indicate the correlations of the variables with the respective factors and furnish the basis for naming them. In the case of oblique factors, to be discussed in later chapters, the structure furnishes the correlations of the variables with the factors, and so it is similarly employed in naming the factors. The investigator is guided by the magnitude of the factor weights in the selection of appropriate names for the factors. The name selected is usually suggested by the nature of the variables having the largest correlations with the factor under consideration. This name should be consistent with the nature of the remaining variables which have a low correlation with the factor.

The common factors for the example are named from the pattern given in Table 6.8 and the brief descriptions of the tests in Appendix **B.1.** The factor B_0 has positive weights throughout and correlates highest with such deductive tests as Series Completion (23), Woody-McCall Arithmetic (24), Problem Reasoning (22), and Word Classification (8). Hence B_0 might be called a "general deductive factor." This name is consistent with the nature of the remaining variables—those involving a lesser amount of deductive ability have correspondingly smaller factor weights.

The remaining common factors are named from the subgroups of tests which have significant correlations with them. The first group factor is named from the "spatial" subgroup (Tests 1–4), the second from the "verbal" subgroup of tests, and similarly for the remaining factors. The names of the six common factors are indicated in Table 6.8. In addition to the common factors, there is one unique factor for each of the twenty-four tests. If a name were desired for any unique factor, it would be obtained from the description of the particular test. The only unnamed factor is the doublet D_1 involved in Speed of Adding (10) and Woody-McCall Arithmetic (24). This doublet appears to measure "arithmetical speed," which might appear as a more significant factor if more tests of this type were introduced in a battery to experiment for this purpose.

For future work with this factor pattern the doublet will be dropped from consideration, since, as was remarked before, it takes at least three variables to define a factor. The six common factors may be referred to by means of symbols or the descriptive names, which are tentatively assigned for that purpose. The particular name by which a factor is designated, however, should not raise an issue for dispute. If another investigator chooses to call these factors by other names, he is free to do so. The naming of factors is not a problem of factor analysis, which is a branch of statistics, but some descriptive names may be highly desirable in a particular subject matter for purposes of classification.

6.11. *A Bi-factor Solution for a Reduced Set of Variables*

It should be evident that any factor solution is dependent upon the sample of individuals and variables. When either of these is altered, it is to be expected that the solution will not remain strictly invariant but may exhibit a certain amount of stability. This stability will be illustrated for

TABLE 6.12

BI-FACTOR PATTERN FOR THIRTEEN
PSYCHOLOGICAL TESTS

TEST	COMMON FACTORS				COMMU-NALITY
	General Deduction	Spatial Relations	Verbal	Perceptual Speed	
j	B_0	B_1	B_2	B_3	h_j^2
1............	.614	.425	....	....	.558
2............	.339	.296	....	....	.203
3............	.369	.475	....	....	.362
4............	.460	.320	....	....	.314
5............	.654	....	.467	....	.646
6............	.604	....	.526	....	.641
7............	.578	....	.645	....	.750
8............	.718	....	.235	....	.571
9............	.532	....	.689	....	.758
10............	.244	....	....	.703	.554
11............	.423	....	....	.520	.449
12............	.346	....	....	.641	.531
13............	.644	....	....	.429	.599
Contribution of factor..	3.538	0.596	1.441	1.360	....

the case of a fixed sample of individuals and a reduction in the number of variables.

A bi-factor solution for the first thirteen of the preceding set of twenty-four psychological tests has been obtained by the methods of this chapter and is presented in Table 6.12. The variables of this subset were selected so that the solution should contain three group factors and include only about half of the original variables.

As might be expected, the form of solution given in Table 6.12 agrees with the corresponding portion of that given in Table 6.8. The respective coefficients for these two patterns are in close agreement throughout. The largest discrepancy occurs in the case of the general-factor coefficients for variable 10, which have the values .388 and .244, respectively. Inasmuch as the standard error of $a_{10,0} = .388$ has already been shown to be .123, the difference .144 is regarded as insignificant. The communalities for corresponding variables are also in close agreement, the greatest discrepancy being .075 for Test 13.

The foregoing illustration is, of course, an example of the stability of one type of solution, when the set of variables is reduced. This type of stability will also be illustrated for other forms of solution for the same data in Chapters X and XI.

CHAPTER VII

THE PRINCIPAL-FACTOR SOLUTION

7.1. *Introduction*

The principal-factor method was developed by Hotelling* at the suggestion of Kelley, who since has developed an alternative procedure,† based on covariances instead of correlations. In a still more recent paper Hotelling‡ has presented an improvement on his original scheme for calculation of principal factors. Hence methods available for calculation include Hotelling's first procedure, Kelley's improvement by use of a simple mathematical device, and Hotelling's latest simplified scheme. For simplicity this latter form of computation only is treated here.

It will be noted that the term "factor" is employed here, as elsewhere in the text, rather than "component," which is used by Hotelling and Kelley. This seems advisable especially in later chapters where comparisons of different solutions are made. Hotelling's objection to the word "factor" arose from its possible confusion with the mathematical term, but general usage would appear to favor retention of "factor."

As indicated in **2.5** the communalities of the variables are usually the desired portions of the variances to be analyzed. In **7.2,** therefore, various methods for estimating communality are presented. The problem of obtaining these estimates is the same for both the principal-factor and the centroid solutions, so the discussion in this section applies also to the method treated in Chapter VIII.

The essential portions of Hotelling's theoretical treatment of the principal-factor solution are given in **7.3,** and certain proofs of the fundamental development are presented in Appendix **B.9.** The method of analysis is applied to a matrix of correlations with communalities in the diagonal rather than ones or reliabilities as Hotelling suggests. Although he has furnished a treatment of the sampling problem, it is not applicable in the present development which involves communalities. When appropriate estimates of the communalities are employed, it is shown in **7.2** that the problem of "when to stop factoring" is obviated.

---

* Harold Hotelling, "Analysis of a Complex of Statistical Variables into Principal Components," *Journal of Educational Psychology*, 1933, pp. 417–41, 498–520.

† Truman L. Kelley, *Essential Traits of Mental Life*, 1935.

‡ "Simplified Calculation of Principal Components," *Psychometrika*, 1936.

Except for the choice of communalities, the solution of a principal-factor pattern can be reduced to a routine procedure. An iterative scheme for calculation is described in **7.4**, and a detailed series of steps for computation is given in Appendix D. In illustrating these steps a set of only eight variables is employed inasmuch as this is a sufficient number to clarify the procedure. Furthermore, it is usually advisable to restrict the application of the direct principal-factor solution to small sets of variables because of the excessive amount of calculation when the number is large. In Chapter IX a method will be given for obtaining a principal-factor solution by rotation from another solution. If the latter method is employed, the labor is greatly reduced, and the principal-factor form of solution may thus be made feasible for larger sets of variables.

In section **7.5** the solutions for four sets of variables are presented. The first of these analyzes the eight physical variables used for illustration in Appendix D. The next application is made for the twenty-four psychological tests of **2.8**, in spite of the large amount of calculation entailed. It was originally intended to employ this example in the outline of steps in Appendix D, but because of the bulk of tabular material it was feared that the reader would fail to see the trees because of the forest. The detailed computations of this example are, therefore, not included in the text, but only a portion of the pattern is exhibited in **7.5**. The third illustration is given for eight emotional traits studied by Cyril Burt. The final example is taken from the field of political science. A discussion of the factors obtained in each example is presented to indicate the effectiveness of the principal-factor form of solution.

7.2. *Estimation of Communalities*

It was pointed out in **2.5** that the portions of the variances to be factored are determined by the diagonal elements of the correlation matrix. When ones are put in the principal diagonal of this matrix, the resulting descriptions of the n variables are in terms of n (sometimes fewer) common factors. This was the approach of Hotelling in his method of analysis. In the present treatment, however, communalities are the basic quantities to be analyzed in accordance with the assumed composition of variables (2.4). The development of the principal-factor method in the following section is based upon the latter assumption of the composition of the variables, and hence good estimates of the communalities are required.

Appropriate communalities, and hence the entire factor pattern, can be obtained directly by the methods of Chapter IV if the rank of the correlation matrix is suitably approximated. Thus in the bi-factor method the rank is approximated by means of the grouping of variables. Then the pattern plan is postulated, and the coefficients are computed directly by formula. If, instead of approximating the rank, estimates of the communalities are employed, it is possible to obtain a solution with a number of factors dependent upon such estimates. In the factorial analyses of this and the succeeding chapter, the procedure of estimating communalities is generally employed.

When no such estimates are feasible, owing to the nature and lack of design in the set of variables, an arbitrary method will be presented in **8.4** in which no explicit use of the diagonal elements is made, and the adequacy of the resulting pattern is tested from the final residuals.

One method for estimating the communality of a variable z_j is to select the highest correlation among all its correlations with all the other variables of the given set. Another method is to employ as an approximation to the communality a triad $h_j^2 = r_{jk}r_{jl}/r_{kl}$, where r_{jk} and r_{jl} are the two highest correlations for z_j. Still another estimate is given by the average of all the correlations of each variable. These "arbitrary estimates" of the communalities have been employed by workers in multiple-factor analysis, who contend that the first method is sufficiently accurate when applied to sets of twenty, or more, variables.

A still more satisfactory procedure for estimating communality can be obtained by employing the methods of Chapter IV. By means of the grouping of variables, the approximate rank of the correlation matrix may be assumed. In contrast to the bi-factor procedure, however, no pattern plan is postulated. The groupings of variables are obtained merely to approximate the rank in order to get suitable estimates of the communality. For any rank, thus determined, the direct method of obtaining the communalities, as described in **4.6**, is theoretically most desirable. This method involves the calculation of the average of all possible expressions (4.27) for each communality, when m is the rank of the correlation matrix. For small sets of variables it is expected that there will be only a few factors.* It may then be sufficiently accurate to assume rank one or two and employ the method of Chapter IV for calculating approximations to the communalities. In practice, when the rank exceeds two, the method of Chapter IV is not feasible because of the complexity of the formulas and large amount of computation involved. One simplification of this technique is accomplished by considering the section of the correlation matrix corresponding to a subgroup of variables as approximately of rank one. The estimates of the communalities may then be readily calculated by means of formula (6.9) applied to the subsets of variables. This procedure seems much more satisfactory than the estimation of the communality by a single triad involving the two highest correlations of a given variable.

* See **4.2**.

In order that a subset of variables shall produce a correlation matrix of rank one, it is necessary that the vectors representing these variables lie in a space of one dimension. Since such a configuration of vectors is not ordinarily to be expected for a complete set of variables, the rank usually will be greater than one. An even better estimate of the communality than the preceding one may be obtained by selecting appropriate variables out of the total set so as to yield a matrix of rank one, and applying the bi-factor technique described in **6.4.** Although the bi-factor pattern is explicitly obtained, it is employed here only as a means of obtaining good estimates of the communalities to be used in the calculation of other types of factor solutions. In general, then, the communalities from any satisfactory solution may be taken as good estimates in further factorial analyses. To contrast an arbitrary estimate for a variable involving only a few correlations with that based upon the entire correlation matrix, the latter will be designated as a "complete estimate" of the communality.

Inasmuch as the arbitrary estimates may not be close to the desired communalities, it has been suggested* that the diagonal values be changed in each table of residual correlations for the calculation of successive factor coefficients. For example, when the highest correlation for each variable is taken as its communality, the perplexing problem as to "when to stop factoring" arises. In the matrix of residual correlations with the first factor removed, the highest value in each column would again be used for the diagonal entry (in place of the value actually computed). By continuing this process, a large number of factors (relative to the number of variables) may be obtained, with some significant coefficients even for the last of many factors.

When the complete estimates of the communalities are employed, the foregoing difficulty disappears. Since these estimates are the best available, the diagonal values are not altered as in the case of arbitrary estimates. Then, in a practical sense, the question of "when to stop factoring" no longer arises. The factoring is carried to the stage where nearly 100 per cent of the total estimated communality is analyzed. When this is accomplished, the number of common factors is relatively small; and, if additional factors are obtained, practically all coefficients are insignificant. An illustration of this "convergence" to a small number of common factors is given in **8.3,** where a centroid pattern for the twenty-four psychological tests is obtained.

The most important advantage in employing the complete estimates of the communalities in the calculation of a principal or centroid factor pattern arises in connection with the statistical adequacy of these solutions. Such estimates are based upon the bi-factor solution, for which sampling error

---

* L. L. Thurstone, *The Vectors of Mind*, 1935, p. 113.

formulas are given in Chapter VI. If the bi-factor pattern is justified by the various standards, including the sampling formulas, the resulting communalities are also validated. Then, by employing these communalities in any other form of analysis, *further tests of adequacy of solution are obviated.*

From the geometrical point of view, the fundamental problem of factor analysis is the determination of the common-factor space. Once this space has been determined, any reference system (corresponding to a set of factors) can be transformed into another preferred type by means of a suitable rotation. In obtaining a bi-factor solution, the common-factor space is thereby fixed. Then in further analyses, employing the bi-factor communalities, the common-factor space is predetermined. Any factor solution in this common-factor space may then be regarded as a linear transformation of any other. In actual practice, however, such alternative solutions are generally obtained by different statistical procedures. Illustrations of these geometric properties are given in Chapter XIII.

7.3. *Principal-Factor Method*

As indicated in **5.2**, when the point representation of a set of variables is employed, the loci of uniform frequency density are essentially concentric, similar, and similarly situated ellipsoids. The axes of these ellipsoids correspond to the factors in the principal-factor solution.* From an algebraic point of view, the selection of these axes is equivalent to choosing a set of factors in decreasing order of their contribution to the total communality. The analysis is begun with a factor F_1 whose contribution to the communalities of the variables has as great a total as possible. Then the first-factor residual correlations are obtained, including the residual communalities. A second factor F_2, independent of F_1, with a maximum contribution to the residual communality is next found. This process is continued until the total communality is analyzed.

A brief theoretical description of the principal-factor method will now be given, and this will be followed by a discussion of a more expedient form of solution in the next section. If the composition of a statistical variable† is again taken to be

$$(7.1) \qquad z_j = a_{j1}F_1 + a_{j2}F_2 + \ldots + a_{jm}F_m$$

$$(j = 1, 2, \ldots, n),$$

with the unique factor omitted, the communality of z_j is then given by

$$(7.2) \qquad h_j^2 = a_{j1}^2 + a_{j2}^2 + \ldots + a_{jt}^2 + \ldots + a_{jm}^2.$$

---

* Hotelling, "Analysis of a Complex of Statistical Variables into Principal Components," Sec. 3.

† See n. *, p. 95.

In general, the term a_{jt}^2 indicates the contribution of the factor F_t to the communality of z_j. The sum of the contributions of the first factor F_1 to the communalities of the n variables is

$$(7.3) \qquad A_1 = a_{11}^2 + a_{21}^2 + \ldots + a_{n1}^2 .$$

The object of the present method is to choose the coefficients a_{j1} so as to make A_1 a maximum, subject to the restrictions that the correlations are reproduced by the pattern (7.1). The conditions may be expressed as follows:

$$(7.4) \qquad r_{jk} = r'_{jk} = \sum_{t=1}^{m} a_{jt} a_{kt} \qquad (j, k = 1, 2, \ldots, n) .$$

In the succeeding analysis the reproduced correlations r'_{jk} will be replaced by the corresponding observed correlations r_{jk}. As indicated in Chapter VI, this procedure implies the assumption of zero residuals.

By the methods of the calculus it is possible to maximize A_1 under the given conditions.* The resulting system of equations for the solution of the unknowns a_{j1} may be written as follows:

$$(7.5) \quad \begin{cases} (h_1^2 - \lambda)a_{11} \quad + r_{12}a_{21} + \quad r_{13}a_{31} + \ldots + \quad r_{1n}a_{n1} = 0, \\ r_{21}a_{11} + (h_2^2 - \lambda)a_{21} + \quad r_{23}a_{31} + \ldots + \quad r_{2n}a_{n1} = 0, \\ r_{31}a_{11} + \quad r_{32}a_{21} + (h_3^2 - \lambda)a_{31} + \ldots + \quad r_{3n}a_{n1} = 0, \\ \cdot \quad \cdot \quad \cdot \quad \cdot \quad \cdot \quad \cdot \quad \cdot \quad \cdot \quad \cdot \quad \cdot \quad \cdot \quad \cdot \\ r_{n1}a_{11} + \quad r_{n2}a_{21} + \quad r_{n3}a_{31} + \ldots + (h_n^2 - \lambda)a_{n1} = 0, \end{cases}$$

where λ is a parameter independent of the a's. A necessary and sufficient condition for the system of equations (7.5) to have a solution (in which not all unknowns are zero) is the vanishing of the determinant of the coefficients† of the a_{j1}. This condition may be written in the form

$$(7.6) \quad \begin{vmatrix} (h_1^2 - \lambda) & r_{12} & r_{13} & \ldots & r_{1n} \\ r_{21} & (h_2^2 - \lambda) & r_{23} & \ldots & r_{2n} \\ r_{31} & r_{32} & (h_3^2 - \lambda) & \ldots & r_{3n} \\ \cdot & \cdot & \cdot & \ldots & \cdot \\ r_{n1} & r_{n2} & r_{n3} & \ldots & (h_n^2 - \lambda) \end{vmatrix} = 0 .$$

* For a proof see Appen. B.9.

† L. E. Dickson, *Modern Algebraic Theories*, 1930, p. 61.

An equation of the form (7.6) is known as a *characteristic equation*, some of its properties being that all the roots are real and that a q-fold multiple root substituted for λ in (7.6) reduces the rank of the determinant to $(n - q)$.

When a simple root of the characteristic equation is substituted for λ in (7.5), a set of homogeneous linear equations of rank $(n - 1)$ is obtained. This set of equations has a family of solutions, all of which are proportional to one particular solution. It follows* from the analysis for maximizing A_1 that the factor of proportionality is $\lambda_1 = \sum_{j=1}^{n} a_{j1}^2 = A_1$. Hence A_1, which is to be maximized, is equal to one of the roots of the characteristic equation, namely, the largest root λ_1.

The problem of finding the coefficients a_{j1} of the first factor F_1, which will account for as much of the total communality as possible, is then solved. The largest root λ_1 of (7.6) is substituted into (7.5), and any solution a_{11}, $a_{21}, \ldots, a_{n1}$ is obtained. Then, to satisfy the relation (7.3), these values are divided by the square root of the sum of their squares and then multiplied by $\sqrt{\lambda_1}$. The resulting quantities are

$$(7.7) \qquad a_{j1} = \frac{a_{j1}\sqrt{\lambda_1}}{\sqrt{a_{11}^2 + a_{21}^2 + \ldots + a_{n1}^2}} \qquad (j = 1, 2, \ldots, n) ,$$

which are the desired coefficients of F_1 in the factor pattern (7.1). It may be observed that these values of a_{j1} satisfy the condition (7.3); for, upon squaring the expressions (7.7) and summing, there results

$$\sum_{j=1}^{n} a_{j1}^2 = \frac{\lambda_1(a_{11}^2 + a_{21}^2 + \ldots + a_{n1}^2)}{a_{11}^2 + a_{21}^2 + \ldots + a_{n1}^2} = \lambda_1 = A_1 .$$

When the largest root of the characteristic equation is a q-fold multiple root (i.e., the q largest roots are equal to λ_1), a set of n homogeneous linear equations of rank $(n - q)$ is obtained upon substituting this value for λ in (7.5). This system of equations has q linearly independent solutions, while every other solution is linearly dependent on them. Designating these solutions by

$$
\begin{array}{cccc}
a_{11} , & a_{21} , & \ldots , & a_{n1} , \\
a_{12} , & a_{22} , & \ldots , & a_{n2} , \\
\ldots & \ldots & \ldots & \ldots \\
a_{1q} , & a_{2q} , & \ldots , & a_{nq} ,
\end{array}
$$

* See Appen. **B.9**, eq. (B.28).

they may be selected so that they are "orthogonal" to each other, in the sense that

(7.8)
$$\begin{cases} \sum_{j=1}^{n} a_{js}^2 = \lambda_1 \\ \sum_{j=1}^{n} a_{js}a_{jt} = 0 \end{cases} \quad \left(\begin{matrix} s, t = 1, 2, \ldots, q \\ s \neq t \end{matrix} \right).$$

The q sets of solutions may then be taken as the coefficients of q independent factors $F_1, F_2, \ldots, F_q$ which account (equally) for as large as possible a part of the total communality. Inasmuch as this case is very unlikely to arise in actual practice, it will not be treated explicitly in the subsequent analysis.

Having determined the coefficients a_{j1} of the first factor F_1, the next problem is to find a factor which will account for a maximum of the residual communality. In order to do this, it is necessary to obtain the first-factor residual correlations. Furthermore, in obtaining still other factors the residual correlations with two, three, $\ldots$, $(m-1)$ factors removed are employed, and hence a suitable notation is required. In the last chapter only residuals with the general factor removed $(\dot{r})$ and final residuals $(\bar{r})$ were explicitly indicated. A convenient notation for the residual correlation of r_{jk} with p factors removed is $_p r_{jk}$. Thus, when the first factor has been obtained, the first-factor residuals are written in the form

(7.9) $_1 r_{jk} = r_{jk} - a_{j1}a_{k1} = a_{j2}a_{k2} + a_{j3}a_{k3} + \ldots + a_{jm}a_{km}$.

In determining the coefficients of the second factor F_2, it is necessary to maximize the quantity

(7.10) $A_2 = a_{12}^2 + a_{22}^2 + \ldots + a_{n2}^2$,

which is the sum of the contributions of F_2 to the residual communality. This maximization is subject to the conditions (7.9), which is analogous to the restrictions (7.4) in the case of the first factor. The analysis for obtaining the coefficients a_{j2} is parallel to that for determining the first-factor coefficients, the only difference being that the residuals $_1 r_{jk}$ are used in place of the correlations r_{jk}. Proceeding in this way, the coefficients of $F_1, F_2, \ldots, F_m$ are determined in the order of their contributions to the total communality.

An important mathematical property of the principal-factor pattern is that of orthogonality. It has been indicated already that in case the largest root of the characteristic equation is a multiple root, this orthogonality is given by (7.8). The property of orthogonality holds, in general, for the coefficients of all the principal factors. These relations may be written as follows:

(7.11)
$$\begin{cases} \sum_{j=1}^{n} a_{jt}^2 = \lambda_t \\ \sum_{j=1}^{n} a_{js}a_{jt} = 0 \end{cases} \qquad \begin{pmatrix} s, t = 1, 2, \ldots, m \\ s \neq t \end{pmatrix}.$$

The properties (7.11) are useful in checking the numerical calculations of the factor coefficients.

The foregoing description of the principal-factor method may be considered as its logical basis but not as a scheme for actual computation. The direct solution of the characteristic equation and sets of linear homogeneous equations such as (7.5) would involve great algebraic difficulties. For this reason, an iterative method which requires only routine computations will be described in the next section.

7.4. *Iterative Form of Solution*

A simplified method for calculating a principal-factor pattern will now be developed. This treatment is based upon the two fundamental papers of Hotelling in which he first presents the iterative scheme and later gives an improved variation of it. Detailed steps for the numerical calculation of the pattern are given in Appendix D.

The iterative form of solution yields a root of the characteristic equation and the corresponding coefficients in the factor pattern simultaneously. The roots appear in descending order of magnitude upon successive applications of the iterative scheme. When complete estimates of the communalities are employed, the number of roots required to account for this total communality is relatively small. The contribution of any factor, say, after 95 per cent of the communality has been analyzed, would be expected to be insignificant. The iterative procedure, based upon complete estimates of the communalities, then affords an adequate factorization.

In the iterative process an arbitrary set of n numbers is selected, and, after manipulating these numbers with the matrix of correlations, they are finally reduced to the desired coefficients of the first principal factor. Thus, take the numbers $a_{11}, a_{21}, \ldots, a_{n1}$ as the arbitrary set and consider the following transformation

(7.12)
$$a'_{j1} = \sum_{k=1}^{n} r_{jk}a_{k1} \qquad (j = 1, 2, \ldots, n)$$

to the new set $(a'_{11}, a'_{21}, \ldots, a'_{n1})$. If the numbers a_{j1} are proportional to the direction cosines of any line through the origin, then the numbers a'_{j1} are proportional to the direction cosines of a new line (through the origin) corresponding to the original line under the rotation (7.12).

In general, the line associated with the numbers a'_{j1} is distinct from the line corresponding to the a_{j1}. There may, however, be lines which remain fixed under the transformation (7.12). Such invariant lines are those for which a quantity λ exists such that

$$(7.13) \qquad\qquad a'_{j1} = \lambda a_{j1} \qquad\qquad (j = 1, 2, \ldots, n).$$

Upon substituting the values (7.13) in (7.12), that expression reduces to

$$\lambda a_{j1} = \sum_{k=1}^{n} r_{jk} a_{k1} = r_{j1} a_{11} + r_{j2} a_{21} + \ldots + h_j^2 a_{j1} + \ldots + r_{jn} a_{n1}$$

or

$$(7.14) \quad r_{j1} a_{11} + r_{j2} a_{21} + \ldots + (h_j^2 - \lambda) a_{j1} + \ldots + r_{jn} a_{n1} = 0.$$

As j takes on the values 1 to n in (7.14), it is readily seen that these equations are identical with (7.5). Thus, for any invariant line, the direction cosines are proportional to a solution of (7.5), where λ is a root of the characteristic equation (7.6). Hence it follows that the invariant lines are the desired principal axes. It is thus apparent that, if a set of numbers $a_{11}, a_{21}, \ldots, a_{n1}$ can be found which when substituted into the right-hand members of (7.12) produce relations (7.13), the numbers $a'_{11}, a'_{21}, \ldots, a'_{n1}$ are proportional to the direction cosines of the principal axes. The coefficients of one of the principal factors can then be obtained from the latter set of numbers. Furthermore, λ in (7.13) is the sum of the contributions of this factor to the communalities of the variables.

In practice, of course, it cannot be expected that the arbitrary numbers a_{j1} will be so selected as to be proportional to the direction cosines of one of the principal axes. The iterative process then involves the use of the derived numbers a'_{j1} as a new set of arbitrary numbers in place of a_{j1}. Now if the numbers a'_{j1} are proportional to the direction cosines of any line through the origin, and if they are substituted in the equations*

$$(7.15) \qquad\qquad a''_{v1} = \sum_{j=1}^{n} r_{vj} a'_{j1} \qquad\qquad (v = 1, 2, \ldots, n),$$

* The symbol a''_{v1} is employed instead of a''_{j1} corresponding to the notation in (7.12) because it will be found convenient for subsequent algebraic manipulation to retain j as a subscript in the right-hand member of (7.15).

then the quantities on the left will be proportional to the direction cosines of a new line (through the origin) corresponding to the original one under the transformation (7.15). This process is continued until the ratios among the quantities obtained at any stage converge to the corresponding ratios among the coefficients of F_1 to any specified degree of accuracy. The proof of the convergence of these ratios to those of the coefficients a_{j1} of the first principal factor is given by Hotelling.* A convenient procedure is to divide each of the trial values by a fixed one of them, say the largest. Then the next value obtained, corresponding to this number, will be an approximation to the characteristic root λ_1.

Instead of calculating the successive values a_{j1}', a_{v1}'', etc., and substituting them in equations like (7.12) and (7.15), a modification will next be introduced which greatly accelerates convergence.† This simplification is accomplished by the formal substitution of the a's in these equations. Thus, upon substituting the values for a_{j1}' from (7.12) into the right-hand member of (7.15), the latter equation takes the form

$$a_{v1}'' = \sum_{k=1}^{n} \sum_{j=1}^{n} r_{vj} r_{jk} a_{k1}.$$

This expression may be written more simply as follows:

$$(7.16) \qquad a_{v1}'' = \sum_{k=1}^{n} c_{vk} a_{k1} \qquad (v = 1, 2, \ldots, n),$$

where

$$(7.17) \qquad c_{vk} = \sum_{j=1}^{n} r_{vj} r_{jk}.$$

Consequently, if the sums of the paired products c_{vk} are first obtained, equation (7.16) may be used instead of (7.12) to calculate the a_{v1}'' values. Hence the two iterations which were involved in obtaining a_{v1}'' (by multiplication with the correlations) are reduced to only one operation with the numbers c_{vk}. The number of iterations required for any degree of accuracy is thus cut in half.

It will be found very convenient to employ matrix notation in dealing with complex expressions of the form (7.17). If $\mathbf{R} \equiv \|r_{jk}\|$ is used to denote the matrix of correlations, the c_{vk} is the element in the vth row and kth column of the product of the symmetric matrix $\mathbf{R}$ by itself. The matrix

---

* "Analysis of a Complex of Statistical Variables into Principal Components," Sec. 4.

† Hotelling, "Simplified Calculation of Principal Components."

of these elements may be represented by $\mathbf{C} \equiv \|c_{vk}\|$. It is, therefore, apparent that

$$\mathbf{C} = \|c_{vk}\| = \|r_{vj}\| \cdot \|r_{jk}\| = \mathbf{R}' \cdot \mathbf{R} = \mathbf{R}^2 \,,$$

where the last equality follows from the fact that the transpose of a symmetric matrix is equal to the matrix itself. Substitution of the trial values $a_{11}, a_{21}, \ldots, a_{n1}$ in (7.12) is equivalent to multiplying them by $\mathbf{R}$ (i.e., obtaining the sums of the paired products with the elements of the columns of $\mathbf{R}$). Substitution in (7.16), on the other hand, amounts to the multiplication by $\mathbf{R}^2$.

The improvement in the iteration process need not end with the employment of $\mathbf{R}^2$. After doubling the speed of convergence by squaring $\mathbf{R}$, it can be doubled again by squaring $\mathbf{R}^2$, i.e., by multiplying a set of trial values by $\mathbf{R}^4$, and thus the equivalent of four multiplications by $\mathbf{R}$ is obtained. Upon squaring again, a matrix $\mathbf{R}^8$ is obtained, and multiplication by it is equivalent to eight multiplications by $\mathbf{R}$, and so forth to any power of the correlation matrix. This squaring process is continued until the convergence is so rapid that additional matrix squaring is not worth while. In Appendix D a scheme for determining the number of times a matrix should be squared is explained.

The second and remaining principal factors may be determined by the same method, and the convergence can be accelerated by the use of a convenient power of the matrix of residual correlations. It is not necessary, however, to obtain this power of the residual matrix by repeated squarings, as was done in the case of the original matrix of correlations. Instead, the determination already made of the power of $\mathbf{R}$ and the following algebraic properties of matrices can be employed for this purpose.

Denoting the matrix of first-factor residuals by $\mathbf{R}_1$, it follows from (7.9) that

(7.18) $$\mathbf{R}_1 = \|_1 r_{jk}\| = \|r_{jk} - a_{j1}a_{k1}\| = \mathbf{R} - \mathbf{Q}_1 \,,$$

where

$$\mathbf{Q}_1 = \|_1 p_{jk}\| = \|a_{j1}a_{k1}\| \qquad (j, k = 1, 2, \ldots, n)$$

is used to represent the matrix of products of first-factor coefficients. Now it is shown in equation (B.30) that

$$\sum_{j=1}^{n} r_{jk}a_{j1} = \lambda_1 a_{k1}$$

and in (7.11) that

$$\sum_{j=1}^{n} a_{j1}^2 = \lambda_1 \,.$$

These lead to the following relationships among the matrices:*

$$(7.19) \qquad \begin{cases} \mathbf{R}\mathbf{Q}_1 = \mathbf{Q}_1\mathbf{R} = \lambda_1\mathbf{Q}_1, \\ \mathbf{Q}_1^2 = \lambda_1\mathbf{Q}_1. \end{cases}$$

By repeated use of (7.19) it can readily be shown that

$$(7.20) \qquad \begin{cases} \mathbf{R}^e\mathbf{Q}_1 = \mathbf{R}\mathbf{Q}_1^e = \lambda_1^e\mathbf{Q}_1, \\ \mathbf{Q}_1^e = \lambda_1^{e-1}\mathbf{Q}_1, \end{cases}$$

where e is any positive integer. Hence employing (7.19),

$$\mathbf{R}_1^2 = (\mathbf{R} - \mathbf{Q}_1)^2 = \mathbf{R}^2 - 2\mathbf{R}\mathbf{Q}_1 + \mathbf{Q}_1^2 = \mathbf{R}^2 - \lambda_1\mathbf{Q}_1,$$

and, in general,

$$(7.21) \qquad \mathbf{R}_1^e = \mathbf{R}^e - \lambda_1^{e-1}\mathbf{Q}_1.$$

Thus the eth power of the residual matrix is expressed in terms of the eth power of the original correlation matrix, obviating actual squaring of the residual matrix.

From the foregoing development the order of procedure of the iterative scheme may be summarized. Using $\mathbf{R}^e$ as the basis of selection of the set of trial values, this set rapidly yields the values of the first-factor coefficients† and the characteristic root λ_1. Furthermore, the value λ_1^e will be determined from the multiplication of the set of trial values by $\mathbf{R}^e$, and λ^{e-1} can be obtained by divison. Then multiplying λ^{e-1} by each element of $\mathbf{Q}_1$ and subtracting from the corresponding element of $\mathbf{R}^e$, the eth power of the residual matrix is obtained. The second-factor coefficients are ob-

---

* To indicate the derivation of (7.19), the algebra leading to the last relation will be given in detail. The square of the matrix $\mathbf{Q}_1 = \|a_{j1}a_{k1}\|$ is given by

$$\mathbf{Q}_1 = \|a_{j1}a_{v1}\|\|a_{v1}a_{k1}\| \qquad (j, k, v = 1, 2, \ldots, n),$$

in which the jth row of the first representation of $\mathbf{Q}_1$ and the kth column of the second representation are obtained by letting v range from 1 to n. Thus a representative row is $\|a_{j1}a_{11}\ a_{j1}a_{21} \ldots a_{j1}a_{n1}\|$ and a representative column (written horizontally to save space) is $\{a_{11}a_{k1}\ a_{21}a_{k1} \ldots a_{n1}a_{k1}\}$. Row-by-column multiplication of the matrices then produces

$$\mathbf{Q}_1^2 = \left\| \sum_{v=1}^{n} a_{j1}a_{v1}a_{v1}a_{k1} \right\| = \left\| a_{j1}a_{k1}\sum_{v=1}^{n}a_{v1}^2 \right\| = \|a_{j1}a_{k1}\lambda_1\| = \lambda_1\mathbf{Q}_1.$$

† In "The Unit Hierarchy and Its Properties" (*Psychometrika*, 1938), Burt has pointed out that to factor a matrix $\mathbf{R}^e$ is equivalent to obtaining a Spearman general factor. This arises from the fact that, with a sufficient number of self-multiplications, any symmetric matrix can be reduced as closely as desired to a matrix of rank one.

tained from R_1 and R_1^e in the same manner as the first-factor coefficients are determined from R and R^e. It may not be necessary to employ the eth power of R_1 in the calculation of the second-factor coefficients when rapid convergence is evident. Then some lower power of R_1, or R_1 itself, is employed. This is illustrated in Appendix D. To calculate the third-factor coefficients, the matrix R_2 of the second-factor residuals and R_2^e (or some lower power of R_2) are employed. The latter matrix is obtained conveniently by an expression of the form (7.21) relating the second- to the first-factor residuals. Further factors are determined similarly until approximately all the communality is analyzed.

7.5. Numerical Applications

1. EIGHT PHYSICAL VARIABLES

The first illustration for the method of principal factors was obtained from Mrs. Mullen's data, which were referred to in **4.6.** Her analysis of seventeen physical variables by the bi-factor method revealed a general size factor and two outstanding group factors identified with longitudinal and horizontal growth. After this solution was obtained, an alternative form, which might be preferred by the biologist, was suggested by the fact that the latter two factors might be considered as opposing measures of a single factor. A solution with a general physical growth factor and a bipolar factor* (representing the longitudinal versus horizontal growth) was then proposed.

For the purpose of making such a principal-factor solution eight of the total set of variables were selected. Of the set of seventeen variables, three indices—of head size, hand squeeze, and lung capacity—were eliminated because they were not measures of the two group factors. The following variables were dropped because of small, or insignificant, group-factor coefficients: sitting height, bi-iliac diameter, chest depth, and shoulder width. The eight variables retained include two subgroups consisting of four longitudinal and four horizontal variables. The correlations among these variables are presented in Table 7.1.

In Mrs. Mullen's study the complete analysis was made by the bi-factor method which furnished the communalities for all variables. The portion of the bi-factor pattern for the eight variables, also including their communalities, is given in Table 7.2. Thus estimates of the communalities of these variables for further analysis into a principal-factor pattern are immediately available. The communalities of these variables were also obtained directly from the correlations by the methods of Chapter IV. The latter values,

* See **5.7.**

which are given in Table 4.5, are compared with the bi-factor estimates of
the communalities in Table 7.3. It is evident from this comparison that
there would be little practical difference between the final solution based
upon these two sets of communalities. Since the communalities of Table 7.2
were available at the time the analysis was first made, they are employed in
Appendix D.

TABLE 7.1

INTERCORRELATIONS OF EIGHT PHYSICAL VARIABLES
FOR 305 FIFTEEN-YEAR-OLD GIRLS

Variable	1	2	3	4	5	6	7	8
1. Height..............								
2. Arm span.............	.846							
3. Length of forearm......	.805	.881						
4. Length of lower leg.....	.859	.826	.801					
5. Weight...............	.473	.376	.380	.436				
6. Bitrochanteric diameter.	.398	.326	.319	.329	.762			
7. Chest girth............	.301	.277	.237	.327	.730	.583		
8. Chest width...........	.382	.415	.345	.365	.629	.577	.539	

TABLE 7.2

PORTION OF BI-FACTOR PATTERN FOR SEVENTEEN
PHYSICAL VARIABLES[a]

Variable	General Physical Growth	Lankiness	Stockiness	Communality
j	A	B	C	h_j^2
1..............	.691	.614	....	.854
2..............	.591	.740	....	.897
3..............	.581	.704	....	.833
4..............	.598	.652	....	.783
5..............	.694	....	.623	.870
6..............	.611	....	.560	.687
7..............	.562	....	.453	.521
8..............	.596	....	.473	.579

[a] Taken from Frances Mullen, "Factors in the Growth of Girls Seven to
Seventeen Years of Age" (Ph.D. dissertation, Department of Education, University of Chicago), 1939, Table 27, p. 45.

The principal-factor pattern for the eight variables is presented in Table
7.4. The adequacy of factorization is shown in several ways. The comparison of communalities in the last column of Table 7.4 shows that the values
obtained from the pattern differ only slightly from those originally employed in the correlation matrix. Actually, the total calculated communality (5.968) accounts for 99.1 per cent of the original communality (6.024).
The completeness of factorization is also indicated in the process of com-

puting the respective factor coefficients. Thus the contribution of the first
factor (i.e., the sum of the squares of its coefficients) is 4.455 or 74.0 per cent
of the original communality. Similarly, the contribution of the second fac-

TABLE 7.3

COMPARISON OF COMMUNALITIES FOR
EIGHT PHYSICAL VARIABLES

Variable	(1) Calculated Directly	(2) Bi-factor Estimates	Difference (1) − (2)
1.............	.842	.854	− .012
2.............	.881	.897	− .016
3.............	.817	.833	− .016
4.............	.815	.783	.032
5.............	.872	.870	.002
6.............	.647	.687	− .040
7.............	.584	.521	.063
8.............	.502	.579	− .077

TABLE 7.4

PRINCIPAL-FACTOR PATTERN FOR EIGHT
PHYSICAL VARIABLES

VARIABLE j	PATTERN COEFFICIENTS[a]			COMMUNALITY		
	G	BT	U_j	(1) Original	(2) Calculated	(1) − (2)
1. Height.................	.858	− .328	.395	.854	.844	.010
2. Arm span..............	.849	− .414	.328	.897	.892	.005
3. Length of forearm.......	.810	− .412	.417	.833	.826	.007
4. Length of lower leg......	.825	− .339	.452	.783	.796	− .013
5. Weight.................	.747	.561	.357	.870	.873	− .003
6. Bitrochanteric diameter..	.637	.507	.581	.687	.663	.024
7. Chest girth.............	.561	.488	.669	.521	.553	− .032
8. Chest width............	.619	.371	.692	.579	.521	.058
Total.................	....	....	....	6.024	5.968	.054
Contribution of factor......	4.455	1.511	....	....	....	....
Per cent of total original communality.................	74.0	25.1	....	....	99.1	.9

[a] Since the reliability of any one of these physical variables is close to unity, the unique factor in each
case may be considered as essentially the specific factor. The index of completeness of factorization (2.14)
is then approximately 100 times the calculated communality of each variable.

tor is 1.511 or 25.1 per cent of the communality. In this example only two
factors are required to account for practically all the common-factor variance. Completeness of factorization is also evident from Table D.13 of final
residuals in Appendix D.

The coefficients of the first factor in Table 7.4 are all large and positive, indicating an important general factor of physical growth (G) among these variables. On the other hand, the second factor has loadings of opposite signs for the two subgroups of variables. From the nature of the variables, this bipolar factor might be called "Stockiness." If desired, of course, the signs of all the coefficients of this factor may be changed. Then this factor might be labeled "Lankiness."

Whatever name is selected for a bipolar factor, it should have a clearly recognizable negation. A more fundamental approach is to find a basic term which connotes the entire continuum. For example, a bipolar factor which is named "Heat" (or, "Cold") would have the opposite characteristic "Cold" (or, "Heat"). A name representing both of these characteristics is "Temperature." These two approaches may be indicated schematically as in Figure 7.1. Another example is a bipolar factor named "Fear," the nega-

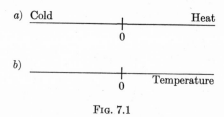

FIG. 7.1

tive of which is clearly "Courage." A fundamental term to describe this continuum, however, is difficult to determine. The investigator may have trouble in finding an appropriate name, of either type, for a bipolar factor because of the psychological difficulty of projecting the interpretation beyond the immediate content of the data.

Inasmuch as "Stockiness" and "Lankiness" are not clearly distinguishable as opposites (according to a of Fig. 7.1), neither of these seems to be an appropriate name for the bipolar factor. In an attempt to get a name, of the type b, which transcends the specific descriptions of the variables, the term "Body Type" (BT) has been adopted. On this continuum, variables describing different body types have projections of opposite sign.

Geometric interpretations of the two factor solutions will now be given. In Figure 7.2 the coordinates of the points representing the eight variables, from Table 7.2, are plotted with respect to the three bi-factor axes. Thus the coordinates of the first point are (.691, .614, 0). It will be noted that all points have a zero coordinate for either B or C, and hence lie in one of the reference planes determined by the A and B axes or the A and C axes. It should be observed that the points lie exactly in the reference planes only because they represent theoretical variables, in the sense of (2.4). The projections of the first four points on the A and B axes are indicated by crosses, and the projections of the last four points on the A and C axes are given by circles. The cluster of positive projections on the A axis is the geometric basis for the naming of the general factor, while the clusters on the other two axes furnish interpretations for the group factors.

The diagram for these eight variables in the plane of the two principal factors is presented in Figure 7.3, the coordinates being taken from Table 7.4. The two subgroups of variables lie in the first and fourth quadrants.

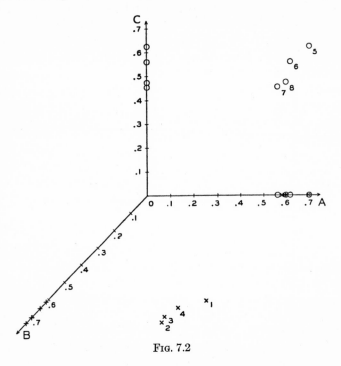

FIG. 7.2

Hence the projections of all the points form a single cluster on the positive end of the G axis. The projections on the BT axis, on the other hand, fall into two clusters which are widely separated. The projections on the respective axes give the geometric basis for the naming of the general and bipolar factors.

The bi-factor analysis of the eight variables, as shown in Table 7.2, indicates a general physical growth factor A, a lankiness factor B, and a stockiness factor C. Such a solution is certainly a satisfactory description of the variables in terms of factors with positive coefficients. For these physical variables, however, the biologist might prefer an analysis in terms of a general factor and another factor which expresses the two preceding factors simultaneously, as indicated in Figure 7.3. This preference might be based upon the opposing nature of the two groups of variables which makes it possible to conceive of them as measures in opposite directions on a common scale. In this example such preference would also lead to parsimony of description, inasmuch as the total number of common factors is reduced from three to two. The biologist would then choose the principal-factor solution of Table 7.4.

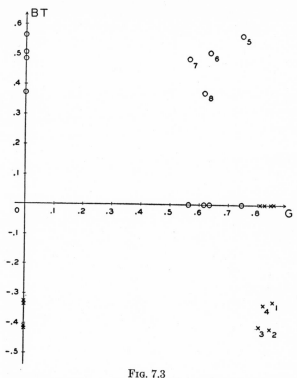

Fig. 7.3

These considerations as to choice of form of solution are in harmony with the principles set down in Chapter V. One of the most important bases for the selection of a preferred type of solution in any field of investigation is the nature of the variables. Statistical standards, such as complexity of variables or parsimony of factors, are of lesser importance in making a decision. The investigator is fortunate when the variables of his study lend themselves to a clear-cut choice of solution. In such a case, the final pattern could be considered almost unique, in the sense that other workers would also accept it as the preferred type.

2. TWENTY-FOUR PSYCHOLOGICAL TESTS

The next illustration is based upon the twenty-four psychological tests of **2.8**. Although it would not be expected that variables of this nature would ordinarily be interpreted in bipolar form by psychologists, it was decided to carry the analysis far enough to see the essence of a principal-factor

TABLE 7.5

FIRST TWO PRINCIPAL FACTORS FOR
TWENTY-FOUR PSYCHO-
LOGICAL TESTS

Variable	G	VR
1.............	.601	−.051
2.............	.371	.018
3.............	.423	.097
4.............	.482	.094
5.............	.690	.321
6.............	.683	.402
7.............	.683	.449
8.............	.676	.206
9.............	.693	.449
10............	.459	−.430
11............	.557	−.355
12............	.471	−.492
13............	.599	−.259
14............	.430	−.072
15............	.393	−.115
16............	.505	−.110
17............	.474	−.238
18............	.523	−.348
19............	.445	−.113
20............	.615	.124
21............	.593	−.210
22............	.612	.096
23............	.692	.056
24............	.652	−.158
Contribution of factor.......	7.657	1.669
Per cent of total original communality....	65.4	14.3

solution. This implied the calculation of the coefficients for only the first two factors, for all the other factors would be of the form of the second. Table 7.5 presents this portion of the principal-factor pattern.

The labor of computation in the direct principal-factor solution increases very rapidly with the number of variables and factors. For the example of eight physical variables, the total time for complete factorization was less than ten hours, indicating the feasibility of this method for such set of variables. In the case of the twenty-four psychological tests, however, the time required for the calculation of the first-factor weights alone was more than seventy hours. Each additional factor would probably require upward of forty hours depending upon the number of iterations. In case a machine is devised which will simplify the type of multiplication involved, the direct principal-factor method will then be appropriate for large sets of variables.

The interpretation of the two factors in Table 7.5 will now be given. As in all cases of principal-factor patterns, based upon a set of positive correlations, the first factor has appreciably high positive loadings for every test. This factor might then be regarded as general ability (G).

The second factor may be named from the tests with significant coefficients. As a rough estimate the standard error of a factor coefficient may be taken from Table H.1. For the present example this approximation to the standard error* is .109 so that the level of significance of .30 may be appropriate. Those variables which have significant coefficients, by this standard, are listed below:

Variable	Coefficient
5. General information	.321
6. Paragraph comprehension	.402
7. Sentence completion	.449
9. Word meaning	.449
10. Speed of addition	−.430
11. Speed of code translation	−.355
12. Speed of counting dots	−.492
18. Number-figure memory	−.348

The first four tests, which are verbal in character have positive correlations with the second factor, while the last four, which are essentially speed tests, have negative correlations with this factor. These subgroups of tests agree substantially with the grouping by the method of B-coefficients described in **2.9.** (Although Test 18 was put in the memory group, it is also a measure of speed of reaction.) It appears difficult to find the common element which underlies the content of these eight variables by which to name the factor. A tentative name which might be attached to this factor is "Verbal Rigidity" (VR).

Subsequent factors will, of course, be of the bipolar form and might be given similar interpretations in terms of the subgroups of tests with significant loadings. Such subgroups may include some variables which were employed in the naming of VR. Owing to this increased complexity of the variables, the naming of later factors may be more involved. A complete derived principal-factor pattern for these twenty-four tests is given in **9.3.**

* See p. 149.

3. EIGHT EMOTIONAL TRAITS

The particular appropriateness of the principal-factor method to another field of psychology will now be indicated. The material for this illustration includes eight emotional traits, the correlations for which were furnished

TABLE 7.6

INTERCORRELATIONS OF EIGHT EMOTIONAL VARIABLES
FOR 172 NORMAL CHILDREN AGED NINE TO TWELVE

Variable	1	2	3	4	5	6	7	8
1. Sociability.....	.94	....	....	....	....	....	....	....
2. Sorrow........	.83	.94	....	....	....	....	....	....
3. Tenderness....	.81	.87	.89	....	....	....	....	....
4. Joy..........	.80	.62	.63	.50	....	....	....	....
5. Wonder.......	.71	.59	.37	.49	.57	....	....	....
6. Disgust.......	.54	.58	.30	.30	.34	.28	....	....
7. Anger........	.53	.44	.12	.28	.55	.38	.63	....
8. Fear..........	.24	.45	.33	.29	.19	.21	.10	.12

TABLE 7.7

PRINCIPAL-FACTOR PATTERN FOR EIGHT EMOTIONAL TRAITS

VARIABLE	COMMON FACTORS		COMMUNALITY		
	GE	E	(1) Original	(2) Calculated	(1) − (2)
1. Sociability...	.98	.06	.94	.96	−.02
2. Sorrow......	.95	−.14	.94	.92	.02
3. Tenderness...	.81	−.51	.89	.92	−.03
4. Joy.........	.72	−.10	.50	.53	−.03
5. Wonder.....	.68	.32	.57	.56	.01
6. Disgust......	.53	.14	.28	.30	−.02
7. Anger.......	.52	.60	.63	.63	.00
8. Fear........	.35	−.14	.12	.14	−.02
Total......	....	....	4.87	4.96	−.09
Contribution of factor........	4.17	.79	....	....	....
Per cent of total original communality.....	85.6	16.2	....	101.8	−1.8

by Burt,* who has also discussed the factorial analyses of variables of this type in a subsequent paper.† Although he does not furnish a principal-factor solution, he does point out the bipolar nature of emotionality factors.

* Cyril Burt, "General and Specific Factors Underlying the Primary Emotions," *Report of the British Association for the Advancement of Science*, 1915, pp. 694–96.

† "The Factorial Analysis of Emotional Traits," *Character and Personality*, 1939, pp. 238–54, 285–99.

The traits which are analyzed here are indicated in Table 7.6, where the correlations are presented. The communalities were determined from a solution essentially of the bi-factor form. It was found that only two principal factors were necessary to account for these communalities. The factor pattern is given in Table 7.7, where only the common factors are presented.

The first factor may appropriately be called "General Emotionality" (GE), although the present sample of emotional traits is small. In the present example the method of naming the bipolar factor is similar to that employed in the case of the twenty-four tests. An approximate measure of the standard error of a factor coefficient for $N = 172$ and an average correlation of .48 is .065 from Table H.1. The traits with significant coefficients are anger (.60), wonder (.32), and tenderness ($-.51$). Since wonder and anger are indicative of an egocentric personality, and tenderness is indicative of timidity, the factor characterizing these two opposing emotions may be called "Egocentricity" (E). If it is desired to change the signs of all the coefficients, then the factor may be called "Timidity." In Burt's discussion fear and sorrow are classed with tenderness, and in the present analysis each of these traits has a coefficient of $-.14$. These values have some statistical significance and help substantiate the naming of the second factor.

4. EIGHT POLITICAL VARIABLES

The final example has been selected from a set of political variables in order to illustrate the applicability of the principal-factor solution in an entirely different field. The data also furnish a solution in which all the factors, including the first, are of the bipolar form. A set of eight variables was selected from a larger group of seventeen political variables, analyzed by Gosnell and Schmidt.* The smaller set, which was taken for simplicity, nevertheless includes the variables which are among the best measures of the factors given in Gosnell's solution. A brief description of these variables, measured in 147 Chicago election areas, follows:

1. *Lewis:* Percentage of the total Democratic and Republican vote cast for Lewis
2. *Roosevelt:* Corresponding percentage for Roosevelt
3. *Party voting:* Percentage that the straight-party votes were of the total
4. *Median rental:* Median rental (in dollars)
5. *Homeownership:* Percentage of the total families that own their homes
6. *Unemployment:* Percentage unemployed in 1921 of the gainful workers ten years of age and over
7. *Mobility:* Percentage of total families that have lived less than one year at present address
8. *Education:* Percentage of population, eighteen years and older, which completed more than ten grades of school

* Harold F. Gosnell and Margaret Schmidt, "Factorial and Correlational Analysis of the 1934 Vote in Chicago," *Journal of the American Statistical Association*, 1936, pp. 507–18.

The intercorrelations of these variables are given in Table 7.8, in which communalities are also recorded. These communalities were computed by the second method of **4.6**, in which grouping of variables is not employed. For example, the calculation of h_1^2 was based upon the stub of Table 4.6. Of the fourteen evaluations of this communality, four were dropped because they involved insignificant denominators. The remaining ten (.57, .42, .52, .55, .61, .39, .66, .45, .47, and .58) were averaged to obtain $h_1^2 = .52$.

The principal-factor pattern is presented in Table 7.9. It may be observed that several variables have large negative coefficients for the first factor, in contrast with the consistently positive coefficients found in the

TABLE 7.8

INTERCORRELATIONS OF EIGHT POLITICAL
VARIABLES FOR 147 ELECTION AREAS

Variable	Lewis (1)	Roosevelt (2)	Party Voting (3)	Median Rental (4)	Home-owner-ship (5)	Unem-ployment (6)	Mobility (7)	Education (8)
1........	.52							
2........	.84	1.00						
3........	.62	.84	.78					
4........	−.53	−.68	−.76	.82				
5........	.03	−.05	.08	−.25	.36			
6........	.57	.76	.81	−.80	.25	.80		
7........	−.33	−.35	−.51	.62	−.72	−.58	.63	
8........	−.63	−.73	−.81	.88	−.36	−.84	.68	.97

preceding solutions. In the present solution the first factor, being of the bipolar type, may be named from the nature of the variables in the subsets (1, 2, 3) and (4, 7, 8). The variables of the first subset may be regarded as measures of the "Traditional Democratic Vote" (*TDV*), which is taken as the name of the factor. The variables of the second subset characterize the sociological level of the election areas and seem to be opposite in nature to the "Traditional Democratic Vote." The high weight for variable 6 (Unemployment) is consistent with the foregoing interpretation inasmuch as high unemployment is associated with traditional vote.

In the case of the second factor, the largest weights appear for variables 5 (Homeownership) and 7 (Mobility), being +.65 and −.56, respectively. Inasmuch as both Homeownership and lack of Mobility are aspects of a single characteristic, the second factor may be termed "Home Permanency" (*HP*). The negative factor weights for the first three variables again appear to verify the naming of this factor. This bipolar factor is conveniently described by a single name because the opposing variables may be considered as measures on a single scale in opposite directions.

From the foregoing illustrations it is apparent that the direct principal-factor solution is well adapted to small sets of variables, say, less than

TABLE 7.9

PRINCIPAL-FACTOR PATTERN FOR EIGHT POLITICAL VARIABLES

VARIABLE j	COMMON FACTORS		COMMUNALITY		
	TDV	HP	(1) Original	(2) Calculated	(1) $-$ (2)
1...............	.69	$-.28$	.52	.55	$-.03$
2...............	.88	$-.48$	1.00	1.00	.00
3...............	.87	$-.17$	.78	.79	$-.01$
4...............	$-.88$	$-.09$	.82	.78	.04
5...............	.28	.65	.36	.50	$-.14$
6...............	.89	.01	.80	.79	.01
7...............	$-.66$	$-.56$	.63	.75	$-.12$
8...............	$-.96$	$-.15$	.97	.94	.03
Total......	....	....	5.88	6.10	$-.22$
Contribution of factor........	5.01	1.10	....	....	....
Per cent of total original com- munality.....	85.2	18.8	....	103.7	-3.7

twelve. The direct method does not appear to be feasible when dealing with larger sets of variables because of the excessive labor involved. In Chapter IX, however, an indirect method is presented for obtaining a principal-factor pattern by rotation from some other form of solution. Thus if some factor solution can be simply obtained, it may be rotated to the principal-factor form. By this procedure a large set of variables can be analyzed in the principal-factor form with only a fraction of the labor required by the direct method.

CHAPTER VIII

THE CENTROID SOLUTION

8.1. *Introduction*

In the two preceding chapters methods have been presented for obtaining two of the preferred types of factor solutions discussed in Chapter V. A third type of preferred pattern, the multiple-factor solution, was indicated in **5.6.** A direct method of analysis for this type of pattern is not available. Instead, any factor pattern which has the property (2.24) of reproducing the correlations may first be obtained and then transformed into the multiple-factor form by the methods of Chapter X. The problem of obtaining a multiple-factor pattern thus consists of two parts: first, the calculation of a preliminary pattern and, second, the transformation of this pattern to the multiple-factor type. In this chapter two such preliminary patterns are developed. These patterns may then be transformed to any desired form of solution. In particular, the rotation to the multiple-factor form is presented in Chapter X. An illustration of the rotation from a preliminary pattern to the principal-factor form is also given in Chapter IX.

The two preliminary solutions are the centroid and averoid patterns. The theoretical development of the first of these is presented in **8.2,** and a list of steps for routine calculation is given in Appendix E. Three illustrations of the centroid pattern are presented in **8.3.** The averoid method of analysis, discussed in **8.4,** is similar to the centroid method, and, therefore, no additional outline for calculation is required.

8.2. *Centroid Method*

The fundamental formula of the centroid solution was first employed by Burt* in obtaining a single general factor of the Spearman form. Later, when the analysis of psychological tests shifted from one to several common factors, Thurstone† provided the complete form for the centroid method, which is followed in the main in the present development for the analysis of any set of statistical variables.

The name of the method connotes its close relationship to the mechani-

---

* Cyril Burt, *The Distribution and Relations of Educational Abilities*, 1917, p. 53.

† L. L. Thurstone, "Multiple Factor Analysis," *Psychological Review*, 1931, pp. 406–27; *The Vectors of Mind*, 1935, Chap. III.

cal concept of a centroid, or center of gravity. For this reason, the centroid form of analysis can best be described in geometric terms. According to Chapter III, the variables may be considered as represented by a set of n vectors which are contained in a space of m dimensions, where m is the number of common factors; and the scalar product of any pair of vectors is the correlation between them, as given in (3.51). The variables may also be considered as represented by the m coordinates of the end points of these vectors with respect to m mutually orthogonal arbitrary reference axes. Since the configuration of the vectors representing the variables completely determines the intercorrelations, the reference system may be rotated without any effect on them. The arbitrary coordinate system may then be rotated so that the centroid point of the set of n points, along with the origin, determines the first axis of reference. Thus it is possible to obtain the projection of each of the vectors, or the coordinate of each variable, on the first axis of reference through the centroid.

Starting with a factor pattern of the usual form (2.16), the correlations are reproduced by means of equation (2.22) when the common factors are uncorrelated. Then, making the same assumption as in the preceding methods of analysis, namely, that the residuals vanish, the observed correlations may be written

$$(8.1) \qquad r_{jk} = r'_{jk} = a_{j1}a_{k1} + a_{j2}a_{k2} + \ldots + a_{jm}a_{km}$$
$$(j, k = 1, 2, \ldots, n),$$

where m is the number of common factors. The numerical values of a_{jt} $(t = 1, 2, \ldots, m)$ are determined by the position of the orthogonal reference axes, since a_{jt} is the tth coordinate of variable z_j.* Now let the frame of reference be so selected that the first axis F_1 passes through the centroid of the system of n points:

$$P_1(a_{11}, a_{12}, \ldots, a_{1m}), \quad P_2(a_{21}, a_{22}, \ldots, a_{2m}), \ldots,$$
$$P_n(a_{n1}, a_{n2}, \ldots, a_{nm}).$$

Any one of the m coordinates of the centroid (say, the first one) is the average of the corresponding coordinates (the first ones) of the n points. Thus, in general, the tth coordinate of the centroid is given by

$$(8.2) \qquad \frac{1}{n}\sum_k a_{kt} \qquad\qquad (t = 1, 2, \ldots, m),$$

---

* More precisely, this variable should be designated by z''_j since it is represented in the common-factor space. See **3.8**.

where the summation is from 1 to n on the indicated index when the limits are not given specifically. In the present case the centroid lies in the first axis of reference, so that its coordinates are all zero except the first, that is,

$$(8.3) \qquad \sum_k a_{k2} = \sum_k a_{k3} = \ldots = \sum_k a_{km} = 0 \, .$$

The m values (8.2) then reduce to

$$\frac{1}{n} \sum_k a_{k1}, \, 0, \, 0, \, \ldots, \, 0 \, ,$$

there being $(m - 1)$ zeros. Since the centroid lies in the first axis, the first coordinate is also the distance of the centroid from the origin.

It is now possible to determine the coefficients of the first centroid factor, i.e., the coordinates a_{j1}, in terms of the observed correlations. For, summing (8.1) for all variables k in a fixed column j of the correlation matrix, there results

$$\sum_k r_{jk} = a_{j1} \left(\sum_k a_{k1} \right) + a_{j2} \left(\sum_k a_{k2} \right) + \ldots + a_{jm} \left(\sum_k a_{km} \right),$$

which, on applying (8.3), becomes

$$(8.4) \qquad \sum_k r_{jk} = a_{j1} \left(\sum_k a_{k1} \right) .$$

Then the sum of all the entries in the correlation matrix is simply

$$(8.5) \qquad \sum_j \sum_k r_{jk} = \left(\sum_j a_{j1} \right) \left(\sum_k a_{k1} \right) = \left(\sum_k a_{k1} \right)^2 .$$

Now substituting $\pm \sqrt{\sum_j \sum_k r_{jk}}$ for $\sum_k a_{k1}$ in (8.4), and arbitrarily taking the positive sign, the expression for a_{j1} may be written explicitly as follows:

$$(8.6) \qquad a_{j1} = \frac{\sum_k r_{jk}}{\sqrt{\sum_j \sum_k r_{jk}}} = \frac{S_j}{\sqrt{T}} \qquad (j = 1, 2, \ldots, n) ,$$

where S_j is the sum of all the correlations in column j of the correlation matrix, and T is the total of all the correlations in the matrix, including the diagonal terms in both of these sums. Of course, if the negative sign of the radical had been chosen, the coefficients of the factor would all be changed in sign, yielding an equally acceptable factor. Formula (8.6) gives the coefficient of the first centroid factor F_1 for each variable z_j, or the first coordinate for each point representing a variable.

The next step is to get the first-factor residuals, from which the second coordinates are found. Since the residual correlations with one, two, . . . , $(m - 1)$ factors removed are employed in successive stages of the centroid method, the notation introduced for the principal-factor method in **7.3** will be employed again. The first-factor residuals are written

$$(8.7) \qquad {}_1r_{jk} = r_{jk} - a_{j1}a_{k1} = a_{j2}a_{k2} + a_{j3}a_{k3} + \ldots + a_{jm}a_{km} .$$

The residual correlations may be regarded as the scalar products of pairs of residual vectors in a space of $(m - 1)$ dimensions—the dimension of the residual space being equal to the number of terms in the right-hand member of (8.7), or the rank of the matrix of residual correlations, according to Theorem 3.5.

In the $(m - 1)$ residual space, the n points representing the variables have the following sets of coordinates:

$$P_1(a_{12}, a_{13}, \ldots , a_{1m}), \qquad P_2(a_{22}, a_{23}, \ldots , a_{2m}), \ldots ,$$

$$P_n(a_{n2}, a_{n3}, \ldots , a_{nm}) .$$

Then the $(m - 1)$ coordinates of the centroid of these n points are

$$\frac{1}{n}\sum_k a_{kt} \qquad\qquad (t = 2, 3, \ldots , m) ,$$

which all vanish according to (8.3). Thus the centroid is at the origin in this $(m - 1)$ space, and formula (8.6) cannot be used directly for calculating the values of the second-factor coefficients. It will be noted that in obtaining (8.6) there was involved the division by $\sum_k a_{k1}$, or n times the distance of the centroid from the origin. It was tacitly assumed that the centroid was not at the origin, for otherwise this division would not have been possible.

The immediate problem, then, is to remove the centroid from the origin of the $(m - 1)$ space, so that the preceding method can again be applied.

By means of rotations of certain of the vectors about the origin through $180°$—also called *reflections in the origin*—the centroid can be removed from the origin. If the coordinates of a point P_j, representing a variable z_j, are

$$(a_{j1}, a_{j2}, \ldots, a_{jm}) ,$$

then the reflected point $-P_j$, with coordinates

$$(-a_{j1}, -a_{j2}, \ldots, -a_{jm}) ,$$

represents the variable $-z_j$. Such a variable may be interpreted as the original variable measured in the opposite direction.

Now it is evident from (8.1) that to reverse the signs of the coordinates of P_j has the effect of reversing the signs of all the correlations of variable z_j with the remaining ones. Thus the reflection of a variable in the origin is accomplished merely by changing the signs of the correlations of this variable in the correlation matrix. Of course, the same argument holds for the residual $(m - 1)$ space as for the original common-factor space of m dimensions. Hence the reflection of a variable in the residual space is accomplished by changing the signs of the residual correlations (8.7) for that variable.

In an attempt to determine which variables to reflect, Thurstone* suggests that "it is desirable to account for as much as possible of the residual variance by each successive factor." It should be observed that the same idea is involved in the principal-factor method, where the maximization is accomplished by a mathematically rigorous procedure.† For the present case the maximization principle indicates that the second reference axis should pass through a cluster of residual vectors. If there is a clustering of a set of residual vectors (i.e., a group of variables having high positive residual correlations), which is balanced by a scattering of vectors on the opposite side of the origin, since the centroid is at the origin, then the second reference axis should be made to pass through this cluster. Thus it would seem that the vectors which scatter, opposite to a cluster, should be reflected so as to fall in with the group, and then the centroid of the n points will be in this group, and the second axis can pass through it and satisfy the foregoing principle of contributing to the variances as great a total as possible. The second centroid coordinates can then be computed as in the first case. In application, those variables which have the greatest number of negative correlations would be reflected first, bringing them into the hemisphere of

* *The Vectors of Mind*, p. 96.

† A further analogy between the centroid and principal-factor methods may be noted. Each centroid factor is actually the first approximation, in the iterative scheme of **7.4**, to the principal factor.

the cluster. For practical problems, Thurstone suggests reversing "the signs of one trait at a time until the number of negative coefficients in the residual table is less than $n/2$,"[*] that is, less than $n/2$ negative signs for any one variable, not the entire table. One need not stop with this, however, for, if it is desired to further "maximize" the variance removed by each successive factor, the reflections of variables may be continued until the sum of the residual correlations for each variable is as large (positively) as possible.

For the remainder of the analytical work it will be convenient to use a symbol to designate whether a point, representing a variable, has been reflected in the origin. Let ϵ_j stand for the algebraic sign of P_j, that is, the point $\epsilon_j P_j$ is $+P_j$ or $-P_j$. If P_j has not been reflected, ϵ_j is plus, but, if P_j has been reflected, then ϵ_j is minus. Furthermore, ϵ_j may be considered as an algebraic operator defined as follows:

$$\epsilon_j = \begin{cases} +1 \text{ if } z_j \text{ has not been reflected,} \\ -1 \text{ if } z_j \text{ has been reflected.} \end{cases}$$

Then ϵ_j can be attached to the coordinates of P_j, and it can be treated as any other algebraic quantity. Thus, if the first-factor residual correlations after reflection of certain variables are designated by r_{1jk} (in distinction to $_1r_{jk}$ before reflection), then they may be written as follows:

(8.8) $$r_{1jk} = \epsilon_j \epsilon_k (a_{j2}a_{k2} + a_{j3}a_{k3} + \ldots + a_{jm}a_{km}) .$$

This result is immediate from (8.7) where each a_{jt} and a_{kt} was replaced by $\epsilon_j a_{jt}$ and $\epsilon_k a_{kt}$, respectively, and then ϵ_j and ϵ_k were factored out algebraically. If neither z_j nor z_k was reflected, or if both variables were reflected, then $r_{1jk} = _1r_{jk}$; but, if only one or the other of z_j and z_k was reflected, then $r_{1jk} = -_1r_{jk}$. In other words, $r_{1jk} = \epsilon_j \epsilon_k (_1r_{jk})$.

The $(m-1)$ coordinates of the centroid of the n points, after reflection of variables, are given by

$$\frac{1}{n} \sum_k \epsilon_k a_{kt} \qquad (t = 2, 3, \ldots, m) .$$

Now the system of reference can be rotated about the first axis F_1 so that the second axis F_2 passes through this centroid.[†] Let it be assumed that

[*] *The Vectors of Mind*, p. 97.

[†] The residual $(m-1)$ space is orthogonal to the first axis of reference F_1. The second axis F_2, i.e., the first one in the $(m-1)$ subspace, may then be rotated to any position in the residual space, and it will be at right angles to F_1.

this has been done, there being no need to change the notation for the co-ordinates. Then the coordinates of the centroid are

$$\frac{1}{n} \sum_k \epsilon_k a_{k2}, \, 0, \, 0, \, \ldots, \, 0 \,,$$

since the centroid lies in the axis F_2. From the values for the last $(m - 2)$ coordinates the following useful expressions may be written:

$$(8.9) \qquad \sum_k \epsilon_k a_{k3} = \sum_k \epsilon_k a_{k4} = \ldots = \sum_k \epsilon_k a_{km} = 0 \,.$$

Now the projections of the vectors on the second centroid axis can be expressed in terms of the residual correlations. For, summing (8.8) for all variables k in a fixed column j of the residual correlation matrix (after re-flection of variables) and applying (8.9), there results

$$(8.10) \qquad \sum_k r_{1jk} = \epsilon_j a_{j2} \sum_k \epsilon_k a_{k2} \,.$$

Then, summing for all columns,

$$(8.11) \qquad \sum_j \sum_k r_{1jk} = \sum_j \epsilon_j a_{j2} \sum_k \epsilon_k a_{k2} = \left(\sum_k \epsilon_k a_{k2} \right)^2 .$$

From (8.10) and (8.11) it follows that

$$\epsilon_j a_{j2} = \frac{\displaystyle\sum_k r_{1jk}}{\sqrt{\displaystyle\sum_j \sum_k r_{1jk}}} = \frac{S_{j1}}{\sqrt{T_1}}$$

or, multiplying both sides by ϵ_j,

$$(8.12) \qquad\qquad a_{j2} = \frac{\epsilon_j S_{j1}}{\sqrt{T_1}} \qquad\qquad (j = 1, 2, \ldots, n) \,,$$

where S_{j1} is the sum of all the entries in column j of the matrix of first-factor residual correlations and T_1 is the total of all the correlations in this matrix, the signs of all the entries being those after reflection. The ϵ_j indicates that, if the variable z_j was reflected, then the algebraic sign must be changed, but, if the variable was not reflected, then ϵ_j is merely $+1$. In other words,

$\epsilon_j S_{j1}$ is the sum of all residual correlations for the unreflected variable z_j with all other variables. Hence, by defining

(8.13)
$$_1S_j = \epsilon_j S_{j1},$$

formula (8.12) may be put in the form

(8.14)
$$a_{j2} = \frac{_1S_j}{\sqrt{T_1}} \qquad\qquad (j = 1, 2, \ldots, n).$$

In this formula the numerator refers to the sum of the residual correlations for the unreflected variable j, while in the denominator T_1 still stands for the sum of all residual correlations after the sign changes. Formula (8.14) gives the coefficients of the second centroid factor F_2 for each variable.

The remaining factor weights can be obtained in a similar manner. In general, the residual correlation of r_{jk} after p factors have been removed is given by

(8.15)
$$_p r_{jk} = r_{jk} - \sum_{t=1}^{p} a_{jt} a_{kt} = a_{j,p+1} a_{k,p+1} + \ldots + a_{jm} a_{km}.$$

The centroid of the n points in this residual $(m - p)$ space usually will be near the origin. Certain variables may then be reflected in the origin, beginning with the one which has the largest number of negative residual correlations. Thus, employing the same principle as before, the centroid may be removed from the new origin, and the factor F_{p+1} determined so as to contribute to the residual variances of the variables as great a total as possible. After reflection of variables, the residual correlations become

(8.16)
$$r_{pjk} = \epsilon_j \epsilon_k (_p r_{jk}) = \pm _p r_{jk},$$

where the plus sign holds if neither z_j nor z_k was reflected, or if both were reflected, and the minus sign holds if only one or the other of the two variables was reflected. Then, proceeding as before, the projections of the vectors on the $(p + 1)$st centroid axis, i.e., the coefficients of F_{p+1}, can be determined. They are given by

(8.17)
$$a_{j,p+1} = \frac{\epsilon_j S_{jp}}{\sqrt{T_p}} = \frac{_p S_j}{\sqrt{T_p}} \qquad \left(\begin{matrix} j = 1, 2, \ldots, n \\ p = 0, 1, \ldots, m - 1 \end{matrix} \right),$$

where S_{jp} is the sum of all the entries in column j of the matrix of residual correlations with p factors removed, and T_p is the sum of all the correlations in this matrix, the signs of the entries being those after reflection of variables. The definition (8.13) is extended to the general case, that is,

$$(8.18) \qquad\qquad _pS_i = \epsilon_j S_{jp} = \pm S_{jp} ,$$

where the column sum S_{jp} is not changed in sign if z_j was not reflected, and changed if it was reflected. Formula (8.17) gives the coefficients of any centroid factor F_{p+1} for each variable.

It is evident that formulas (8.6) and (8.12) are special cases of (8.17) for $p = 0$ and $p = 1$, respectively. The same type of formula is used to calculate the coefficients of the successive centroid factors. Since a basic principle of the centroid method is to account for as much as possible of the variances of the variables by each factor, the variables are reflected in the residual subspaces to bring them into a cluster. When the sign changes have been made, the centroid of the system of points in the residual space lies somewhere in the cluster of variables, and the next reference axis is selected through this centroid. Each successive centroid axis is at right angles to every one of the preceding axes because the residual space is orthogonal to the space of the centroid axes already established. Upon extracting each centroid factor, the residual correlations are reduced in magnitude, and the rank of each residual matrix is reduced by one. The foregoing development was made without any restrictions on the diagonal elements. The number of factors ultimately obtained is dependent upon these diagonal values, leading to the question of "when to stop factoring."

Thurstone[*] recommends that the largest correlation in each column of the correlation matrix be selected for the diagonal element of that column. In each subsequent residual matrix the calculated diagonal term is not retained but replaced by the largest residual correlation, regardless of sign, in each column. This procedure does not furnish a standard for determining the number of common factors.

If, instead of modifying the diagonal entries at each stage, the analysis is applied directly, keeping the diagonal terms as calculated, then the number of factors is determined when the original diagonal values have been completely resolved. Only the common factors will be obtained if the correlation matrix contains communalities in the principal diagonal and these values are completely analyzed. In practice, it is recommended that appropriate estimates of the communalities, discussed in **7.2**, be employed. When such estimates are used and the straightforward centroid analysis is applied, the resulting solution terminates in a definite number of common factors. This feature is illustrated in the next section.

[*] *The Vectors of Mind*, Appen. I.

8.3. *Illustrations of Centroid Method*

1. THIRTEEN PSYCHOLOGICAL TESTS

The first illustration of the centroid method is based upon the reduced set of thirteen psychological tests of **6.11.** The intercorrelations of these tests are given in Table 2.2 and are repeated in Appendix E, where the

TABLE 8.1

CENTROID PATTERN FOR THIRTEEN PSYCHOLOGICAL TESTS

Test[a]	COMMON-FACTOR COEFFICIENTS			COMMUNALITY		
	C_1	C_2	C_3	(1) Original	(2) Calculated	(1) − (2)
1	.607	−.060	−.443	.558	.568	−.010
2	.355	.038	−.266	.203	.198	.005
3	.418	.148	−.429	.362	.381	−.019
4	.478	.083	−.287	.314	.318	−.004
5	.729	.257	.244	.646	.657	−.011
6	.707	.354	.167	.641	.653	−.012
7	.721	.367	.257	.750	.721	.029
8	.705	.197	.062	.571	.540	.031
9	.698	.409	.252	.758	.718	.040
10	.455	−.482	.399	.554	.599	−.045
11	.537	−.390	.145	.449	.461	−.012
12	.487	−.553	.033	.531	.544	−.013
13	.674	−.368	−.135	.599	.608	−.009
Total	....	....	....	6.936	6.966	−.030
Contribution of factor	4.620	1.392	.954	....	....	....
Per cent of total original communality	66.6	20.1	13.8	....	100.4	−0.4

[a] The names and brief descriptions of the tests appear in Appen. **B.1.**

complete centroid analysis of these data is exhibited. According to the discussion of choice of communality in **7.2,** it is desirable that "complete estimates" be employed. As the best available estimates, the bi-factor communalities of Table 6.13 are used in the centroid analysis.

The centroid pattern for these thirteen tests is presented in Table 8.1, where the centroid factors are denoted by C's and the unique factors have been omitted. Inasmuch as this solution is regarded as a preliminary one, the three common factors will not be named. Nevertheless, the common-factor space is definitely determined by this solution. The adequacy of this solution is indicated both by the magnitude of the final residuals, given in Table E.10, and by the degree to which the original communalities are analyzed. The comparison of the calculated and original communalities for each test, which is given in the last three columns of Table 8.1, shows that the factorization is quite adequate. The total calculated communality accounts for 100.4 per cent of the original communality, indicating a slight overfactorization. The stage to which the factorization should be carried is also evident in the actual process of calculation, for, after each factor is obtained, the cumulative contributions of the factors can be compared with the total original communality. Thus, in the example, the first factor accounts for 4.620, or 66.6 per cent, of the communality, the first two factors account for 6.012, or 86.7 per cent, of the communality, while the three common factors account for 6.966, or 100.4 per cent, of the total original communality. By all standards, it is clear that three common factors are sufficient to describe the given data.

The form of this solution is very similar to that of the principal-factor pattern, including general and bipolar factors. The centroid pattern might thus be retained as a final preferred type of solution. As indicated in the preceding section, however, the maximization of the contributions of the factors is mathematically more rigorous in the case of the principal solution, so it would generally be preferred as a final form. It will be shown in the next chapter that this more desirable form can be simply obtained by a transformation from some preliminary solution, such as the centroid.

2. TWENTY-FOUR PSYCHOLOGICAL TESTS

The centroid pattern for the twenty-four psychological tests of 2.8 is given in Table 8.2. This pattern may be shown to fit the original data by the standards employed in the preceding section. A multiple-factor solution will also be obtained in Chapter X by rotation of this centroid pattern.

This example gives a practical illustration of the nature of the "convergence" to a relatively small number of common factors when complete estimates of the communalities are employed. As already noted, the solution of Table 8.2 is statistically adequate as judged by the magnitude of the fourth-factor residuals and also by the fact that these factors account for over 97 per cent of the total original communality. To check the adequacy of this solution still further, the coefficients of a fifth factor have been calculated and are presented in Table 8.3. It will be observed that except for one value all the coefficients are insignificant, so that the factor may be dropped. This example indicates how an analysis based upon complete estimates of the communalities shunts to a fixed number of factors.

TABLE 8.2
CENTROID PATTERN FOR TWENTY-FOUR PSYCHOLOGICAL TESTS

Test[a]	COMMON-FACTOR COEFFICIENTS				COMMUNALITY		
	C_1	C_2	C_3	C_4	(1) Original	(2) Calculated	(1) − (2)
1	.608	−.116	.300	−.250	.581	.536	.045
2	.372	−.119	.207	−.135	.209	.214	−.005
3	.427	−.220	.262	−.155	.390	.323	.067
4	.477	−.211	.206	−.184	.315	.348	−.033
5	.668	−.306	−.344	.108	.668	.670	−.002
6	.661	−.337	−.258	.216	.643	.664	−.021
7	.652	−.396	−.384	.124	.786	.745	.041
8	.662	−.225	−.153	−.060	.530	.516	.014
9	.664	−.394	−.240	.308	.708	.749	−.041
10	.462	.455	−.365	−.136	.503	.572	−.069
11	.569	.397	−.208	−.063	.500	.529	−.029
12	.484	.360	−.149	−.388	.575	.537	.038
13	.608	.130	−.099	−.402	.524	.558	−.034
14	.442	.199	−.013	.293	.448	.321	.127
15	.407	.170	.146	.266	.350	.287	.063
16	.523	.077	.300	.076	.371	.375	−.004
17	.492	.317	.082	.338	.551	.464	.087
18	.547	.307	.248	.072	.484	.460	.024
19	.452	.125	.129	.111	.273	.249	.024
20	.612	−.174	.128	.004	.415	.421	−.006
21	.601	.114	.080	−.171	.416	.410	.006
22	.608	−.144	.145	.136	.415	.430	−.015
23	.691	−.164	.129	−.116	.539	.534	.005
24	.654	.151	−.150	−.003	.507	.473	.034
Total					11.701	11.385	.316
Contribution of factor	7.637	1.600	1.145	1.001			
Per cent of total original communality	65.3	13.7	9.8	8.6		97.3	2.7

[a] The names and brief descriptions of the tests appear in Appen. **B.1.**

TABLE 8.3
FIFTH CENTROID FACTOR WEIGHTS FOR TWENTY-FOUR PSYCHOLOGICAL TESTS

Test j	a_{j5}	Test j	a_{j5}	Test j	a_{j5}	Test j	a_{j5}
1	.116	7	.048	13	.071	19	.128
2	−.048	8	−.068	14	−.406	20	−.118
3	−.204	9	.068	15	−.146	21	.140
4	.074	10	.122	16	−.179	22	.192
5	.001	11	−.025	17	−.019	23	−.066
6	−.006	12	.030	18	.121	24	.152

3. EIGHT PHYSICAL VARIABLES

An additional illustration of a centroid solution is given in Table 8.4 for the physical variables of **7.5**. This example is included to furnish a simple illustration of a transformation from a centroid to a principal solution, which is given in the next chapter. Since the direct principal-factor solution is already available in Table 7.4, a comparison of these two methods of obtaining such a solution can then be made.

TABLE 8.4

CENTROID PATTERN FOR EIGHT PHYSICAL VARIABLES

VARIABLE	COMMON-FACTOR COEFFICIENTS		COMMUNALITY		
	c_1	c_2	(1) Original	(2) Calculated	(1) − (2)
1. Height..............	.830	− .396	.854	.846	.008
2. Arm span............	.818	− .469	.897	.889	.008
3. Length of forearm.....	.777	− .470	.833	.825	.008
4. Length of lower leg....	.798	− .401	.783	.798	− .015
5. Weight..............	.786	.500	.870	.868	.002
6. Bitrochanteric diameter.	.672	.458	.687	.661	.026
7. Chest girth...........	.594	.444	.521	.550	− .029
8. Chest width..........	.647	.333	.579	.529	.050
Total...............	....	....	6.024	5.966	.058
Contribution of factor....	4.439	1.526	....	....	....
Per cent of total original communality..........	73.7	25.3	....	99.0	1.0

8.4. *Averoid Method*

It has been seen that estimates of the communalities are required in the principal-factor and centroid methods of analysis. In this section a method is developed which may be employed when good estimates of the communalities are not available. This situation may arise when the original design of the variables fails to produce intercorrelations that clearly indicate distinct subgroups of variables.

It will now be shown that, if the average correlation for each variable is employed as the estimate of its communality in formula (8.6), a simplification of the method of analysis results. The sum S_j in this formula, where the average correlation is employed for r_{jj}, is given by

$$(8.19) \qquad S_j = \left(1 + \frac{1}{n-1}\right) \Sigma(r_{jk}; \ k \neq j, \ k = 1, 2, \ldots, n),$$

or, denoting the sum on the right by S'_j,

$$(8.20) \qquad S_j = \left(\frac{n}{n-1}\right) S'_j \qquad (j = 1, 2, \ldots, n) .$$

The total T of formula (8.6), with average correlations in the diagonal, reduces to

$$(8.21) \quad \begin{cases} T = \Sigma(S_j; \; j = 1, 2, \ldots, n) \\[2mm] \quad = \left(\frac{n}{n-1}\right) \Sigma(r_{jk}; \; j \neq k, \; j, k = 1, 2, \ldots, n) \\[2mm] \quad = \left(\frac{n}{n-1}\right) T' . \end{cases}$$

Under the foregoing assumption, the first-factor coefficients are given by

$$(8.22) \qquad a'_{j1} = \frac{\left(\dfrac{n}{n-1}\right) S'_j}{\sqrt{\left(\dfrac{n}{n-1}\right) T'}} = S'_j \sqrt{\frac{n}{(n-1) T'}}$$

$$(j = 1, 2, \ldots, n) ,$$

where the prime is used on a_{j1} to distinguish it from the general value given by formula (8.6).

The simplification of (8.22) over (8.6) is due to the fact that diagonal values are not explicitly involved. The values obtained by use of (8.22) are identical, of course, with the values which would be obtained by means of (8.6) with average correlations in the diagonal. The expression (8.22) can also be shown to be equivalent to the ratio of the average of the $(n-1)$ correlations in S'_j to the square root of the average of the $n(n-1)$ correlations in T'. Inasmuch as averages are employed in (8.22), the analysis based upon this formula is called the *averoid method*.

After the coefficients of the first averoid factor have been obtained, the first-factor residuals are calculated. Certain variables are then reflected, as in the usual centroid method, in order to increase the contribution of the second factor to the residual variance. Then a formula of the form (8.22) is applied to the residual correlations for the calculation of the second-factor coefficients. This process is continued until the final residuals are considered as insignificant. In contrast to the centroid procedure discussed in **8.2**, at each stage of the averoid analysis the calculated communalities are replaced, in effect, by the new average residual correlations.

Inasmuch as precise standards for "when to stop factoring" are not known for such solutions, some crude basis must be employed. One such basis might be the numerical magnitude of the factor coefficients at a given stage of the analysis. If the largest of these values are considered to have little significance, then the last factor obtained would be rejected as negligible.

8.5. *Illustrations of Averoid Method*

To illustrate the averoid method, the thirteen psychological tests are again employed. It has been seen that very good estimates of the communalities are available for this set of variables, and a centroid solution dependent on such estimates is given in Table 8.1. The centroid pattern based on the complete estimates of the communalities will therefore serve as a check on the adequacy of the averoid solution.

TABLE 8.5

CALCULATION OF THE A_1 COEFFICIENTS FROM THE INTERCORRELATIONS OF THIRTEEN PSYCHOLOGICAL TESTS

Variable	1	2	3	4	5	6	7	8	9	10	11	12	13
1..													
2..	.318												
3..	.403	.317											
4..	.468	.230	.305										
5..	.321	.285	.247	.227									
6..	.335	.234	.268	.327	.622								
7..	.304	.157	.223	.335	.656	.722							
8..	.332	.157	.382	.391	.578	.527	.619						
9..	.326	.195	.184	.325	.723	.714	.685	.532					
10..	.116	.057	−.075	.099	.311	.203	.246	.285	.170				
11..	.308	.150	.091	.110	.344	.353	.232	.300	.280	.484			
12..	.314	.145	.140	.160	.215	.095	.181	.271	.113	.585	.428		
13..	.489	.239	.321	.327	.344	.309	.345	.395	.280	.408	.535	.512	
S_j'..	4.034	2.484	2.806	3.304	4.873	4.709	4.705	4.769	4.527	2.889	3.615	3.159	4.504
a_{j1}'..	.592	.364	.411	.484	.715	.691	.690	.699	.664	.424	.530	.463	.660

The intercorrelations of the thirteen tests are given in Table 8.5. The sums S_j' of the correlations of each variable with all the others are recorded in the table. The total T' of all the intercorrelations is merely the sum of all the S_j'. Then the radical in formula (8.22) becomes

$$\sqrt{\frac{13}{12(50.378)}} = .14664 ,$$

and, upon multiplying this number by each sum S'_j, the corresponding coefficient a_{j1} of the first averoid factor A_1 is obtained.

The first-factor residuals are calculated by the same procedure as outlined for the centroid method in Appendix E and are presented in the lower half of Table 8.6. It will be noted that more than half of the signs in this part of the table are negative, and hence a factor determined from these residuals would be inappreciable. In order to increase the contribution of the second averoid factor, certain tests are reflected in the origin. The number of negative residuals for any test is reduced to six or less by the methods

TABLE 8.6

FIRST-FACTOR RESIDUALS AND THE CALCULATION OF THE A_2 COEFFICIENTS

Variable	−1	2	3	4	5	6	7	8	9	−10	−11	−12	−13
1	......	−.103	−.160	−.181	.102	.074	.104	.082	.067	−.135	−.006	.040	.098
2	.103	......	.167	.054	.025	−.018	−.094	−.097	−.047	.097	.043	.024	.001
3	.160	.167	......	.106	−.047	−.016	−.061	.095	−.089	.249	.127	.050	−.050
4	.181	.054	.106	......	−.119	−.007	.001	.053	.004	.106	.147	.064	−.008
5	−.102	.025	−.047	−.119	......	.128	.163	.078	.248	−.008	.035	.116	.128
6	−.074	−.018	−.016	−.007	.128	......	.245	.044	.255	.090	.013	.225	.147
7	−.104	−.094	−.061	.001	.163	.245	......	.137	.227	.047	.134	.138	.110
8	−.082	−.097	.095	.053	.078	.044	.137	......	.068	.011	.070	.053	.066
9	−.067	−.047	−.089	.004	.248	.255	.227	.068	......	.112	.072	.194	.158
10	−.135	−.097	−.249	−.106	.008	−.090	−.047	−.011	−.112	......	.259	.389	.128
11	−.006	−.043	−.127	−.147	−.035	−.013	−.134	−.070	−.072	.259	......	.183	.185
12	.040	−.024	−.050	−.064	−.116	−.225	−.138	−.053	−.194	.389	.183	......	.206
13	.098	−.001	.050	.008	−.128	−.147	−.110	−.066	−.158	.128	.185	.206	......
S'_{j1}	−.018	.052	.371	.220	.849	1.180	1.151	.660	1.269	1.345	1.262	1.682	1.169
a'_{j2}	.006	.016	.115	.068	.264	.367	.358	.205	.395	−.419	−.393	−.523	−.364

for reflection outlined in Steps 11–26 of Appendix E. The residuals after such reflections are recorded in the upper half of Table 8.6. Then the second-factor coefficients are calculated by means of the formula

$$(8.23) \qquad a'_{j2} = \epsilon_j S'_{j1} \sqrt{\frac{n}{(n-1)T'_1}},$$

where S'_{j1} is the sum of all the first-factor residuals for variable j, and T'_1 is the total of all the residuals, the signs being those after reflection. The symbol ϵ_j again indicates that if variable z_j has been reflected then the algebraic sign of the factor coefficient is changed. The sums S'_{j1} and the factor coefficients a'_{j2} are also given in Table 8.6.

The second-factor residuals, before and after reflection, are presented in Table 8.7. Then, applying a formula like (8.23), the coefficients a'_{j3} of the third averoid factor A_3 are obtained. The residuals with the third factor removed are given in Table 8.8. Since the number of negative residuals for any variable is less than six, no reflections were made in calculating the coefficients a'_{j4}.

In contrast to the magnitude of the third-factor coefficients, all but one of the a'_{j4}'s are very small. The largest of the latter values is only $a'_{14} =$

TABLE 8.7

SECOND-FACTOR RESIDUALS AND THE CALCULATION OF THE A_3 COEFFICIENTS

Variable	-1	-2	-3	-4	5	6	7	8	9	10	11	12	-13
1	.....	.103	.159	.181	.104	.076	.106	.083	.069	.132	.004	-.043	.100
2	.103	.....	.165	.053	-.021	.024	.100	.100	.053	.090	.037	.016	.005
3	.159	.165	.....	.098	.077	.058	.102	-.071	.134	.201	.082	-.010	.092
4	.181	.053	.098	.....	.137	.032	.023	-.039	.023	.078	.120	.028	.033
5	-.104	.021	-.077	-.137	.....	.031	.068	.024	.144	.119	.069	.022	.032
6	-.076	-.024	-.058	-.032	.031	.....	.114	-.031	.110	.064	.131	-.033	.013
7	-.106	-.100	-.102	-.023	.068	.114	.....	.064	.086	.103	.007	.049	-.020
8	-.083	-.100	.071	.039	.024	-.031	.064	.....	-.013	.075	.011	.054	-.009
9	-.069	-.053	-.134	-.023	.144	.110	.086	-.013	.....	.054	.083	.013	.014
10	-.132	-.090	-.201	-.078	.119	.064	.103	.075	.054	.....	.094	.170	.025
11	-.004	-.037	-.082	-.120	.069	.131	.007	.011	.083	.094	.....	-.023	-.042
12	.043	-.016	.010	-.028	.022	-.033	.049	.054	.013	.170	-.023	.....	-.016
13	.100	.005	.092	.033	-.032	-.013	.020	-.009	-.014	-.025	.042	.016	.....
S'_{j2}	1.074	.725	1.087	.767	.806	.589	.802	.248	.770	1.205	.573	.227	.227
a'_{j3}	-.371	-.250	-.375	-.265	.278	.203	.277	.086	.266	.416	.198	.078	-.078

TABLE 8.8

THIRD-FACTOR RESIDUALS

(Final Residuals)

Variable	1	2	3	4	5	6	7	8	9	10	11	12	13
1	.....												
2	.010	.....											
3	.020	.071	.....										
4	.083	-.013	-.001	.....									
5	-.001	.091	.027	-.063	.....								
6	-.001	.027	.018	.022	-.025	.....							
7	-.003	-.031	.002	.050	-.009	.058	.....						
8	-.051	-.078	.103	.062	.000	-.048	.040	.....					
9	.030	.013	-.034	.047	.070	.056	.012	-.036	.....				
10	.022	.014	-.045	.032	.003	-.020	-.012	.039	-.057	.....			
11	.069	.013	-.008	-.068	.014	.091	-.048	-.006	.030	.012	.....		
12	.072	.004	.039	-.007	.000	-.049	.027	.047	-.008	.138	-.038	.....	
13	.071	-.015	.063	.012	-.010	.003	.042	.016	-.007	.007	.057	.022	.....
S'_{j3}	.321	.106	.255	.156	.097	.132	.128	.088	.130	.133	.118	.247	.275
a'_{j4}	.226	.075	.180	.110	.068	.093	.090	.062	.092	.094	.083	.174	.194

.226. It is then clear that the fourth factor may be rejected as negligible. This, of course, is also evident from the magnitude of the third-factor residuals, all of which appear to be insignificant. The first three factors are then retained in the final averoid pattern, which is exhibited in Table 8.9.

Further tests of the adequacy of this solution may also be considered. The reliabilities of these psychological tests may be compared with the calculated communalities in order to check whether the factorization is in harmony with the assumptions of **2.3**. This check is afforded by the index of factorization (2.14), which is given for each test in Table 8.9. It will be noted that only one index of factorization, namely, $H_6 = 100.3$, slightly exceeds 100 per cent. Hence this standard indicates that the factorization has not been carried too far. The preceding test, however, showed that three factors were quite sufficient. Taken together these standards imply that three factors, and no more, are required to give an adequate description of the original data.

TABLE 8.9

AVEROID PATTERN FOR THIRTEEN PSYCHOLOGICAL TESTS

Test	Common Factors			Calculated Commu- nality	Relia- bility	Index of Factori- zation
j	A_1	A_2	A_3	h_j^2	r_{jj}	$H_j = 100 \dfrac{h_j^2}{r_{jj}}$
1...........	.592	.006	−.371	.488	.756	64.6
2...........	.364	.016	−.250	.195	.568	34.3
3...........	.411	.115	−.375	.323	.544	59.4
4...........	.484	.068	−.265	.309	.922	33.5
5...........	.715	.264	.278	.658	.808	81.4
6...........	.691	.367	.203	.653	.651	100.3
7...........	.690	.358	.277	.681	.754	90.3
8...........	.699	.205	.086	.538	.680	79.1
9...........	.664	.395	.266	.668	.870	76.8
10...........	.424	−.419	.416	.528	.952	55.5
11...........	.530	−.393	.198	.475	.712	66.7
12...........	.463	−.523	.078	.494	.937	52.7
13...........	.660	−.364	−.078	.574	.889	64.6
Contribution of factor.......	4.391	1.285	.909	....	....	....

The averoid solution of Table 8.9 may now be compared with the centroid solution of Table 8.1. The corresponding coefficients in these two patterns are very much alike, and the calculated communalities of the respective variables are not appreciably different. The total contribution of the three centroid factors is just 0.351 greater than the contribution of the three averoid factors. Thus the averoid solution accounts for all but 5 per cent of the total centroid communality. These discrepancies are due to employing average correlations (in effect) at successive stages of analysis in place of complete estimates of the communalities. With larger sets of variables, it is to be expected that these discrepancies will be even smaller.

Evidently, one would prefer the centroid solution based upon complete estimates of the communalities if such a solution was feasible. The real need for a solution such as the averoid becomes apparent when an analysis

is attempted of a set of variables for which good estimates of communalities
are difficult to determine.*

Another illustration of the averoid solution is given in Table 8.10 for the
complete set of twenty-four psychological tests. The agreement of this solu-

TABLE 8.10

AVEROID PATTERN FOR TWENTY-FOUR PSYCHOLOGICAL TESTS

VARIABLE	COMMON FACTORS				CALCULATED COMMUNALITY	RELIABILITY	INDEX OF FACTORIZATION
j	A_1	A_2	A_3	A_4	h_j^2	r_{jj}	$H_j = 100\dfrac{h_j^2}{r_{jj}}$
1..........	.596	$-$ .143	.273	$-$ .235	.505	.756	66.9
2..........	.376	$-$ .127	.210	$-$ .190	.238	.568	41.8
3..........	.421	$-$ .237	.250	$-$ .055	.299	.544	55.0
4..........	.479	$-$ .240	.216	$-$ .103	.344	.922	37.3
5..........	.653	$-$ .285	$-$ .345	.112	.639	.808	79.1
6..........	.648	$-$ .311	$-$ .256	.255	.647	.651	99.4
7..........	.626	$-$ .366	$-$ .359	.200	.695	.754	92.1
8..........	.658	$-$ .239	$-$ .166	.014	.518	.680	76.2
9..........	.646	$-$ .353	$-$ .226	.312	.690	.870	79.4
10..........	.449	.401	$-$ .393	$-$ .272	.591	.952	62.1
11..........	.562	.335	$-$ .236	$-$ .069	.489	.712	68.6
12..........	.466	.242	$-$ .113	$-$ .452	.493	.937	52.6
13..........	.601	.113	$-$ .092	$-$ .387	.532	.889	59.9
14..........	.431	.198	.022	.351	.349	.648	53.8
15..........	.402	.199	.110	.275	.289	.507	57.0
16..........	.524	.083	.293	.091	.376	.600	62.7
17..........	.476	.330	.018	.242	.394	.725	54.4
18..........	.539	.310	.226	$-$ .004	.438	.610	71.8
19..........	.456	.134	.115	.017	.239	.569	42.1
20..........	.614	$-$ .140	.127	.095	.422	.649	65.0
21..........	.602	.093	.060	$-$ .207	.418	.784	53.3
22..........	.609	$-$ .121	.142	.070	.411	.787	52.2
23..........	.687	$-$ .164	.122	$-$ .025	.514	.931	55.2
24..........	.651	.168	$-$ .172	$-$ .061	.485	.836	58.1
Contribution of factor...	7.441	1.395	1.099	1.080	....	....	....

tion with the centroid pattern of Table 8.2 is very close. As in the preceding
illustration, the coefficients and calculated communalities of corresponding
variables differ only slightly. The total calculated communality in the averoid solution is about 97 per cent of the total centroid communality, illustrating closer agreement than in the preceding case when only thirteen tests
were employed.

* An example of such a situation may be found in W. L. Miller, "The Relative Ability
of the States To Finance Public Education" (Ph.D. dissertation, University of Chicago),
1940.

PART III

DERIVED SOLUTIONS: ORTHOGONAL AND OBLIQUE

CHAPTER IX

DERIVED PRINCIPAL-FACTOR SOLUTION

9.1. *Introduction*

When any direct solution is obtained, a description of the variables is given in the common-factor space thereby determined. The resulting pattern equations are linear expressions in terms of the common factors for theoretical variables which approximate the observed ones. Geometrically, any such theoretical variable is the orthogonal projection of the corresponding observed variable into the common-factor space. The coefficients in a pattern equation are the coordinates of a point representing a variable in this space. Since the pattern (or reproduced) communalities and correlations are describable in terms of these coordinates (see **3.8**), such values are generally different from those used in the original analysis. These discrepancies have been illustrated in the preceding analyses by the residual correlations.

The problem of obtaining a derived principal-factor solution involves the transformation of some simply calculated initial pattern. The initial solutions which will be employed in this chapter are the centroid, bi-factor, and averoid forms. Inasmuch as the principal-factor solution can be obtained directly, comparison with the transformed solution can be made in each case. It will be convenient to designate the three solutions as follows:

$\mathbf{I} \equiv$ pattern matrix of initial solution,
$\mathbf{P}_I \equiv$ pattern matrix of transformed principal-factor solution, based upon the matrix $\mathbf{I}$,
$\mathbf{P} \equiv$ pattern matrix of direct principal-factor solution.

In obtaining $\mathbf{P}_I$, reproduced communalities and correlations based upon the values in $\mathbf{I}$ are involved, whereas $\mathbf{P}$ is obtained directly from the observed correlation matrix. Since the reproduced correlation matrix generally differs from the observed correlation matrix, it is to be expected that the solutions $\mathbf{P}_I$ and $\mathbf{P}$ will be somewhat different. If the solutions $\mathbf{I}$ and $\mathbf{P}$ fit the original correlations equally well, then the discrepancies between $\mathbf{P}_I$ and $\mathbf{P}$ can be regarded as negligible. These points will be illustrated with numerical examples.

After presentation of the theoretical basis for transformation to a principal-factor form in **9.2**, several illustrations of the method are given in detail. As pointed out in Chapter VII, the chief difficulty of the direct analysis for a principal-factor pattern is the large amount of labor involved when the number of variables is fairly large. The present method of transformation is employed to effect a great reduction in the total labor of computation. The economy of labor becomes more pronounced as the number of variables increases. A method for obtaining the roots of a polynomial, which arises in the process of transformation, is given in Appendix F.

9.2. *Transformation of a Given Pattern to a Principal-Factor Solution*

The order of procedure for obtaining a derived principal-factor solution consists of the determination of a given factor pattern which can be simply calculated, followed by a rotation of this coordinate system so that the principal axes constitute the new orthogonal reference system. The definition of the principal axes given in **7.4** may be taken for this purpose, namely, those lines which remain fixed under the transformation (7.12). The principal axes may also be considered as the orthogonal reference axes on each of which the sum of the squares of the projections of the vectors representing the variables is stationary.*

Employing the geometric ideas of Chapter III, any factor, or reference variable, may be regarded as a unit vector in the common-factor space of m dimensions. In this space the computed variables of the initial pattern are represented by vectors whose lengths are less than unity. Let the reference vectors of the given solution be designated by $F_1, F_2, \ldots, F_m$, and let the projections upon these axes of the vectors representing the variables be denoted by $a_{j1}, a_{j2}, \ldots, a_{jm}, (j = 1, 2, \ldots, n)$. Denote the principal reference vectors by $P_1, P_2, \ldots, P_m$ and their direction cosines with respect to the axes $F_1, F_2, \ldots, F_m$ by

$$(\lambda_{11}, \lambda_{21}, \ldots, \lambda_{m1}) , \qquad (\lambda_{12}, \lambda_{22}, \ldots, \lambda_{m2}), \ldots,$$
$$(\lambda_{1m}, \lambda_{2m}, \ldots, \lambda_{mm}) ,$$

respectively. The problem is to determine the values of these direction cosines so that the transformation from the known solution to a principal-factor solution can be accomplished.

The correlation between any variable z_j and the first principal factor P_1 may be considered as the sum of the paired products of their respective direction cosines multiplied by the lengths of their vectors in the common-factor space. The direction cosines of the vector representing z_j are $(a_{j1}/h_j^2,$ $a_{j2}/h_j^2, \ldots, a_{jm}/h_j^2)$, and the length of this vector is h_j^2. The length of the

---

* For general theorems on maxima and minima see William F. Osgood, *Advanced Calculus*, 1932, Chap. VII.

reference vector representing P_1 is, of course, equal to unity. The desired correlation may then be written simply as follows:

$$(9.1) \quad r_{jP_1} = a_{j1}\lambda_{11} + a_{j2}\lambda_{21} + \ldots + a_{jm}\lambda_{m1} \quad (j = 1, 2, \ldots, n).$$

This expression will give the coefficients p_{j1} $(=r_{jP_1})$ of the first principal factor when the values of the λ's are obtained. Inasmuch as the values p_{j1} are the projections of the variable z_j on the first principal axis, the sum of their squares must be maximized. The expression (9.1) for p_{j1} may be written in condensed form as follows

$$(9.1') \qquad\qquad p_{j1} = \sum_{s=1}^{m} a_{js}\lambda_{s1} \qquad\qquad (j = 1, 2, \ldots, n).$$

Squaring both sides of this expression, and summing over the n variables, yields

$$(9.2) \qquad \sum_{j=1}^{n} p_{j1}^2 = \sum_{j=1}^{n} \left(\sum_{s=1}^{m} a_{js}\lambda_{s1} \right)^2.$$

For convenience, the left-hand member of this expression will be designated by A_1.

The sum of the squares of the projections, A_1, must be maximized under the condition that the sum of the squares of the direction cosines is equal to unity. This condition may be written in the form

$$(9.3) \qquad\qquad B_1 = \sum_{s=1}^{m} \lambda_{s1}^2 - 1 = 0.$$

In maximizing A_1 by the method of Lagrange's multipliers,* the function

$$(9.4) \qquad\qquad 2w = A_1 - \mu B_1$$

is employed. In this expression, μ is a parameter which will be determined in the following analysis. Consider w as a function of the m variables λ_{11}, $\lambda_{21}, \ldots, \lambda_{m1}$, and write the necessary conditions for w to be stationary, namely,

$$(9.5) \qquad \frac{\partial w}{\partial \lambda_{s1}} = \frac{1}{2}\left(\frac{\partial A_1}{\partial \lambda_{s1}} - \mu \frac{\partial B_1}{\partial \lambda_{s1}} \right) = 0 \quad (s = 1, 2, \ldots, m).$$

* Ibid.

Now, the derivative of A_1 with respect to any variable λ_{s1} is given by

$$
(9.6) \quad \begin{cases} \dfrac{\partial A_1}{\partial \lambda_{s1}} = 2 \displaystyle\sum_{j=1}^{n} \left(\sum_{t=1}^{m} a_{jt}\lambda_{t1} \right) a_{js} \\[2em] \qquad\qquad = 2 \displaystyle\sum_{j=1}^{n} a_{js}(a_{j1}\lambda_{11} + a_{j2}\lambda_{21} + \ldots + a_{jm}\lambda_{m1}) , \end{cases}
$$

and the derivative of B_1 is

$$
(9.7) \qquad\qquad \frac{\partial B_1}{\partial \lambda_{s1}} = 2\lambda_{s1} \qquad\qquad (s = 1, 2, \ldots, m) .
$$

Substituting (9.6) and (9.7) in (9.5), the latter conditions may be written explicitly for $s = 1, 2, \ldots, m$, as follows:

$$
(9.8) \quad \begin{cases} \lambda_{11}(\Sigma a_{j1}^2 - \mu) + \lambda_{21}\Sigma a_{j1}a_{j2} \quad + \ldots + \lambda_{m1}\Sigma a_{j1}a_{jm} \quad = 0 , \\ \lambda_{11}\Sigma a_{j2}a_{j1} \quad + \lambda_{21}(\Sigma a_{j2}^2 - \mu) + \ldots + \lambda_{m1}\Sigma a_{j2}a_{jm} \quad = 0 , \\ \quad \cdot \quad \cdot \quad \cdot \quad \cdot \quad \cdot \quad \cdot \quad \cdot \quad \cdot \quad \cdot \quad \cdot \quad \cdot \quad \cdot \quad \cdot \quad \cdot \\ \lambda_{11}\Sigma a_{jm}a_{j1} \quad + \lambda_{21}\Sigma a_{jm}a_{j2} \quad + \ldots + \lambda_{m1}(\Sigma a_{jm}^2 - \mu) = 0 , \end{cases}
$$

where each of the summations extends from $j = 1$ to $j = n$.

A necessary condition for the m equations (9.8) to have solutions (in which not all of the values λ are zero) is the vanishing of the determinant of coefficients. This condition leads to the characteristic equation, which may be written in the form

$$
(9.9) \quad f(\mu) \equiv \begin{vmatrix} (\Sigma a_{j1}^2 - \mu) & \Sigma a_{j1}a_{j2} & \ldots & \Sigma a_{j1}a_{jm} \\ \Sigma a_{j2}a_{j1} & (\Sigma a_{j2}^2 - \mu) & \ldots & \Sigma a_{j2}a_{jm} \\ \cdot \quad \cdot \quad \cdot & \cdot \quad \cdot \quad \cdot & \cdot \quad \cdot & \cdot \quad \cdot \\ \Sigma a_{jm}a_{j1} & \Sigma a_{jm}a_{j2} & \ldots & (\Sigma a_{jm}^2 - \mu) \end{vmatrix} = 0 .
$$

Upon expanding this determinant, this equation can be written as follows:

$$
(9.10) \qquad f(\mu) = \mu^m - c_1\mu^{m-1} + c_2\mu^{m-2} - \ldots (-1)^m c_m = 0 ,
$$

where the c's are positive numbers.* Each of the m roots of this equation can be obtained to any desired degree of accuracy by methods such as those outlined in Appendix F.

Evidently any root μ_s $(s = 1, 2, \ldots, m)$ of (9.10) will make the determinant in (9.9) vanish and yield a solution for the unknowns in (9.8). The solution is labeled $(\lambda_{11}, \lambda_{21}, \ldots, \lambda_{m1})$, however, only in the case that the largest

* See Appen. F.

root μ_1 of (9.10) is employed. When the other roots μ_2, μ_3, $\ldots$, μ_m of (9.10) are employed, the sets of direction cosines $(\lambda_{12}, \lambda_{22}, \ldots, \lambda_{m2}), \ldots, (\lambda_{1m}, \lambda_{2m}, \ldots, \lambda_{mm})$ of the remaining principal axes are obtained. This follows from the preceding form of analysis by a simple substitution of indices. For example, in order to obtain the direction cosines of the second principal axis, all that is necessary is to replace p_{j1}, λ_{s1}, A_1, B_1 by p_{j2}, λ_{s2}, A_2, B_2, respectively, and equations (9.1') to (9.8) follow as before. The new equations (9.8) will be formally identical with the old, except that the unknowns will be $(\lambda_{12}, \lambda_{22}, \ldots, \lambda_{m2})$ instead of $(\lambda_{11}, \lambda_{21}, \ldots, \lambda_{m1})$. The determinant of coefficients, nevertheless, will be the same and the characteristic equation (9.9), or (9.10), will be unchanged.

It is clear, then, that the problem of making any sum of squares, A_1, A_2, $\ldots$, A_m, stationary leads to the same characteristic equation. Thus the direction cosines of the respective principal-factor axes may, in effect, be obtained by employing the roots μ_s $(s = 1, 2, \ldots, m)$ of (9.10) successively in (9.8), changing the second subscript of the λ's in each case to agree with the index of μ.

Furthermore, it can be shown that the roots of the characteristic equation are equal to the respective sums of squares, i.e., $\mu_s = A_s$ $(s = 1, 2, \ldots, m)$. Hence if a root is very small, indicating that the contribution of the corresponding factor is insignificant, the direction cosines of that factor axis need not be obtained.

When all the desired λ's have been determined, it is then possible to transform the given solution to the principal-factor form. The first column of the transformed pattern is given by equation (9.1) in which the direction cosines of the first principal axis are now known. The complete transformation can be exhibited most conveniently in matrix form, as follows:

$$
\begin{Vmatrix} a_{11} & a_{12} & \ldots & a_{1m} \\ a_{21} & a_{22} & \ldots & a_{2m} \\ \cdot & \cdot & \cdot & \cdot \\ a_{n1} & a_{n2} & \ldots & a_{nm} \end{Vmatrix} \cdot \begin{Vmatrix} \lambda_{11} & \lambda_{12} & \ldots & \lambda_{1m} \\ \lambda_{21} & \lambda_{22} & \ldots & \lambda_{2m} \\ \cdot & \cdot & \cdot & \cdot \\ \lambda_{m1} & \lambda_{m2} & \ldots & \lambda_{mm} \end{Vmatrix} = \begin{Vmatrix} p_{11} & p_{12} & \ldots & p_{1m} \\ p_{21} & p_{22} & \ldots & p_{2m} \\ \cdot & \cdot & \cdot & \cdot \\ p_{n1} & p_{n2} & \ldots & p_{nm} \end{Vmatrix}
$$

$$(9.11) \qquad \mathbf{A} \qquad \cdot \qquad \mathbf{T} \qquad = \qquad \mathbf{P}$$

The pattern matrix $\mathbf{A}$ is that of the given solution, $\mathbf{T}$ is the matrix of transformation, and $\mathbf{P}$ is the resulting principal pattern matrix. The multiplication is performed by the conventional row-by-column procedure, i.e., the element p_{jk} is the sum of the paired products of the elements in the jth row of $\mathbf{A}$ by the corresponding elements in the kth column of $\mathbf{T}$. This completes the analysis for obtaining a derived principal-factor solution.

9.3. *Numerical Rotations to the Principal-Factor Form*

When a principal-factor solution is desired, the most economical procedure for obtaining this form is by a rotation of a simply calculated initial solution. The reduction in labor over the direct method of Chapter VII is especially great for a large number of variables. The initial solutions considered for this purpose are the centroid, bi-factor, and averoid patterns.

1. ROTATION FROM CENTROID SOLUTION

In order to illustrate the method of transformation very simply, a set of only eight variables involving two factors will be employed. These data are the physical variables which were analyzed directly into a principal-factor solution in **7.5**. Thus a comparison between the direct and indirect solutions may be made. The centroid pattern of these variables, which is given in Table 8.3, is taken as the initial solution for purposes of rotation. This pattern may be exhibited as follows:

$$\mathbf{C} = \begin{Vmatrix} & C_1 & C_2 \\ & .830 & -.396 \\ & .818 & -.469 \\ & .777 & -.470 \\ & .798 & -.401 \\ & .786 & .500 \\ & .672 & .458 \\ & .594 & .444 \\ & .647 & .333 \end{Vmatrix},$$

where $\mathbf{C}$ is used to denote the centroid pattern matrix, and C_1, C_2 represent the centroid factors whose coefficients appear in the columns.

In the process of obtaining the matrix of transformation, a characteristic equation of the form (9.9) is involved. For the given data the elements appearing in the characteristic equation are the sums of the squares of the elements in the respective columns of $\mathbf{C}$, and the sum of the paired-products of the corresponding elements in the two columns, as follows:

$$\sum_{j=1}^{8} a_{j1}^2 = 4.4394, \qquad \sum_{j=1}^{8} a_{j1}a_{j2} = -.2175, \qquad \sum_{j=1}^{8} a_{j2}^2 = 1.5263.$$

The characteristic equation may then be written in the form

$$(9.12) \qquad f(\mu) \equiv \begin{vmatrix} (4.4394 - \mu) & -.2175 \\ -.2175 & (1.5263 - \mu) \end{vmatrix} = 0,$$

or

$$f(\mu) \equiv \mu^2 - 5.9657\mu + 6.7285 = 0 .$$

The two roots of this quadratic equation are readily found to be

$$\mu_1 = 4.4556 , \qquad \mu_2 = 1.5102 .$$

Employing the larger root, the direction cosines of the first principal-factor axis can be obtained by means of equations (9.8), as follows:

(9.13)
$$\begin{cases} -.0162\lambda_{11} - .2175\lambda_{21} = 0 , \\ -.2175\lambda_{11} - 2.9293\lambda_{21} = 0 . \end{cases}$$

In order to obtain unique solutions for the two unknowns λ_{11}, λ_{21}, it is necessary to employ the auxiliary condition (9.3), which in this case is simply

(9.14)
$$\lambda_{11}^2 + \lambda_{21}^2 = 1 .$$

The two homogeneous equations (9.13) have a matrix of coefficients of rank one, as is evident from (9.12), and so one of these equations may be used to solve for one unknown in terms of the other. This solution will also satisfy the second equation.* From the first of equations (9.13), the solution

(9.15)
$$\lambda_{11} = -13.43\lambda_{21}$$

is obtained, which gives an infinite number of values λ_{11} corresponding to arbitrary values of λ_{21}. To obtain a determinate solution, the condition (9.14) is now employed, yielding

$$(-13.43\lambda_{21})^2 + \lambda_{21}^2 = 1 ,$$

or

$$\lambda_{21} = \pm.07426 .$$

Substituting this value in (9.15) gives

$$\lambda_{11} = \mp.9973 ,$$

where the minus sign is associated with the positive value of λ_{21} and vice versa. The positive sign will be taken for the larger direction cosine for convenience, i.e., $\lambda_{11} = .9973$, $\lambda_{21} = -.0743$.

The second root, $\mu_2 = 1.5102$, is next employed in order to determine the direction cosines of the second principal-factor axis. Substitution of μ_2 for μ

* L. E. Dickson, *Modern Algebraic Theories*, p. 61.

in (9.8), and replacing the second subscript on the λ's by 2, gives the following pair of simultaneous homogeneous equations:

$$(9.16) \qquad \begin{cases} 2.9292\lambda_{12} - .2175\lambda_{22} = 0 , \\ -.2175\lambda_{12} + .0161\lambda_{22} = 0 . \end{cases}$$

The solution of these equations, under the restriction

$$\lambda_{12}^2 + \lambda_{22}^2 = 1 ,$$

is $\lambda_{12} = .0740$, $\lambda_{22} = .9972$.

The direction cosines having been determined, the matrix of transformation can be written as follows:

$$\mathbf{T}_C = \left\| \begin{array}{cc} .9973 & .0740 \\ -.0743 & .9972 \end{array} \right\| .$$

Then, upon multiplying the centroid pattern matrix $\mathbf{C}$ by $\mathbf{T}_C$, the following principal pattern matrix is obtained:

$$\mathbf{P}_C = \begin{array}{cc} P_1 & P_2 \end{array}$$

$$\mathbf{P}_C = \left\| \begin{array}{cc} .857 & -.333 \\ .851 & -.407 \\ .810 & -.411 \\ .826 & -.341 \\ .747 & .557 \\ .636 & .506 \\ .559 & .487 \\ .621 & .380 \end{array} \right\| .$$

It will be noted that there was an ambiguity in choice of algebraic signs in the determination of the direction cosines of the principal-factor axes. The effect of choosing a particular set of signs may now be indicated. If the signs of the direction cosines of a principal axis are changed, the elements of the corresponding column in the matrix $\mathbf{P}_C$ are changed in sign. The adequacy of the solution is not changed, however, by the reversal of all the signs in a column of a pattern matrix, as pointed out in **2.5**.

The derived principal-factor pattern, the coefficients of which are given in the matrix $\mathbf{P}_C$, agrees very closely with the solution obtained directly in Chapter VII and exhibited in Table 7.4. The coefficients of the first factor in the two cases have a maximum discrepancy of only .002, while the coefficients of the second factor have a maximum difference of .009.

2. ROTATION FROM BI-FACTOR SOLUTION

An example will be presented now in which a derived principal-factor solution is obtained from an initial bi-factor pattern. The illustration is for the same set of eight physical variables which were just employed in passing from a centroid solution to a principal-pattern. It will be evident then that the derived solution from either of these initial patterns is essentially the same as the principal-factor solution obtained directly in Chapter VII.

The bi-factor pattern matrix for the eight physical variables is taken from Table 7.2 and may be written as follows:

$$B = \begin{Vmatrix} B_0 & B_1 & B_2 \\ .691 & .614 & 0 \\ .591 & .740 & 0 \\ .581 & .704 & 0 \\ .598 & .652 & 0 \\ .694 & 0 & .623 \\ .611 & 0 & .560 \\ .562 & 0 & .453 \\ .596 & 0 & .473 \end{Vmatrix}.$$

For these data the characteristic equation (9.9) takes the form

$$(9.17) \quad f(\mu) \equiv \begin{vmatrix} (3.0479 - \mu) & 1.6605 & 1.3110 \\ 1.6605 & (1.8453 - \mu) & 0 \\ 1.3110 & 0 & (1.1307 - \mu) \end{vmatrix} = 0.$$

In the determinant of the characteristic equation arising from a bi-factor pattern there will generally be zeros for the elements off the diagonal, except for those in the first row and column. This property holds true when the subsets of variables measuring the group factors are distinct. When there is some overlap of group factors, then some small values will appear for these elements.

Upon expansion of the determinant in (9.17), the characteristic equation may be written

$$(9.18) \qquad f(\mu) = \mu^3 - 6.0239\mu^2 + 6.6810\mu - .0701 = 0.$$

This equation may be solved by the methods of Appendix F, yielding the three roots

$$(9.19) \qquad \begin{cases} \mu_1 = 4.5631, \\ \mu_2 = 1.4502, \\ \mu_3 = .0106. \end{cases}$$

Then, substituting the largest root for μ in equations (9.8), the following three equations arise:

$$(9.20) \quad \begin{cases} -1.5152\lambda_{01} + 1.6605\lambda_{11} + 1.3110\lambda_{21} = 0 \,, \\ 1.6605\lambda_{01} - 2.7178\lambda_{11} \qquad\qquad = 0 \,, \\ 1.3110\lambda_{01} \qquad\qquad - 3.4324\lambda_{21} = 0 \,, \end{cases}$$

where the direction cosines of the first principal axis with respect to the three bi-factor axes are denoted by λ_{01}, λ_{11}, λ_{21}. The solution for λ_{01}, λ_{11}, λ_{21} is subject to the restriction

$$(9.21) \qquad\qquad \lambda_{01}^2 + \lambda_{11}^2 + \lambda_{21}^2 = 1 \,.$$

The last two of equations (9.20) may be considered as linearly independent, and the variables λ_{11}, λ_{21} solved in terms of λ_{01}. The resulting expressions may be written

$$\lambda_{11} = \frac{1.6605\lambda_{01}}{2.7178} = .61097\lambda_{01} \quad \text{and} \quad \lambda_{21} = \frac{1.3110\lambda_{01}}{3.4324} = .38195\lambda_{01} \,.$$

By making use of the condition (9.21), the direction cosines of the first principal-factor axis are found to be

$$\lambda_{01} = .8113 \,, \qquad \lambda_{11} = .4957, \qquad \text{and} \qquad \lambda_{21} = .3099 \,.$$

The direction cosines of the second principal axis are similarly obtained, the values being

$$\lambda_{02} = .1678 \,, \qquad \lambda_{12} = -.7053 \,, \qquad \text{and} \qquad \lambda_{22} = .6888 \,.$$

It will be observed that the third root of the characteristic equation, $\mu_3 = .0106$, is very small in comparison with the others. Inasmuch as this value is equal to the contribution of the third principal factor, this factor will not be obtained because of its insignificance.[*]

The two sets of direction cosines are recorded in the following matrix of transformation:

$$\mathbf{T}_B = \left\| \begin{matrix} .8113 & .1678 \\ .4957 & -.7053 \\ .3099 & .6888 \end{matrix} \right\| \,.$$

[*] Precise methods for determining the significance of principal factors are given by Harold Hotelling, "Analysis of a Complex of Statistical Variables into Principal Components," *Journal of Educational Psychology*, 1933, pp. 417–42.

By multiplying the bi-factor pattern matrix $\mathbf{B}$ by $\mathbf{T}_B$, the derived principal-factor pattern matrix is obtained, as follows:

$$\mathbf{P}_B = \begin{Vmatrix} & P_1 & P_2 \\ & .865 & -.317 \\ & .846 & -.423 \\ & .820 & -.399 \\ & .808 & -.360 \\ & .756 & .546 \\ & .669 & .488 \\ & .596 & .406 \\ & .630 & .426 \end{Vmatrix}.$$

It may be observed that the principal-factor pattern derived from the bi-factor solution agrees very closely with the direct solution given in Table 7.4. The sum of the contributions of the derived principal factors P_1 and P_2 is 6.011, or 99.8 per cent of the total original communality used in obtaining the direct solution. The slight discrepancies between the derived and direct principal-factor patterns are due to the fact that the total communality of the latter solution did not agree exactly with the original communality, which the former solution reproduces.

From the foregoing illustrations, it is apparent that a principal-factor form of solution may be derived from either a centroid pattern based upon good estimates of communalities or a bi-factor pattern. If the communalities of two initial solutions are the same, then the derived solutions will agree. Such agreement is illustrated by the two derived matrices $\mathbf{P}_C$ and $\mathbf{P}_B$, the minor discrepancies being due to the slight variations in the communalities calculated in the initial solutions. In case no initial solution of the preceding type is available and a principal-factor solution is desired, a preliminary pattern such as the averoid may be employed. A derived principal-factor solution may be considered as appropriate provided it is based upon any initial pattern which is statistically adequate.

3. ROTATION FROM AVEROID SOLUTION

To illustrate the method of rotation to a principal-factor pattern for a fairly large set of variables, the twenty-four psychological tests are employed. After obtaining such a derived solution for these variables, it may be compared with the first two principal factors which were obtained directly and are given in Table 7.5. Although both a bi-factor and a centroid solution are available for these data, the present analysis will be based upon the averoid solution of Table 8.10. The averoid was selected as the initial form of solution in order to indicate the procedure when good estimates of the communalities are not available. The total time required to calculate a direct principal-factor solution for these data was estimated to be two hundred hours, while the time required for the computation of the averoid solution and the subsequent rotation was about twenty-five hours. The economy of labor for a set of variables of this size is clearly evident.

The necessary sums for the characteristic equation (9.9) are calculated from the averoid pattern of Table 8.10, producing

$$(9.22) \quad f(\mu) \equiv \begin{vmatrix} (7.4406 - \mu) & -.3136 & -.2753 & .0360 \\ -.3136 & (1.3950 - \mu) & .0413 & -.3222 \\ -.2753 & .0413 & (1.0987 - \mu) & -.0917 \\ .0360 & -.3222 & -.0917 & (1.0799 - \mu) \end{vmatrix} = 0 \,.$$

This determinant can be expanded most simply by Laplace's development by columns,* using the first two columns as a base, and then the characteristic equation becomes

$$(9.23) \quad f(\mu) = \mu^4 - 11.0142\mu^3 + 30.5260\mu^2 - 31.7349\mu + 11.1727 = 0 \,.$$

The complete procedure for the transformation from the averoid pattern to the principal-factor form is described in Appendixes F and G. In the first of these appendixes a general method for calculating the roots of a polynomial of any degree is presented. As an illustration of this method, the roots of the characteristic equation of the present example are evaluated. There are four roots in this case so that four sets of equations of the form (9.8) arise. The solution of such sets of simultaneous equations is presented in Appendix G.2, in which the data of this example are used again as an illustration. The derived principal-factor pattern is given in Table 9.1.

Since the axes representing the derived principal factors are obtained by rotation of an initial set of axes in a fixed common-factor space, the calculated communalities in the two cases are, of course, the same. This agreement may be seen by comparing the corresponding values of Tables 8.10 and 9.1. It then follows that the total contributions of these two sets of factors must be equal, which is again evident from these tables. As would

* See, e.g., L. E. Dickson, *First Course in the Theory of Equations*, p. 122.

be expected, however, the contributions of the individual factors are allocated differently.

The coefficients of the first two factors of the above pattern may be compared with the corresponding values of the direct solution given in Table

TABLE 9.1

DERIVED PRINCIPAL-FACTOR PATTERN FOR TWENTY-FOUR
PSYCHOLOGICAL TESTS (BASED UPON THE
AVEROID PATTERN OF TABLE 8.10)

TEST	COMMON FACTORS				CALCULATED COMMUNALITY
	General	Verbal Rigidity	Spatial	Memory	
j	P_1	P_2	P_3	P_4	h_j^2
1.........	.588	$-$ .079	.350	$-$.174	.505
2.........	.371	$-$ .047	.273	$-$.153	.238
3.........	.421	.109	.321	$-$.083	.299
4.........	.480	.087	.298	$-$.132	.344
5.........	.682	.309	$-$ .252	$-$.120	.639
6.........	.676	.396	$-$ .182	.009	.647
7.........	.661	.427	$-$ .259	$-$.092	.695
8.........	.676	.193	$-$ .079	$-$.131	.518
9.........	.676	.457	$-$ .151	.043	.690
10.........	.442	$-$ .449	$-$ .425	$-$.118	.592
11.........	.553	$-$ .312	$-$ .285	.063	.488
12.........	.453	$-$ .454	$-$ .089	$-$.270	.492
13.........	.594	$-$ .323	$-$ .041	$-$.271	.532
14.........	.422	$-$ .000	$-$ .071	.407	.349
15.........	.388	$-$ .053	.024	.367	.289
16.........	.506	$-$ .089	.259	.210	.375
17.........	.459	$-$ .170	$-$ .091	.382	.394
18.........	.512	$-$ .319	.151	.226	.438
19.........	.443	$-$ .142	.086	.125	.239
20.........	.615	.116	.161	.062	.421
21.........	.591	$-$ .230	.082	$-$.091	.417
22.........	.608	.085	.174	.054	.410
23.........	.688	.068	.183	$-$.049	.514
24.........	.648	$-$ .183	$-$ .179	.007	.485
Contribution of factor..	7.467	1.591	1.093	.859	....

7.5. The agreement of the individual coefficients is remarkably close in the case of both factors, and the total contributions of the respective factors are practically the same. It would therefore appear that a very close approximation to the principal-factor solution calculated directly from the correlations can be obtained by the preceding rotational method. From the foregoing discussion it would appear that, if a principal-factor pattern is desired for a large set of variables, a satisfactory solution can be obtained effectively by rotation of an initial averoid pattern.

Since the first two factors agree with those obtained by the direct analysis, they may be named "General" and "Verbal Rigidity," as in **7.5.** The third factor has been designated as "Spatial" because the largest positive coefficients appear for spatial tests. This factor might also have been named "Spatial-Speed" because of the negative coefficients for the speed tests. The last factor has been called "Memory" because of the consistent positive weights for the six memory tests.

CHAPTER X

ORTHOGONAL TRANSFORMATIONS AND THE MULTIPLE-FACTOR SOLUTION

10.1. *Introduction*

In the preceding chapter rotations from simple initial patterns to the principal-factor form were discussed. Such rotations were expressed completely in analytical form because of the exact mathematical properties of the principal-factor solution. Other preferred types of solution may not be defined in such precise mathematical terms. The transformation of an initial pattern to a preferred type such as the multiple-factor solution, therefore, cannot be developed directly as in Chapter IX but must be constructed somewhat subjectively. The guiding principles in formulating such a transformation are given by the criteria set forth in Table 5.1.

Before considering the applications of transformations to factor analysis, the theoretical development of orthogonal rotations is first presented. In **10.2** the rotations in the plane are developed and are used as the basis of the rotations in three- and higher dimensional spaces in **10.3** and **10.4**. Specific application to the multiple-factor form of solution is made in **10.5**. Other types of transformations leading to multiple-factor solutions are available[*] but will not be treated in the present work. Multiple-factor patterns are obtained for the eight physical variables, the thirteen psychological tests, and the complete set of twenty-four tests. In the first and third of these illustrations the centroid is used as the initial solution, whereas for the second example the averoid solution is employed.

10.2. *Rotations in a Plane*

When an initial factor pattern involves only two factors, the variables may be represented as points in a plane, with the coefficients of the factors as the coordinates. Then a transformation to some other form of solution implies the representation of these points with respect to the axes denoting the new factors. Inasmuch as the origin is assumed to be fixed, such a transformation is merely a rotation of axes in this common-factor space. The transformations considered in this chapter are orthogonal, and hence final patterns involve uncorrelated factors.

---

[*] See, e.g., L. L. Thurstone, "A New Rotational Method in Factor Analysis," *Psychometrika*, 1938.

In deriving an orthogonal transformation in the plane, the required terms may be indicated conveniently as follows:

$F_1, F_2 \equiv$ axes representing the original factors,
$\quad P_j \equiv$ point representing variable z_j $(j = 1, 2, \ldots, n)$,
$a_{j1}, a_{j2} \equiv$ coordinates of P_j with respect to F_1, F_2, i.e., the coefficients in the original factor pattern,
$M_1, M_2 \equiv$ axes representing the final factors,
$\quad b_{j1}, b_{j2} \equiv$ coordinates of P_j with respect to M_1, M_2, i.e., the coefficients in the final factor pattern,
$\quad\quad \theta \equiv$ angle of rotation from original to final axes.

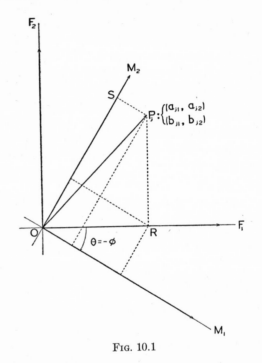

Fig. 10.1

Employing the above notation, any variable may be represented by a point P_j, referred to either system of reference F_1, F_2 or M_1, M_2, as shown in Figure 10.1. The problem is to express the coordinates (b_{j1}, b_{j2}) in terms of the original coordinates (a_{j1}, a_{j2}). This is equivalent to obtaining the final factor pattern from the initial one.

The required transformation is accomplished by making use of the following property on projections of lines: the sum of the projections upon a straight line of the segments of any broken line connecting two points is equal to the corresponding sum for any other broken line connecting the same two points. The points O and P_j are joined by two broken lines, namely, ORP_j and OSP_j. It follows that the projections of these broken lines along any direction are equal:

$$(10.1) \qquad \text{Proj. } OR + \text{Proj. } RP_j = \text{Proj. } OS + \text{Proj. } SP_j.$$

If the direction is taken, first, as the positive axis of M_1 and, second, as the positive axis of M_2, the resulting expressions are

$$(10.2) \qquad \begin{cases} OR \cos \theta - RP_j \sin \theta = 0 + SP_j, \\ OR \sin \theta + RP_j \cos \theta = OS + 0, \end{cases}$$

Now, employing the definitions of the coordinates,

$$OR = a_{j1}, \qquad RP_j = a_{j2}, \qquad SP_j = b_{j1}, \qquad OS = b_{j2},$$

the result may finally be written in the form

$$(10.3) \qquad \begin{cases} b_{j1} = a_{j1} \cos \theta - a_{j2} \sin \theta, \\ b_{j2} = a_{j1} \sin \theta + a_{j2} \cos \theta, \end{cases}$$

in which the angle θ is negative. There are n such sets of equations corresponding to the number of variables.

In the above analysis it was convenient to take θ negative in order to get direct expressions for the final coordinates in terms of the original ones. If this angle θ is denoted by $-\phi$, then formulas (10.3) become

$$(10.4) \qquad \begin{cases} b_{j1} = a_{j1} \cos \phi + a_{j2} \sin \phi, \\ b_{j2} = -a_{j1} \sin \phi + a_{j2} \cos \phi. \end{cases}$$

It may be noted that these formulas reduce to (10.3) if the angle ϕ is negative. Hence (10.4) may be taken as the general equations of transformation. This transformation may also be expressed in matrix notation, as follows:

$$(10.5) \qquad \|b_{j1} \quad b_{j2}\| = \|a_{j1} \quad a_{j2}\| \cdot \left\| \begin{matrix} \cos \phi & -\sin \phi \\ \sin \phi & \cos \phi \end{matrix} \right\|,$$

or

$$(10.6) \qquad \mathbf{M} = \mathbf{AT},$$

where $\mathbf{M}$ is the $n \times 2$ matrix of final factor coefficients, $\mathbf{A}$ is the $n \times 2$ matrix of initial factor coefficients, and $\mathbf{T}$ is the 2×2 matrix of the transformation. Formulas (10.4) express the new coordinates (b_{j1}, b_{j2}) as functions of the old coordinates (a_{j1}, a_{j2}), involving only one parameter ϕ. Thus, when a value is assigned to ϕ, the final factor pattern can be obtained. The manner in which such an angle of rotation is selected is demonstrated in **10.5**.

To illustrate the analytical properties of orthogonal transformations, the foregoing equations may be written in the general form (3.16) as a set of linear homogeneous equations:

$$(10.7) \qquad \begin{cases} b_{j1} = \lambda_{11} a_{j1} + \lambda_{21} a_{j2} \, , \\ b_{j2} = \lambda_{12} a_{j1} + \lambda_{22} a_{j2} \, , \end{cases}$$

where the λ's are the coefficients expressed in terms of the angle ϕ. These coefficients, by rows, are the direction cosines of M_1 and M_2 with respect to the original axes F_1 and F_2 and are conveniently indicated in tabular form as follows:

	F_1	F_2
M_1	$\lambda_{11} = \quad \cos \phi$	$\lambda_{21} = \sin \phi$
M_2	$\lambda_{12} = -\sin \phi$	$\lambda_{22} = \cos \phi$

Inasmuch as the direction cosines satisfy the conditions (analogous to eq. [3.15])

$$\lambda_{11}^2 + \lambda_{21}^2 = 1, \qquad \lambda_{11}\lambda_{12} + \lambda_{21}\lambda_{22} = 0, \qquad \text{and} \qquad \lambda_{12}^2 + \lambda_{22}^2 = 1 \, ,$$

it is clear that (10.7) represents an orthogonal transformation.

Besides enabling the analyst to rotate one solution involving two factors to another, the above type of transformation forms the basis of the analysis for a solution including several factors. It will be shown that a transformation in higher dimensional space may be reduced to successive rotations in planes.

10.3. *Rotations in Three-Space*

In the case of three factors the transformation from an initial to a final pattern may be exhibited as follows:

$$(10.8) \qquad \begin{cases} b_{j1} = \lambda_{11} a_{j1} + \lambda_{21} a_{j2} + \lambda_{31} a_{j3} \, , \\ b_{j2} = \lambda_{12} a_{j1} + \lambda_{22} a_{j2} + \lambda_{32} a_{j3} \, , \\ b_{j3} = \lambda_{13} a_{j1} + \lambda_{23} a_{j2} + \lambda_{33} a_{j3} \, , \end{cases}$$

where the notation of **10.2** has been extended to an additional factor. The transformation (10.8) may again be expressed in matrix form

$$(10.9) \qquad \mathbf{M} = \mathbf{AT} \, ,$$

where, now, $\mathbf{M}$ is $n \times 3$, $\mathbf{A}$ is $n \times 3$, and $\mathbf{T}$ is 3×3.

The elements of **T** are direction cosines which must satisfy the six independent conditions

$$\lambda_{11}^2 + \lambda_{21}^2 + \lambda_{31}^2 = 1 ,$$
$$\lambda_{12}^2 + \lambda_{22}^2 + \lambda_{32}^2 = 1 ,$$
$$\lambda_{13}^2 + \lambda_{23}^2 + \lambda_{33}^2 = 1 ,$$
$$\lambda_{11}\lambda_{12} + \lambda_{21}\lambda_{22} + \lambda_{31}\lambda_{32} = 0 ,$$
$$\lambda_{11}\lambda_{13} + \lambda_{21}\lambda_{23} + \lambda_{31}\lambda_{33} = 0 ,$$
$$\lambda_{12}\lambda_{13} + \lambda_{22}\lambda_{23} + \lambda_{32}\lambda_{33} = 0 .$$

Each of these equations is an instance of the following general expression:

$$\lambda_{1s}\lambda_{1t} + \lambda_{2s}\lambda_{2t} + \lambda_{3s}\lambda_{3t} = \delta_{st} \qquad (s, t = 1, 2, 3, \ s \leqq t) ,$$

which may be written compactly in the form

(10.10)
$$\sum_{u=1}^{3} \lambda_{us}\lambda_{ut} = \delta_{st} \qquad (s, t = 1, 2, 3, \ s \leqq t) ,$$

where δ_{st} is the Kronecker δ which is equal to unity if $s = t$ and equal to zero if $s \neq t$. Thus the nine coefficients of (10.8), being subject to six conditions, afford only three degrees of freedom of rotation in ordinary space. Explicit equations for the b's in terms of the a's, involving only three independent parameters can be obtained.* Since such equations are not employed in practical analyses, they are not exhibited here.

A form of transformation that is not only practical but which can be readily generalized to any number of factors will now be discussed. The fundamental principle underlying this method is that the result of successive orthogonal transformations is itself an orthogonal transformation. This final transformation is said to be the *product* of the successive rotations. Since a planar rotation is the simplest type, a transformation in three-space is built up from rotations of essentially this form. Thus a transformation in ordinary space may involve the displacement of any two axes about the third, being, in effect, a rotation in a plane. Finally, a product of such rotations may be taken as the complete transformation.

The rotations can be arranged in a systematic order so that each axis is rotated with every other axis only once. The three rotations of pairs of axes in ordinary space may be indicated conveniently in the following manner:

Old Axes	Angle of Rotation	New Axes
F_1F_2	θ_{12}	Y_1Y_2
Y_1F_3	θ_{13}	M_1Y_3
Y_2Y_3	θ_{23}	M_2M_3

* Virgil Snyder and C. H. Sisam, *Analytic Geometry of Space*, 1914, p. 42.

It will be noted that the angle of rotation is denoted by θ with subscripts corresponding to the numbers of the axes involved in the rotation. The first rotation is made in the plane of F_1 and F_2, leaving F_3 unaltered. The new axes in this plane are designated by Y_1 and Y_2. Since F_3 is perpendicular to the plane of F_1 and F_2, it is perpendicular to any line in this plane. In particular, F_3 is perpendicular to the new axis Y_1. The next rotation is made in the plane of Y_1 and F_3, leaving Y_2 unchanged. The new first axis, denoted by M_1, may be regarded as final because it is the result of rotations with each of the other axes. The last rotation transforms Y_2 and Y_3 into the final coordinate axes M_2 and M_3. It will be observed that the Y's are merely auxiliary axes and, taken alone, do not form an orthogonal system. Both sets of axes Y_1, Y_2, F_3 and M_1, Y_2, Y_3 are orthogonal, and either one may be taken, in some instances, as the final reference system. The solution ordinarily desired, however, is one based upon the complete transformation of the original axes F_1, F_2, F_3 to the final M_1, M_2, M_3.

Denoting the matrix of transformation of F_1 and F_2, leaving F_3 unchanged, by

$$\mathbf{T}_{12} = \left\| \begin{array}{ccc} \cos \theta_{12} & -\sin \theta_{12} & 0 \\ \sin \theta_{12} & \cos \theta_{12} & 0 \\ 0 & 0 & 1 \end{array} \right\| ,$$

the first of the above rotations may be denoted by

(10.11) $$\mathbf{Y} = \mathbf{AT}_{12} ,$$

where $\mathbf{A}$ is the initial pattern matrix and $\mathbf{Y}$ is an intermediate matrix of coordinates with respect to Y_1, Y_2, F_3. The second and third rotations may be designated similarly, as follows:

(10.12) $$\mathbf{Z} = \mathbf{YT}_{13}$$

and

(10.13) $$\mathbf{M} = \mathbf{ZT}_{23} ,$$

where $\mathbf{Z}$ is another intermediate matrix, $\mathbf{M}$ is the final matrix of coordinates, and

$$\mathbf{T}_{13} = \left\| \begin{array}{ccc} \cos \theta_{13} & 0 & -\sin \theta_{13} \\ 0 & 1 & 0 \\ \sin \theta_{13} & 0 & \cos \theta_{13} \end{array} \right\| , \qquad \mathbf{T}_{23} = \left\| \begin{array}{ccc} 1 & 0 & 0 \\ 0 & \cos \theta_{23} & -\sin \theta_{23} \\ 0 & \sin \theta_{23} & \cos \theta_{23} \end{array} \right\| .$$

The three preceding rotations may be combined into a single transformation. Substituting (10.12) for $\mathbf{Z}$ in (10.13) gives

$$\mathbf{M} = \mathbf{YT}_{13}\mathbf{T}_{23} ,$$

and substituting (10.11) for $\mathbf{Y}$ in the last equation yields

(10.14) $$\mathbf{M} = \mathbf{AT}_{12}\mathbf{T}_{13}\mathbf{T}_{23}.$$

Denoting the product of the three successive rotations by

(10.15) $$\mathbf{T} = \mathbf{T}_{12}\mathbf{T}_{13}\mathbf{T}_{23},$$

the expression (10.14) reduces to (10.9). In practice this matrix $\mathbf{T}$ cannot be obtained directly, but the final pattern is calculated by means of the successive rotations. When each of the partial transformations has been obtained, however, the complete product matrix $\mathbf{T}$ may be recorded and used as a check on the coefficients of the final factors.

10.4. *Rotations in Higher Dimensional Space*

The preceding methods can now be generalized to a common-factor space of m dimensions. In this space let the initial pattern matrix be denoted by

$$\mathbf{A} = \|a_{js}\| \qquad (j = 1, 2, \ldots, n; \ s = 1, 2, \ldots, m)$$

and the final matrix by

$$\mathbf{M} = \|b_{js}\| \qquad (j = 1, 2, \ldots, n; \ s = 1, 2, \ldots, m).$$

Then the transformation from the initial to the final pattern may be expressed as follows:

(10.16) $$b_{js} = \sum_{u=1}^{m} \lambda_{us} a_{ju}$$

$$(j = 1, 2, \ldots, n; \ s = 1, 2, \ldots, m)$$

or in the equivalent matrix form

(10.17) $$\mathbf{M} = \mathbf{AT},$$

where the matrix of transformation is now

$$\mathbf{T} = \begin{Vmatrix} \lambda_{11} & \lambda_{12} & \ldots & \lambda_{1m} \\ \lambda_{21} & \lambda_{22} & \ldots & \lambda_{2m} \\ \cdot & \cdot & \cdot & \ldots & \cdot & \cdot \\ \lambda_{m1} & \lambda_{m2} & \ldots & \lambda_{mm} \end{Vmatrix}.$$

The sets of λ's, by columns, are the direction cosines of the final reference axes $M_1, M_2, \ldots, M_m$ with respect to the original axes $F_1, F_2, \ldots, F_m$.

These direction cosines are subject to the following set of independent conditions for orthogonality of the matrix $\mathbf{T}$ (see **3.5**):

$$(10.18) \qquad \sum_{u=1}^{m} \lambda_{us}\lambda_{ut} = \delta_{st} \qquad \binom{s,\, t = 1,\, 2,\, \ldots,\, m}{s \leq t}.$$

Since $s \leq t$ and these indices range from 1 to m, the number of such conditions is $\binom{m}{2} + m$ or $m(m + 1)/2$. There is a total of m^2 parameters in matrix $\mathbf{T}$, and, since these are subject to $m(m + 1)/2$ restrictions, there remain

$$(10.19) \qquad m^2 - \frac{m(m + 1)}{2} = \frac{m(m - 1)}{2}$$

degrees of freedom of rotation in m-space. The number of independent parameters given in (10.19) may be associated with the same number of rotations in planes. The planes in which the rotations are made are determined by all possible pairs of reference axes. These rotations then involve $\binom{m}{2}$ angles corresponding to the number of independent parameters.

As in the case of three variables, the above rotations may be organized in a systematic manner. For example, when four factors are involved, the scheme may be indicated as follows:

Old Axes	Angle of Rotation	New Axes
$F_1 F_2$	θ_{12}	$Y_1 Y_2$
$Y_1 F_3$	θ_{13}	$Z_1 Y_3$
$Z_1 F_4$	θ_{14}	$M_1 Y_4$
$Y_2 Y_3$	θ_{23}	$Z_2 Z_3$
$Z_2 Y_4$	θ_{24}	$M_2 Z_4$
$Z_3 Z_4$	θ_{34}	$M_3 M_4$

10.5. *Applications to the Multiple-Factor Solution*

In obtaining a multiple-factor solution, the reference axes are chosen in conformity with the discussion in **5.6**. It is first necessary that the initial solution shall satisfy the criteria of composition of variables, parsimony of factors, and uncorrelated factors. Then an orthogonal rotation of such an initial pattern, in its common-factor space, will preserve these properties. The purpose of the transformation is to obtain a final pattern which also satisfies the criteria of low complexity, level contributions of factors, and hyperplanar fit (i.e., as many zeros as possible in the columns).

Although any pattern with uncorrelated factors could be used as the initial solution from which to rotate to a multiple-factor pattern, in the present treatment only centroid and averoid initial patterns are considered. The procedure is begun by plotting the points representing the variables in the plane of the first two initial factors F_1 and F_2. Since in an initial solution of the centroid form the second factor has both positive and negative weights, the points will lie in the first and fourth quadrants (see Fig. 10.6). The first rotation is then made through an angle θ_{12} such that all variables will have positive projections on the new axes Y_1, Y_2. Usually the angle θ_{12} so selected will be about $-45°$. Then, by applying equations of the type (10.4), the coordinates with respect to Y_1 and Y_2 are obtained. The next rotation is made in the plane of Y_1 and F_3 as indicated in the scheme exhibited in **10.4.** The angle θ_{13} is obtained again by inspection of the graph. The new reference axis Z_1 should pass near a cluster of points while at the same time the other axis Y_3 also should be near some other points. The variables represented by the first cluster of points will have high positive weights for the Z_1 factor, and the variables given by the second set of points will have low weights for this factor. Additional rotations may be made according to the outline given in **10.4.** It will be evident from the following examples that the above procedure yields a final solution which agrees with the criteria of low complexity, level contributions of factors, and hyperplanar fit.

1. EIGHT PHYSICAL VARIABLES

The first illustration of a multiple-factor solution is based upon the centroid pattern of the eight physical variables, given in Table 8.4. The coefficients in this pattern are the coordinates, with respect to the two centroid axes, of the eight points representing the variables. The plot of these points is given in Figure 10.2, in which it is apparent that the points fall into two distinct clusters. If two lines were passed through these clusters of points, they would produce excellent geometric fit to the data. Such axes, however, are not orthogonal and therefore not appropriate for the present method. The case of correlated factors will be treated in the next chapter.

If one axis is passed through a cluster and the other orthogonal to it, the standard of uncorrelated factors is met, but other standards are not well satisfied. Thus if an axis M_1' is passed through the first four points, the other axis M_2' will be far removed from the second cluster. The coefficients of such new factors would have the following properties:

Variables	Coefficients of M_1'	Coefficients of M_2'
1, 2, 3, 4	Very high	Near zero
5, 6, 7, 8	Fairly high	High

The first four variables would be of complexity one while the last four would be of complexity two. Variables 5–8 would not satisfy the criterion of low complexity for the present example involving only two factors.

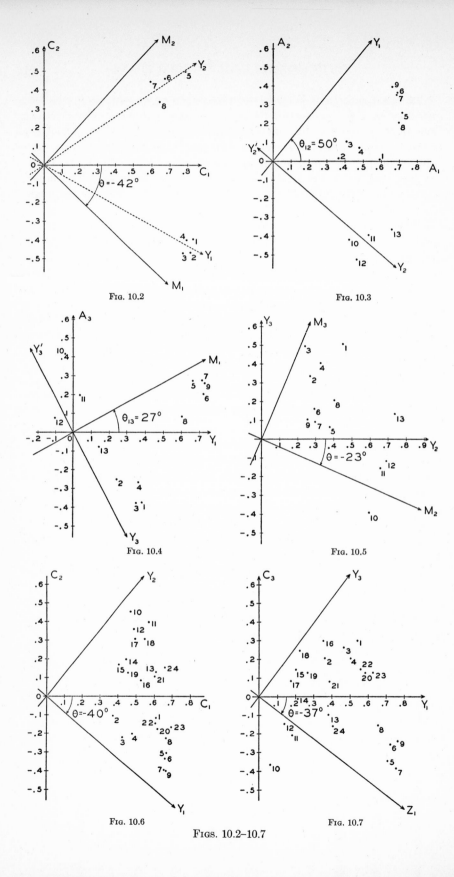

FIG. 10.2

FIG. 10.3

FIG. 10.4

FIG. 10.5

FIG. 10.6

FIG. 10.7

FIGS. 10.2–10.7

In an attempt to meet the basic standards for a multiple-factor pattern, the axes M_1 and M_2 are selected so as to be about equally removed from the two clusters of points. By inspection the resulting angle of rotation is taken to be $\theta_{12} = -42°$. Another worker, of course, might select a slightly different angle. The necessary trigonometric functions are

$$\cos(-42°) = .7431, \qquad \sin(-42°) = -.6691.$$

Substituting these values in equations (10.4), there results

(10.20)
$$\begin{cases} b_{j1} = .7431a_{j1} - .6691a_{j2}, \\ b_{j2} = .6691a_{j1} + .7431a_{j2}, \end{cases}$$

which is the transformation from the old coordinates (a_{j1}, a_{j2}) to the new ones (b_{j1}, b_{j2}). Equations (10.20) may also be written in the equivalent form

(10.21)
$$\mathbf{M} = \mathbf{C} \left\| \begin{matrix} .7431 & .6691 \\ -.6691 & .7431 \end{matrix} \right\|,$$

where $\mathbf{C}$ is the centroid pattern matrix of Table 8.4 and $\mathbf{M}$ is the final pattern which is presented in Table 10.1. For example, the first entry in Table 10.1 is given by

$$.830(.7431) - .396(-.6691) = .882.$$

The pattern of Table 10.1 may be examined now to see how well it conforms to the standards for a multiple-factor solution. Since there are no

TABLE 10.1

MULTIPLE-FACTOR PATTERN FOR EIGHT
PHYSICAL VARIABLES

Variable j	M_1	M_2	COMMU-NALITY h_j^2
1. Height..............	.882	.261	.846
2. Arm span...........	.922	.199	.890
3. Length of forearm.....	.892	.171	.825
4. Length of lower leg....	.861	.236	.797
5. Weight..............	.250	.897	.867
6. Bitrochanteric diameter	.193	.790	.661
7. Chest girth..........	.144	.727	.549
8. Chest width.........	.258	.680	.529
Contribution of factor....	3.352	2.612	....

sampling error formulas for this type of solution, the analyst usually must set some arbitrary level of insignificance. The present example is based on a large number of observations ($N = 305$), and hence the coefficients which ordinarily might be judged as insignificant may not be so. In the analysis of these data by the bi-factor method, the standard error of a general-factor coefficient was shown to have the approximate value .066 (see p. 141). If this standard error were applied to the coefficients in Table 10.1, even the smallest value might be judged significant. While the foregoing test is not strictly applicable in the present case, it nevertheless throws some doubt on the insignificance of the small values. The multiple-factor pattern for these data is therefore not a good example of this type of solution.

2. THIRTEEN PSYCHOLOGICAL TESTS

The next example is based upon the averoid pattern, given in Table 8.9, for the thirteen psychological tests. The transformation to a multiple-factor solution in this case is made in accordance with the scheme outlined in **10.3**. In Figure 10.3 the thirteen points are plotted in the plane of the first two averoid axes. The procedure in the present example differs somewhat from that employed in the preceding one. The first rotation is made in order to accomplish a leveling of the contributions of the first two factors. An angle $\theta_{12} = 50°$ is selected by inspection for this purpose. In such a rotation all points have negative projections on the second axis, designated as Y_2'. This rotation is immediately followed by the reflection of the second axis, namely,

$$Y_2 = -Y_2',$$

so as to yield positive coordinates. Although many points will have appreciable loadings for both Y_1 and Y_2, this can be adjusted by subsequent rotations. The equations of transformation (10.4) may be written as follows:

$$(10.22) \qquad \begin{cases} Y_1 = \quad\; .6428A_1 + .7660A_2, \\ Y_2' = -.7660A_1 + .6428A_2, \end{cases}$$

where it is understood that for given values of A_1 and A_2 the corresponding coordinates with respect to Y_1 and Y_2' are obtained. This notation, in which the coordinates are not given explicitly, will be found convenient in specifying the axes when several successive rotations are involved. The transformation (10.22) is followed by

$$(10.23) \qquad Y_2 = -Y_2' = .7660A_1 - .6428A_2.$$

Then, writing the resulting matrix of transformation in the form

$$\mathbf{T}_{12} = \left\| \begin{matrix} .6428 & .7660 \\ .7660 & -.6428 \end{matrix} \right\|,$$

and postmultiplying the first two columns of Table 8.9 by $\mathbf{T}_{12}$, yields the first two columns of Table 10.2. The numerical calculations may be checked at this stage. The new factors Y_1, Y_2, and the factor A_3 are mutually orthogonal, and their total contribution should be the same as that of the original system A_1, A_2, A_3. Thus,

$$2.878 + 2.798 + .909 = 4.391 + 1.285 + .909 = 6.585.$$

The next rotation is made in the Y_1, A_3-plane. The plot of points is presented in Figure 10.4, in which the coordinates are obtained from the first column of Table 10.2 and the third column of Table 8.9. In this trans-

TABLE 10.2

INTERMEDIATE COORDINATES

Test	Y_1	Y_2	Y_3
1.........	.385	.450	.508
2.........	.246	.269	.336
3.........	.352	.241	.496
4.........	.363	.327	.404
5.........	.662	.378	.065
6.........	.725	.293	.161
7.........	.718	.298	.093
8.........	.606	.404	.209
9.........	.729	.255	.107
10.........	− .048	.594	− .390
11.........	.040	.659	− .156
12.........	− .103	.691	− .117
13.........	.145	.740	.137
Contribution of factor...	2.878	2.798	1.083

formation the first multiple-factor axis is selected. Therefore, it is important that this axis pass near a cluster of points and also be about 90° removed from a number of other points. To satisfy these requirements, the angle $\theta_{13} = 27°$ is chosen. In this case one of the axes is reflected again to obtain positive coordinates. The final transformation in this plane may be written in matrix form:

$$(10.24) \qquad \left\| M_1 \quad Y_3 \right\| = \left\| Y_1 \quad A_3 \right\| \left\| \begin{matrix} .8829 & .4695 \\ .4695 & -.8829 \end{matrix} \right\|.$$

The resulting values of M_1 and Y_3 may be recorded in the appropriate columns of Tables 10.2 and 10.3.

The final rotation is made in the Y_2, Y_3-plane. For this transformation the last two multiple-factor axes are selected so as to pass as closely as possible to clusters of points. Thus M_2 passes near points *10, 11, 12*, and *13*, while M_3 lies close to the points *1, 2, 3*, and *4* when the angle of rotation is

TABLE 10.3

MULTIPLE-FACTOR PATTERN FOR THIRTEEN
PSYCHOLOGICAL TESTS

Test[a]	Verbal	Speed	Spatial Relations	Commu- nality
j	M_1	M_2	M_3	h_j^2
1.............	.166	.216	.643	.488
2.............	.100	.116	.414	.195
3.............	.135	.028	.551	.323
4.............	.196	.143	.500	.309
5.............	.715	.323	.208	.659
6.............	.735	.207	.263	.652
7.............	.764	.238	.202	.681
8.............	.575	.290	.350	.537
9.............	.769	.193	.198	.668
10.............	.153	.699	− .127	.528
11.............	.128	.668	.114	.476
12.............	− .054	.682	.162	.494
13.............	.091	.628	.415	.575
Contribution of factor.......	2.703	2.201	1.681	....

[a] The names and brief descriptions of the tests appear in Appen. **B.1.**

taken to be $\theta_{23} = -23°$. The transformation to the new axes may then be indicated by

$$(10.25) \qquad \| M_2 \quad M_3 \| = \| Y_2 \quad Y_3 \| \cdot \left\| \begin{array}{cc} .9205 & .3907 \\ -.3907 & .9205 \end{array} \right\| .$$

The coefficients of the factors M_2 and M_3 are recorded in Table 10.3. The numerical check on the total contribution of a factor system, which can be made after each rotation, may again be employed on the final set of factors. Thus the numbers appearing in the last line of Table 10.3 sum to 6.585, which is the same as the total contribution of the original averoid factors.

The multiple-factor pattern of Table 10.3 satisfies the standards listed above quite well. The contributions of the factors are relatively level in comparison with other types of preferred solutions. The criteria of low complexity and good geometric fit also appear to be satisfied. For the present sample ($N = 145$) it is judged that a factor coefficient of two-tenths is insignificant. In the present solution at least four entries in each column and one in each row would be considered as essentially zero. The only exception occurs for variable 8, which might be considered of complexity two or possibly three if the small value .290 is considered significant. The above solution thus affords a good illustration of the multiple-factor type.

In the naming of the multiple factors, those variables having definitely significant weights, say, greater than four-tenths, are considered. The subgroups of tests identifying the multiple factors are the same as those employed in naming the group factors in the bi-factor solution of Table 6.13. The same names are then assigned to the multiple factors, as indicated in Table 10.3. It may be noted that each test is essentially a measure of only one of these factors, except Test 13. This variable appears to be a measure of both speed and spatial abilities. This description is reasonable inasmuch as the test is a measure of speed of perception of simple geometric forms.

3. TWENTY-FOUR PSYCHOLOGICAL TESTS

The last example of a multiple-factor solution is based upon the centroid pattern of Table 8.2 for the twenty-four psychological tests. The transformations follow the scheme previously outlined for four factors. The diagrams from which the angles of rotation are determined are given in Figures 10.6 to 10.11. Then the successive transformations of coordinates may be summarized as follows:

$$
(10.26) \begin{cases}
\|Y_1 \quad Y_2\| = \|C_1 \quad C_2\| \cdot \left\| \begin{matrix} .7660 & .6428 \\ -.6428 & .7660 \end{matrix} \right\|, & \theta_{12} = -40°, \\[2ex]
\|Z_1 \quad Y_3\| = \|Y_1 \quad C_3\| \cdot \left\| \begin{matrix} .7986 & .6018 \\ -.6018 & .7986 \end{matrix} \right\|, & \theta_{13} = -37°, \\[2ex]
\|M_1' \quad Y_4\| = \|Z_1 \quad C_4\| \cdot \left\| \begin{matrix} .9848 & -.1737 \\ .1737 & .9848 \end{matrix} \right\|, & \theta_{14} = 10°, \\[2ex]
\|Z_2 \quad Z_3\| = \|Y_2 \quad Y_3\| \cdot \left\| \begin{matrix} .9962 & .0872 \\ -.0872 & .9962 \end{matrix} \right\|, & \theta_{23} = -5°, \\[2ex]
\|M_2' \quad Z_4\| = \|Z_2 \quad Y_4\| \cdot \left\| \begin{matrix} .8988 & .4384 \\ -.4384 & .8988 \end{matrix} \right\|, & \theta_{24} = -26°, \\[2ex]
\|M_3' \quad M_4'\| = \|Z_3 \quad Z_4\| \cdot \left\| \begin{matrix} .8829 & .4695 \\ -.4695 & .8829 \end{matrix} \right\|, & \theta_{34} = -28°.
\end{cases}
$$

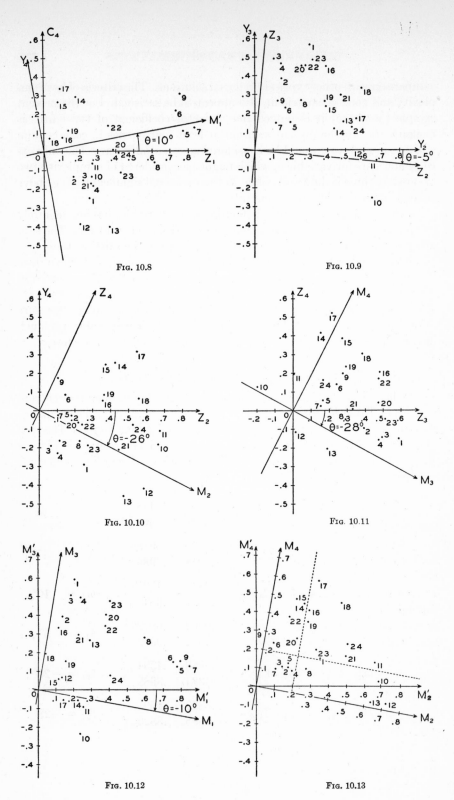

FIG. 10.8

FIG. 10.9

FIG. 10.10

FIG. 10.11

FIG. 10.12

FIG. 10.13

FIGS. 10.8–10.13

The transformed coordinates from the rotations (10.26) are presented in the single Table 10.4 for convenience. The axes of the last reference system have been designated by primes inasmuch as additional transformations will be made.

Upon inspection of the pattern involving M'_1, M'_2, M'_3, and M'_4 in Table 10.4, it is evident from the contribution of the first factor that it probably has been given too much emphasis in the successive transformations. The

TABLE 10.4

INTERMEDIATE COORDINATES

Test	Y_1	Y_2	Y_3	Y_4	Z_1	Z_2	Z_3	Z_4	M'_1	M'_2	M'_3	M'_4
1	.540	.302	.565	−.290	.251	.252	.589	−.150	.204	.354	.590	.144
2	.361	.148	.383	−.161	.164	.114	.394	−.095	.138	.173	.392	.101
3	.468	.106	.491	−.190	.216	.063	.498	−.143	.186	.140	.507	.108
4	.501	.145	.466	−.229	.276	.104	.477	−.160	.240	.194	.496	.083
5	.708	.195	.151	−.028	.772	.181	.167	.054	.779	.175	.122	.126
6	.723	.167	.229	.085	.733	.146	.243	.140	.759	.094	.149	.238
7	.754	.116	.147	−.023	.833	.103	.157	.024	.842	.103	.127	.095
8	.652	.253	.270	−.166	.613	.228	.291	−.049	.593	.278	.280	.093
9	.762	.125	.267	.173	.753	.101	.277	.200	.795	.015	.151	.307
10	.061	.646	−.255	−.180	.268	.666	−.198	.130	.240	.678	−.236	.022
11	.181	.670	−.057	−.109	.270	.672	.002	.197	.255	.652	−.091	.175
12	.139	.587	−.035	−.417	.201	.588	.016	−.117	.132	.711	.069	−.096
13	.382	.490	.151	−.459	.365	.475	.193	−.204	.290	.628	.266	−.089
14	.211	.437	.117	.258	.176	.425	.155	.418	.224	.269	−.059	.442
15	.202	.392	.238	.249	.073	.370	.271	.386	.118	.223	.058	.468
16	.351	.395	.451	.057	.100	.354	.484	.206	.112	.293	.331	.409
17	.173	.559	.170	.317	.089	.542	.218	.523	.146	.348	−.053	.564
18	.222	.587	.332	.066	.028	.556	.382	.303	.040	.471	.195	.447
19	.266	.386	.263	.086	.135	.362	.296	.236	.152	.288	.151	.347
20	.581	.260	.452	−.063	.387	.220	.473	.040	.382	.225	.399	.257
21	.387	.474	.297	−.214	.261	.446	.337	.003	.227	.495	.296	.161
22	.558	.281	.452	.072	.358	.241	.475	.170	.376	.185	.340	.373
23	.635	.319	.485	−.189	.429	.275	.511	−.049	.402	.330	.474	.197
24	.404	.536	.123	−.075	.413	.523	.169	.162	.406	.503	.073	.222
Contribution of factor	5.416	3.822	2.487	1.034	4.075	3.516	2.793	1.100	4.040	3.450	2.071	1.821

contribution of M'_1 is about twice that of M'_3 or M'_4. In order to obtain a more level distribution of the total variance, and a solution with more inappreciable weights for the first two factors and larger weights for the variables identifying the last two factors, two additional rotations will be made. The twenty-four points are plotted in the planes M'_1, M'_3 and M'_2, M'_4 in Figures 10.12 and 10.13, respectively. By selecting a small angle of rotation in each case, the desired adjustments are made. These supplementary rotations may be indicated as follows:

$$(10.27) \quad \begin{cases} \|M_1 \quad M_3\| = \|M'_1 \quad M'_3\| \cdot \left\| \begin{matrix} .9848 & .1737 \\ -.1737 & .9848 \end{matrix} \right\|, & \theta'_{13} = -10° \\ \\ \|M_2 \quad M_4\| = \|M'_2 \quad M'_4\| \cdot \left\| \begin{matrix} .9848 & .1737 \\ -.1737 & .9848 \end{matrix} \right\|, & \theta'_{24} = -10° \end{cases}$$

The final multiple-factor pattern is presented in Table 10.5. The checks on the calculation of the coefficients in Tables 10.4 and 10.5 after each rotation are summarized in Table 10.6. The sets of four factors comprising an orthogonal system are indicated, and their total contribution is compared with that of the original four centroid factors. Since the contributions of the

TABLE 10.5

MULTIPLE-FACTOR PATTERN FOR TWENTY-FOUR
PSYCHOLOGICAL TESTS

Test[a] j	Verbal M_1	Speed M_2	Deduction M_3	Memory M_4	Communality h_j^2
1.........	.098	.324	.616	.203	.535
2.........	.068	.153	.410	.130	.213
3.........	.095	.119	.532	.131	.323
4.........	.150	.177	.530	.115	.348
5.........	.746	.150	.255	.154	.668
6.........	.722	.051	.279	.251	.665
7.........	.807	.085	.271	.111	.744
8.........	.535	.258	.379	.140	.516
9.........	.757	− .039	.287	.305	.750
10........	.277	.664	− .191	.139	.573
11........	.267	.612	− .045	.286	.530
12........	.128	.717	.091	.029	.540
13........	.239	.634	.312	.021	.557
14........	.231	.188	− .019	.482	.321
15........	.106	.138	.078	.500	.286
16........	.053	.218	.345	.454	.375
17........	.153	.245	− .027	.616	.464
18........	.006	.386	.199	.522	.461
19........	.123	.223	.175	.392	.249
20........	.307	.177	.459	.292	.422
21........	.172	.460	.331	.245	.411
22........	.311	.117	.400	.399	.430
23........	.314	.291	.537	.251	.535
24........	.387	.457	.142	.306	.472
Contribution of factor..	3.430	2.917	2.683	2.358	....

[a] The names and brief descriptions of the tests appear in Appen. B.1.

respective systems agree with the number 11.383, except for errors due to rounding, it may safely be assumed that the calculations are accurate.

Using the same level for judging significance of factor coefficients as in the preceding example, it is clear that the solution of Table 10.5 is a good one. There are at least nine insignificant entries in each column, indicating good geometric fit. Each column also has a sufficient number of definitely significant weights for the naming of the factors. From the descriptions of the variables with large coefficients for M_1, M_2, and M_4, these factors may be appropriately named "verbal," "speed," and "memory," respectively. The third factor has appreciable loadings for Tests 1, 2, 3, 4, 20, 22, and 23. The first four of these have been called "spatial" tests and involve the deduction of relations among geometric objects. The last three tests involve logical and arithmetical relations. The common element of all these tests appears to be the deduction of relations, regardless of the specific content of the respective tests. The factor M_3 might then be named "deduction."

TABLE 10.6

TOTAL CONTRIBUTIONS OF SYSTEMS OF FACTORS

$C_1C_2C_3C_4$	$Y_1Y_2C_3C_4$	$Z_1Y_2Y_3C_4$	$M_1'Y_2Y_3Y_4$	$M_1'Z_2Z_3Y_4$	$M_1'M_2'Z_3Z_4$	$M_1'M_2'M_3'M_4'$	$M_1M_2M_3M_4$
11.383	11.384	11.385	11.383	11.383	11.383	11.382	11.388

The factor pattern of Table 10.5 for the first thirteen tests may be compared with the pattern of Table 10.3 for the same tests. A remarkably close agreement is evident in general. Even in the case of the third factor, which is given a different name in the two solutions, there is a close agreement for the variables common to the two sets. The first four tests, which were employed in the naming of this factor in Table 10.3, have very similar weights in the second solution. As pointed out above, however, the high loadings on this factor for the three additional tests suggested a somewhat different name in the latter solution. This illustrates the principle, stated in **5.8,** that a factor solution cannot be considered as independent of the set of variables employed. Thus the larger battery of tests leads to a different name for the third factor and to the inclusion of a "memory" factor which is not present in the smaller set. The agreement of the common portions of Tables 10.3 and 10.5 is evidence of the stability of factor patterns when a particular form of solution has been selected. Similar stability was indicated in **6.11** for the bifactor form of solution.

CHAPTER XI

OBLIQUE SOLUTION

11.1. *Introduction*

In Chapter V a number of preferred types of solutions involving uncorrelated factors were introduced. Methods for the calculation of such factor patterns were developed in subsequent chapters. Now the assumption of uncorrelated factors will be discarded, and the procedures leading to oblique solutions will be considered. It is clear that a certain simplicity of interpretation is sacrificed upon relinquishing the standard of orthogonality. This disadvantage may be offset, however, if the linear descriptions of the variables in terms of correlated factors can be made simpler than in the case of uncorrelated ones. Generally this is possible. Hence the preferred type of oblique pattern which is proposed is one which approximates the uni-factor form.

The method of analysis of this chapter consists in the rotation of some initial orthogonal pattern to an oblique solution. The communalities of the variables, which are determined by the common-factor space of the preliminary solution, remain invariant under this transformation. Hence the uniqueness for the oblique solution will be the same as that of the original. Therefore, the entire development will be made in the common-factor space.

The geometric setting for the oblique form of solution is presented in **11.2,** where the distinction between pattern and structure is again made. This is followed by a detailed outline of procedure illustrated by a simple example. Then several additional numerical illustrations are given in **11.4.** In the final section an illustration is given of the inapplicability of the oblique form of solution for variables which lack a clear design. It will be shown, however, that a suitable oblique uni-factor pattern can generally be achieved when there is evidence of grouping or clustering of the variables of a set.

11.2. *Geometric Basis for an Oblique Solution*

In **2.4** the definitions of factor patterns and structures were formulated. It was also pointed out that, when the factors are uncorrelated, these concepts become identical. In the foregoing chapters, therefore, no distinction was necessary, and the term "pattern" was used synonymously with "solution." When correlated factors are employed, however, the solution consists of two essential parts, i.e., the pattern and the structure. Now this distinction will be shown geometrically.

A pattern, in terms of common factors only, may be represented as follows:

$$z_j'' = b_{j1}F_1 + b_{j2}F_2 + \ldots + b_{jm}F_m \qquad (j = 1, 2, \ldots, n) ,$$

where b's are employed to denote coefficients of correlated factors. As pointed out in **3.8,** the double prime denotes a variable projected into the common-factor space. Since the analysis of this chapter is entirely in the common-factor space, the primes will be dropped for simplicity, and the foregoing equation written

(11.1) $$z_j = b_{j1}F_1 + b_{j2}F_2 + \ldots + b_{jm}F_m \qquad (j = 1, 2, \ldots, n) .$$

The coefficients may be considered as the coordinates of a point z_j with respect to the factor axes. This interpretation may be made whether the factors are represented by orthogonal or oblique axes. In the latter case the theory of **3.6** is employed.

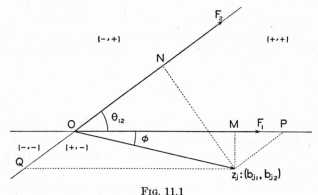

F$_{IG}$. 11.1

For the case of two factors these ideas may be illustrated by Figure 11.1. When the correlation between the factors F_1 and F_2 is known, the unit vectors representing F_1 and F_2 are separated by an angle $\theta_{12} = $ arc cos $r_{F_1 F_2}$. The oblique reference system is thus determined. The algebraic signs of the coordinates in the "quadrants" are the same as in the conventional orthogonal system. Any variable z_j is represented by a vector whose length and direction are determined by its coordinates. These coordinates are taken to be the coefficients of the respective factors in the analytic expression for the variable

(11.2) $$z_j = b_{j1}F_1 + b_{j2}F_2 \qquad (j = 1, 2, \ldots, n) .$$

From the definition of general Cartesian coordinates, given in **3.6**, it may be noted that the coordinates b_{j1}, b_{j2} are given by the line segments OP and OQ, respectively. For the hypothetical variable z_j, the first coordinate is positive and greater than unity, while the second coordinate is negative and less than unity.

The length of the vector z_j can be determined by means of formula (3.32), which in this case may be written as follows:

$$(11.3) \quad \begin{cases} D^2(Oz_j) = \sum_{s=1}^{2} \sum_{t=1}^{2} b_{js} b_{jt} \cos \theta_{st} \\[2mm] \quad = b_{j1} b_{j1} \cos \theta_{11} + b_{j1} b_{j2} \cos \theta_{12} + b_{j2} b_{j1} \cos \theta_{21} + b_{j2} b_{j2} \cos \theta_{22} \,. \end{cases}$$

In this formula each of the angles θ_{11} and θ_{22} is equal to zero, and θ_{12} is the angle between the reference axes. Hence $\cos \theta_{11} = \cos \theta_{22} = 1$ and $\cos \theta_{12} = r_{F_1 F_2}$. The expression (11.3) then reduces to

$$(11.4) \qquad D^2(Oz_j) = b_{j1}^2 + b_{j2}^2 + 2 b_{j1} b_{j2} r_{F_1 F_2} \,.$$

The right-hand member is the communality h_j^2 of the variable z_j, the projection of which is represented in the common-factor space by (11.2). The length of the vector is then equal to the square root of the communality, that is,

$$(11.5) \qquad D(Oz_j) = h_j \,.$$

The geometric interpretation of the correlation of a variable with a factor will now be given. Let the angle between the vector z_j and the reference vector F_1 be denoted by ϕ. Also let the projections of the end point of the vector z_j upon the F_1 and F_2 axes be given by M and N, respectively, as indicated in Figure 11.1. From the right triangle OMz_j, it is apparent that

$$\cos \phi = \frac{D(OM)}{D(Oz_j)} \,.$$

This formula reduces to

$$(11.6) \qquad D(OM) = h_j \cos \phi$$

upon making use of (11.5). Formula (11.6) may be simplified further by applying (3.51), which for variables z_j and F_1 becomes

$$(11.7) \qquad r'_{jF_1} = h_j h_{F_1} \cos \phi \,.$$

Since the length, or "communality," of any factor is unity, this expression may be written in the form

(11.8) $$r_{jF_1} = h_j \cos \phi .$$

In this formula, and in all other representations of correlations of variables with factors, the prime will be dropped for simplicity. Substituting (11.8) into (11.6), the projection of a vector upon a reference axis may finally be expressed as follows:

(11.9) $$D(OM) = r_{jF_1} .$$

In a similar manner it can be shown that the projection, $D(ON)$, of the vector z_j on the F_2 axis is the correlation of the variable with the second factor. Of course, the correlation between two factors is also given by the projection of either reference vector upon the other.

By referring to Figure 11.1, the distinction between a coordinate and a correlation can clearly be seen. The coordinates may be positive or negative and may be greater than one. A correlation coefficient also may be positive or negative but can never exceed unity. It may also be observed that the coordinates and correlations approach coincidence as the reference vectors approach orthogonality.

A complete solution involving correlated factors must consist of a pattern and a structure. The factor pattern may be exhibited as in equation (11.1) or, more compactly, in a table giving the coefficients of the factors. The structure may be presented in tabular or matrix form. For the preceding hypothetical example of two factors and n variables the structure may be recorded as follows:

$$\left\| \begin{matrix} r_{1F_1} & r_{1F_2} \\ r_{2F_1} & r_{2F_2} \\ \cdots & \cdots \\ r_{jF_1} & r_{jF_2} \\ \cdots & \cdots \\ r_{nF_1} & r_{nF_2} \end{matrix} \right\| .$$

In addition to the pattern and structure, the oblique solution should also include a table of intercorrelations of factors.

11.3. *Procedure for Obtaining an Oblique Solution*

An oblique solution can be obtained by means of a rotation of some preliminary orthogonal pattern such as the bi-factor, centroid, or averoid. In this sense, the method of analysis is similar to that employed in the last two chapters. Unlike the procedures employed there, however, the angles between the reference vectors in the present case are permitted to take on values other than 90°.

A complete theoretical development, employing literal notation throughout, would be unnecessarily complex and tend to conceal the actual simplicity of the procedure. For clarity, then, the development will be applied to the example of eight physical variables and may be readily generalized to larger sets of variables. The various stages of analysis are presented in outline form, including a detailed description of method in each step of the procedure.

1. INITIAL ORTHOGONAL PATTERN

As pointed out in **2.7** it is advisable in factor analysis to select the variables according to a design which is later verified or modified by the factor solution. If the resulting pattern reveals distinct subsets of variables, it will be especially effective for a clear interpretation of the oblique solution. Such a preliminary pattern sometimes may arise without an explicit formulation of a design. In either case, a pattern furnishing evidence of subsets will be regarded as "efficient."

Geometrically, the points representing a set of variables which have been analyzed into an efficient orthogonal pattern will form distinct clusters. For such a configuration new reference vectors can be taken through these clusters so as to meet the standard of linear fit.* In general, of course, the new reference system will be oblique.

If an orthogonal solution for a given set of variables is efficient, then any other orthogonal pattern based upon these data is also efficient. The first step in obtaining an oblique solution is, then, to select any such initial pattern. In the present development the centroid solution of the eight physical variables, given in Table 8.4, is selected arbitrarily as the initial form. This pattern is repeated here for convenience.

2. SUBSETS OF VARIABLES

If the initial pattern is an efficient one, the clusters of variables will usually be evident by inspection. Another approach is to apply the B-coefficient technique† to the original correlations. In the case of large sets of variables it is particularly advisable to employ both methods. The latter technique decomposes the set of variables into its fundamental groups, and then the pattern should be inspected for verification.

* See Standard 5a of Sec. **5.2.**   † See **2.7.**

For the eight physical variables the B-coefficients were determined in **4.6** and have the values

$$B(1, 2, 3, 4) = 235 , \qquad B(5, 6, 7, 8) = 179 ,$$

indicating two distinct subgroups. By noting the signs of the coefficients in Table 11.1, it is clear that the vectors representing the first four variables form a cluster in the fourth quadrant, while those representing the last four variables form another cluster in the first quadrant. The above grouping of variables is thus verified.

TABLE 11.1

INITIAL CENTROID PATTERN OF EIGHT
PHYSICAL VARIABLES

VARIABLE	COEFFICIENTS OF COMMON FACTORS	
	a_{j1}	a_{j2}
1. Height..............	.830	− .396
2. Arm span............	.818	− .469
3. Length of forearm.....	.777	− .470
4. Length of lower leg....	.798	− .401
5. Weight..............	.786	.500
6. Bitrochanteric diameter	.672	.458
7. Chest girth..........	.594	.444
8. Chest width.........	.647	.333
Sum...............	5.922	− .001
Contribution of factor....	4.439	1.526

In the case of an initial pattern involving only two or three common factors, the clusters can be seen directly from the plot of points with respect to the original axes. The eight variables, whose coordinates are given in Table 11.1, are plotted in Figure 11.2, where the two distinct clusters are clearly evident. Although the figure is very simple for two factors, the geometric representation for many factors becomes exceedingly complex. Then the methods of B-coefficients and inspection of the coefficients in the pattern must be employed.

3. DIRECTION COSINES OF OBLIQUE REFERENCE AXES

The next stage in the analysis is to determine the directions of the oblique reference vectors. Lines may be drawn, by inspection, from the origin through the clusters. The angles which these new axes make with the old may be measured, and the transformation may be determined thereby.

This procedure is rather subjective, however, and will be replaced by a more objective analytic method.

The average, or centroid, of each cluster of variables can be determined from the coordinates of the corresponding subset of points. These values

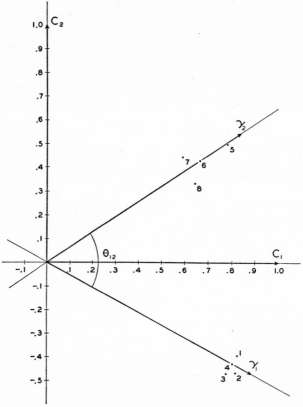

FIG. 11.2

can be calculated directly from the initial factor pattern. For the illustrative example the centroid of the cluster 1, 2, 3, 4 is the point whose coordinates are given by (.8058, −.4340), while that of the cluster 5, 6, 7, 8 is (.6748, .4337). In Figure 11.2 the new oblique reference axes are drawn from the origin through these points. Although geometric concepts are employed here, it is neither necessary nor feasible to actually plot points and draw the axes for many factors. Instead, the coordinates of these points can be calculated from the initial pattern, as indicated above, and axes through them can be imagined.

Knowing the coordinates of a point on a line through the origin, the direction cosines of that line can be determined. As indicated in **3.5,** the direction cosines are given by the ratios of the respective coordinates to the distance of the point from the origin. The distance of the first point from the origin is

$$\sqrt{(.8058)^2 + (-.4340)^2} = .9152 .$$

Then the direction cosines of the line through this point, with respect to the C_1 and C_2 axes, are given by

$$\lambda_{11} = \frac{.8058}{.9152} = .8805 , \qquad \lambda_{21} = \frac{-.4340}{.9152} = -.4742 .$$

These are then the direction cosines of the new axis γ_1 with respect to the original axes. In a similar manner, the direction cosines of the γ_2 axis are found to be

$$\lambda_{12} = .8412 , \qquad \lambda_{22} = .5406 .$$

Now an alternative approach for obtaining these direction cosines will be indicated. Instead of employing the centroid of a cluster, the point corresponding to the composite* of this subset of variables is used. Let the composite variables be defined by

$$(11.10) \qquad \begin{cases} v_1 = z_1 + z_2 + z_3 + z_4 , \\ v_2 = z_5 + z_6 + z_7 + z_8 . \end{cases}$$

The standard deviations of these variables may be computed by means of (2.40), as follows:

$$(11.11) \qquad \begin{cases} \sigma_{v_1} = \sqrt{4 + 2(5.018)} = 3.7465 , \\ \sigma_{v_2} = \sqrt{4 + 2(3.820)} = 3.4117 . \end{cases}$$

Then the correlations of the composite variables with the C_1 and C_2 factors can be calculated by means of formula (2.43). In this case, the z_0 of the formula is taken as a factor. The correlation of the first composite variable with C_1 is thus given by

$$r_{v_1 C_1} = \frac{.830 + .818 + .777 + .798}{3.7465} = .8603 ,$$

where the values in the numerator are taken from Table 11.1. Since the centroid factors are uncorrelated, this value is also the coefficient of C_1 in

* See **2.10.**

the linear expression for the standardized composite variable. In a similar manner the remaining correlations, or coefficients, can be obtained and arranged in the form of a *reduced pattern* as follows:

$$(11.12) \quad \begin{cases} u_1 = \dfrac{v_1}{\sigma_{v_1}} = .8603C_1 - .4634C_2 \,, \\[2ex] u_2 = \dfrac{v_2}{\sigma_{v_2}} = .7911C_1 + .5085C_2 \,. \end{cases}$$

Such pattern equations have the same properties as those for individual variables.

The coefficients of the reduced pattern may be interpreted as the coordinates of two points representing u_1 and u_2. The direction cosines of the lines from the origin through these points can be calculated as before by dividing the coordinates by the appropriate distances. These values are found to be

$$(11.13) \quad \begin{cases} \lambda_{11} = .8804 \,, & \lambda_{21} = -.4742 \,, \\ \lambda_{12} = .8412 \,, & \lambda_{22} = .5407 \,. \end{cases}$$

The equivalence of the direction cosines of γ_1 and γ_2 with respect to C_1 and C_2 obtained by the two methods is proved in Appendix **B.10**.

The method of reduced patterns will be employed in the remaining examples. Although the arithmetic is somewhat more involved than in the method of averages, the reduced pattern furnishes additional interpretations of the variables and factors. The correlations of reduced variables with factors are also employed for the estimation of factors in the next chapter.

4. INTERCORRELATIONS OF FACTORS

After the direction cosines of the oblique reference vectors have been obtained, the correlations between these factors can be determined. By employing (3.41) and (3.29), the correlation between γ_1 and γ_2 in the present example is found to be

$$r_{\gamma_1 \gamma_2} = .8804(.8412) - .4742(.5407) = .4842 \,.$$

The self-correlations, or variances, of the factors may be calculated in the same manner. Thus,

$$\sigma_{\gamma_1}^2 = (.8804)^2 + (-.4742)^2 = 1.0000 \,,$$
$$\sigma_{\gamma_2}^2 = (.8412)^2 + (.5407)^2 = 1.0000 \,.$$

These calculations serve as a check on the values (11.13) because the sum of squares of the direction cosines of any line must be unity. From the correlation between factors the angle of separation of the reference vectors can readily be determined. In the present case this angle is given by

$$\theta_{12} = \text{arc cos } .4842 = 61°2' \, .$$

5. FACTOR STRUCTURE

The projections of the vectors representing the variables upon the oblique reference axes can now be determined.* As indicated in (11.9), such projections are the correlations of the variables with the factors, i.e., the elements

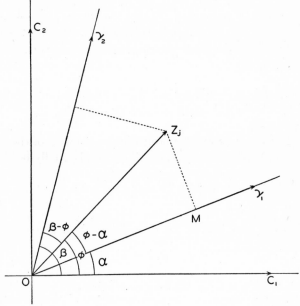

FIG. 11.3

of the factor structure. In order to indicate clearly the derivation of the formulas for the structure values, Figure 11.3 has been constructed. In this figure the oblique reference vectors γ_1 and γ_2 have been taken in the first quadrant of the C_1, C_2 reference system. This has been done merely to

* It is possible to obtain the coordinates of the points with respect to the oblique reference system directly by transformation of the original coordinates. Since, in factor analysis, both the coordinates and the projections (i.e., the coefficients and the correlations) are desired, the present approach is suggested as the simplest and the one best adapted to systematic calculations. First the projections are obtained, and then in the next stage of the analysis the coordinates are calculated.

clarify the development, the results being the same even if the oblique axes fall in other quadrants. The angles from the C_1 axis to the γ_1 and γ_2 axes are denoted by a and β, respectively.

Any variable z_j may be represented in this figure by a point whose co-ordinates (a_{j1}, a_{j2}) with respect to the original centroid axes are the coefficients in the initial pattern equation. The variable may also be represented by the vector from the origin to the point z_j: (a_{j1}, a_{j2}). The angle from the C_1 axis to this vector is denoted by ϕ. Then the projection of the vector z_j upon the γ_1 axis is given by

$$(11.14) \qquad D(OM) = D(Oz_j) \cos (\phi - a) .$$

As already noted, the projection $D(OM)$ is equivalent to the correlation $r_{j\gamma_1}$, and the length of the vector is $D(Oz_j) = h_j$. Making these substitutions in (11.14), and expanding the cosine of the difference of two angles, this formula becomes

$$r_{j\gamma_1} = h_j \left[\cos \phi \cos a + \sin \phi \sin a\right],$$
$$= (h_j \cos \phi) \cos a + (h_j \sin \phi) \sin a .$$

Now, $h_j \cos \phi$ and $h_j \sin \phi$ are the projections a_{j1} and a_{j2} of the vector z_j on the C_1 and C_2 axes, respectively. Then the formula finally becomes

$$(11.15) \qquad r_{j\gamma_1} = a_{j1} \cos a + a_{j2} \sin a .$$

In a similar manner it can be shown that the projection, $D(ON)$, of the vector z_j on the γ_2 axis, that is, the correlation $r_{j\gamma_2}$, is given by

$$(11.16) \qquad r_{j\gamma_2} = a_{j1} \cos \beta + a_{j2} \sin \beta .$$

The results of (11.15) and (11.16) may be summarized in the following matrix form:

$$(11.17) \quad \|r_{j\gamma_1} \quad r_{j\gamma_2}\| = \|a_{j1} \quad a_{j2}\| \cdot \left\|\begin{matrix} \lambda_{11} = \cos a & \lambda_{12} = \cos \beta \\ \lambda_{21} = \sin a & \lambda_{22} = \sin \beta \end{matrix}\right\| ,$$

where, in the last matrix, the elements of the first column are the direction cosines of γ_1 with respect to C_1 and C_2, and those of the second column are the direction cosines of γ_2. Although (11.17) was developed on the basis of Figure 11.3, this expression is true for different positions of the new axes γ_1 and γ_2, as, for example, that indicated in Figure 11.2. Written in the form (11.17), the determination of the elements of a structure can be generalized to problems involving more than two factors.

For the example the direction cosines are given in (11.13) and may be put in a matrix as follows:

$$(11.18) \qquad \left\| \begin{array}{cc} .8804 & .8412 \\ -.4742 & .5407 \end{array} \right\| .$$

Then multiplying the centroid pattern matrix of Table 11.1 by this matrix, the structure values of Table 11.2 are obtained. The correlations of the composite variables with the oblique factors are obtained by multiplying the reduced pattern matrix of (11.12) by the matrix (11.18). These values are presented in the reduced structure of Table 11.2.

TABLE 11.2

OBLIQUE SOLUTION FOR EIGHT
PHYSICAL VARIABLES

VARIABLE	STRUCTURE		PATTERN	
j	$r_{j\gamma_1}$	$r_{j\gamma_2}$	Lankiness γ_1	Stockiness γ_2
1.........	.919	.484	.894	.051
2.........	.943	.435	.956	−.027
3.........	.907	.399	.932	−.052
4.........	.893	.454	.879	.029
5.........	.455	.932	.005	.930
6.........	.374	.813	−.025	.825
7.........	.312	.740	−.060	.769
8.........	.412	.724	.080	.685
	Reduced Structure		Reduced Pattern	
u_1.........	.977	.473	.977	.000
u_2.........	.455	.940	.000	.940

A check on the calculation of the oblique factor structure can be made by changing the order of the multiplications and additions in the calculations of the sums of the structure values. For two factors this may be written in the form

$$(11.19) \qquad \lambda_{1t}\Sigma a_{j1} + \lambda_{2t}\Sigma a_{j2} = \Sigma r_{j\gamma_t} \qquad (t = 1, 2) ,$$

where the range of j is arbitrary but the same for all three sums. To illustrate the application of this check, consider the correlations of the eight variables with γ_1. Then $t = 1$ and j ranges from 1 to 8 in (11.19). The check on the first column of Table 11.2 then consists in the agreement of the sum of this column with the evaluation of the left-hand member of (11.19). This sum is

$$\sum_{j=1}^{8} r_{j\gamma_1} = 5.215 \,,$$

while

$$\lambda_{11} \sum_{j=1}^{8} a_{j1} + \lambda_{21} \sum_{j=1}^{8} a_{j2} = .8804(5.922) - .4742(-.001) = 5.214 \,.$$

Since the discrepancy is evidently due only to rounding, the calculations of this column of the factor structure are accepted as accurate. Of course, the check might have been applied to the entire first column, including the composite variables or, again, to the calculations of the correlations of the composite variables alone. Similarly, the second column of the factor structure is checked.

6. FACTOR PATTERN

In order to have a complete solution in terms of correlated factors, the linear descriptions of the variables are required as well as their correlations with the factors. The pattern coefficients are the coordinates with respect to the oblique axes of the points representing the variables and could have been obtained directly* from the initial factor pattern. It is more convenient, however, to calculate these values after the oblique factor structure has been obtained by means of the relationship between the pattern and structure which is described in Appendix **B.11**.

If the oblique factor pattern for the illustrative example is denoted by

$$(11.20) \qquad\qquad z_j = b_{j1}\gamma_1 + b_{j2}\gamma_2 \qquad\qquad (j = 1, 2, \ldots, 8) \,,$$

the problem is to determine the coefficients b_{j1}, b_{j2}. For any variable z_j, multiply (11.20) by γ_1 and γ_2, in turn, sum for the N values, and divide by N. The resulting equations are

$$(11.21) \qquad\qquad \begin{cases} r_{j\gamma_1} = b_{j1} \quad\;\; + b_{j2}r_{\gamma_1\gamma_2} \,, \\ r_{j\gamma_2} = b_{j1}r_{\gamma_2\gamma_1} + b_{j2} \,. \end{cases}$$

There is such a pair of simultaneous equations for the determination of the two unknowns b_{j1}, b_{j2} for each variable z_j. In equations (11.21) the terms

---

* See n.*, p. 243.

$r_{j\gamma_1}$ and $r_{j\gamma_2}$ are known from the factor structure, and the correlation between the factors is known from the fourth step in the analysis. The determinant of coefficients of the unknowns b_{j1}, b_{j2} is

$$\begin{vmatrix} 1 & .4842 \\ .4842 & 1 \end{vmatrix}$$

and remains the same for successive calculations of the b's. The determination of the factor coefficients may be calculated by the method of determinants, but, especially when many factors are involved, a more efficient procedure is desired. Such a procedure is described in Appendix **G.3,** where the present example is used as an illustration. The resulting values of the factor coefficients appear in the pattern matrix in Table 11.2. In this table the reduced oblique factor pattern is also presented.

7. CONTRIBUTIONS OF OBLIQUE FACTORS

After an oblique factor pattern has been obtained, the direct and joint contributions of these factors can be determined. The communality of a variable z_j, as given by (11.1), may be expressed as follows:

$$(11.22) \quad \begin{cases} h_j^2 = b_{j1}^2 + b_{j2}^2 + \ldots + b_{jm}^2 + 2b_{j1}b_{j2}r_{F_1F_2} + \ldots \\ \\ \qquad\qquad\qquad\qquad\qquad\qquad + 2b_{j,m-1}b_{jm}r_{F_{m-1}F_m} . \end{cases}$$

The direct contributions of the factors to z_j are given by the first m terms in this expression, while the joint contributions of the factors are furnished by the remaining terms. The total direct contributions of the factors are obtained by summing the direct contributions of the respective factors for all the variables as follows

$$(11.23) \qquad \sum_{j=1}^{n} b_{j1}^2 , \qquad \sum_{j=1}^{n} b_{j2}^2 , \quad \ldots , \qquad \sum_{j=1}^{n} b_{jm}^2 .$$

The total joint contributions of pairs of factors are given by

$$(11.24) \quad 2r_{F_1F_2}\sum_{j=1}^{n} b_{j1}b_{j2} , \qquad 2r_{F_1F_3}\sum_{j=1}^{n} b_{j1}b_{j3} , \quad \ldots , \qquad 2r_{F_{m-1}F_m}\sum_{j=1}^{n} b_{j,m-1}b_{jm} .$$

These two sets of expressions can be arranged conveniently in a triangular matrix in which the direct contributions are put in the diagonal and the joint contributions in the remainder of the triangle.

In the illustrative example the total direct contributions of the two factors are given by

$$\sum_{j=1}^{8} b_{j1}^2 = .894^2 + .956^2 + \ldots + .080^2 = 3.365 ,$$

$$\sum_{j=1}^{8} b_{j2}^2 = .051^2 + (-.027)^2 + \ldots + .685^2 = 2.613 ,$$

while the total joint contribution of these factors is

$$2r_{\gamma_1 \gamma_2} \sum_{j=1}^{8} b_{j1} b_{j2}$$

$$= 2(.4842)[.894(.051) + .956(-.027) + \ldots + .080(.685)] = -.010 .$$

The contributions of the respective factors may then be arranged in the form of Table 11.3. The grand total of the contributions of a set of oblique factors should, of course, be equal to the total communality of the original

TABLE 11.3

TOTAL CONTRIBUTIONS
OF FACTORS

	γ_1	γ_2
γ_1........	3.365	....
γ_2........	$-$ .010	2.613

Grand total $= 5.968$

solution. In the present example this total agrees closely with the value 5.965, which is the sum of the contributions in Table 11.1. The direct contributions of the factors account for all but a negligible amount of the total common-factor variance.

11.4. *Numerical Illustrations*

Four oblique solutions will now be presented, employing the psychological tests of **2.8.** Two of these will be based upon initial centroid patterns, for the sets of thirteen and twenty-four variables. The other two solutions will be based upon the bi-factor patterns for the same sets of variables. Then it will be possible to examine the stability of each pair of oblique solutions.

It will also be possible to compare the oblique solutions, for a given set of variables, based on two different initial patterns.

Since the same data are employed in all four solutions, the determination of the subsets of variables may be indicated now. According to the method of B-coefficients of **2.9**, the twenty-four psychological tests are grouped into the following composites:

$$(11.25) \quad \begin{cases} v_1 = z_1 + z_2 + z_3 + z_4, \\ v_2 = z_5 + z_6 + z_7 + z_8 + z_9, \\ v_3 = z_{10} + z_{11} + z_{12} + z_{13}, \\ v_4 = z_{14} + z_{15} + z_{16} + z_{17} + z_{18} + z_{19}, \\ v_5 = z_{20} + z_{21} + z_{22} + z_{23} + z_{24}. \end{cases}$$

When only the first thirteen variables are employed, these are grouped into three subsets which are in agreement with the first three composites of (11.25). This grouping is verified in each case by inspection of the initial factor pattern.

1. SOLUTIONS BASED UPON INITIAL CENTROID PATTERNS

The first illustration is based upon the initial centroid pattern of Table 8.1. The grouping of the thirteen variables into the three composites, v_1, v_2, and v_3, is substantiated by the preliminary solution. These composites are then employed in the determination of the direction cosines of the oblique

TABLE 11.4

REDUCED CENTROID PATTERN FOR THIRTEEN
PSYCHOLOGICAL TESTS

Variable	C_1	C_2	C_3	$D(Ou_j)$
u_1	.6535	.0735	−.5012	.8268
u_2	.8448	.3759	.2330	.9536
u_3	.6841	−.5697	.1405	.9013

reference axes. The standard deviations of the variables v_1, v_2, and v_3 have been computed in **2.11** and are given by $\sigma_{v_1} = 2.843$, $\sigma_{v_2} = 4.214$, and $\sigma_{v_3} = 3.147$. The reduced centroid pattern may then be calculated and written as in Table 11.4. In this table the composite variables, which are in standard form, are designated by u's; and the distances of the points, representing these variables, from the origin are given in the last column. The direction cosines of the oblique reference axes γ_1, γ_2, and γ_3 (which are the lines from the origin through the points representing the composite variables) are obtained by dividing the elements (coordinates) in the rows of Table 11.4 by the respective distances. The resulting values can be recorded in matrix form as follows:

$$(11.26) \quad \begin{matrix} & \lambda_{s1} & \lambda_{s2} & \lambda_{s3} \\ C_1 & .7904 & .8859 & .7590 \\ C_2 & .0889 & .3942 & -.6321 \\ C_3 & -.6062 & .2443 & .1559 \end{matrix} .$$

In this matrix the direction cosines of the respective oblique axes with respect to the centroid axes are recorded in columns.

The correlation between any two oblique factors is obtained simply by summing the paired products of corresponding direction cosines of the reference axes representing them. In like manner, the variances of the factors can be obtained by taking the sum of the squares of the respective columns of (11.26). Of course, these variances must be equal to unity, and hence they can serve as a check on the preceding calculations. The correlations among the factors are presented in Table 11.5. If it is desired, the

TABLE 11.5

INTERCORRELATIONS OF FACTORS

	γ_1	γ_2	γ_3
γ_1.........	1.000	....	....
γ_2.........	.587	1.000	....
γ_3.........	.449	.461	1.000

angles between these oblique axes can be determined from the correlations. In the succeeding analysis, however, the actual values of these angles are not required, but only their cosines, i.e., the correlations.

The oblique factor structure can be determined as indicated by (11.17). Upon multiplying the initial pattern matrix of Table 8.1 by the matrix of direction cosines (11.26), the factor structure of Table 11.6 is obtained. Similarly, the reduced structure is found upon multiplying the reduced pattern matrix of Table 11.4 by the matrix of (11.26). The calculation of the structure of Table 11.6 can be checked by the application of formula (11.19) extended to three factors.

From the intercorrelations of the factors and the structure, the factor pattern can be determined. Employing the method of **G.3,** the oblique factor pattern for the thirteen tests and the reduced pattern are calculated and are presented in Table 11.6 also. The total direct and joint contributions of the three oblique factors are given in Table 11.7. The grand total of the contributions differs from the total original communality only by 0.015, so that the entire oblique solution may be said to check.

TABLE 11.6[a]

OBLIQUE SOLUTION FOR THIRTEEN
PSYCHOLOGICAL TESTS

Test _j_	Structure			Pattern		
	$r_{j\gamma_1}$	$r_{j\gamma_2}$	$r_{j\gamma_3}$	Spatial Relations γ_1	Verbal γ_2	Speed γ_3
1.......	.743	.406	.430	**.731**	−.089	.142
2.......	.445	.264	.204	**.441**	.004	.004
3.......	.604	.324	.157	**.721**	−.090	−.142
4.......	.559	.386	.266	**.508**	.090	−.003
5.......	.451	.807	.429	−.058	**.801**	.087
6.......	.489	.807	.339	.037	**.809**	−.051
7.......	.447	.846	.355	−.068	**.901**	−.030
8.......	.537	.717	.420	.155	**.591**	.078
9.......	.435	.841	.311	−.068	**.919**	−.081
10.......	.075	.311	.712	−**.385**	.164	**.809**
11.......	.302	.357	.677	−.039	.077	**.659**
12.......	.316	.222	.724	.073	−.177	**.773**
13.......	.582	.419	.723	**.351**	−.061	**.594**
	Reduced Structure			Reduced Pattern		
u_1.......	.827	.485	.371	**.827**	.000	.000
u_2.......	.560	.954	.440	−.000	**.954**	.001
u_3.......	.405	.416	.901	.000	.001	**.900**

[a] Based upon centroid solution of Table 8.1.

TABLE 11.7

TOTAL CONTRIBUTIONS OF FACTORS

	γ_1	γ_2	γ_3
γ_1..........	1.823	....	....
γ_2..........	− .272	3.394	....
γ_3..........	− .052	− .015	2.103

Grand total = 6.981

The second illustration is based upon the initial centroid pattern of Table 8.2 for the twenty-four psychological tests. Since this preliminary solution involves only four factors, the common-factor space for the succeeding oblique solution consists of four dimensions, at most, according to Theorem 3.5. Hence only four composite variables are desired, inasmuch as each of these variables determines a direction for one of the oblique axes. Of the composites (11.25) determined by B-coefficients, the first four agree most favorably with the centroid solution of Table 8.2. The points representing the variables of each of these subsets fall into distinct "sedecimants"* with only two minor exceptions, as may be indicated symbolically by

$$v_1 : (+, -, +, -),$$
$$v_2 : (+, -, -, +),$$
$$v_3 : (+, +, -, -),$$
$$v_4 : (+, +, +, +).$$

On the other hand, the points representing the variables of the last subset do not fall into a single "sedecimant" but overlap with the preceding subsets. Thus, from inspection of Table 8.2, variables 20 and 23 might be grouped with those of v_1, variables 21 and 24 with those of v_3, and variable 22 might be included with those of v_4. For simplicity, however, these variables are not regrouped, and the first four composites of (11.25) are accepted. It

TABLE 11.8

REDUCED CENTROID PATTERN FOR TWENTY-FOUR
PSYCHOLOGICAL TESTS

Variable	C_1	C_2	C_3	C_4	$D(Ou_j)$
u_1.......	.6627	−.2343	.3429	−.2547	.8225
u_2.......	.7848	−.3935	−.3272	.1652	.9514
u_3.......	.6746	.4264	−.2609	−.3143	.8965
u_4.......	.7257	.3029	.2261	.2930	.8691

is to be expected that the last five tests will be expressed, in the final oblique pattern, in terms of the same factors which are determined by the composite variables most nearly related to them.

In order to calculate the reduced centroid pattern, the standard deviations of the composite variables are required. These were obtained in **2.11,** and the first three were employed in the previous example. The standard deviation of the fourth composite variable is $\sigma_{v_4} = 3.945$. The elements of the reduced pattern are obtained by dividing the sums of coefficients of the variables comprising a composite by the corresponding standard deviation. The reduced pattern is presented in Table 11.8. The direction cosines of

---

* A "sedecimant" is one of the sixteen regions into which the four-space is divided by the four reference axes. These regions are analogous to the four quadrants in the plane, and the eight octants in ordinary space.

the oblique reference axes γ_1, γ_2, γ_3, and γ_4 with respect to the original frame of reference are given in the columns of the following matrix:

(11.27)

	λ_{s1}	λ_{s2}	λ_{s3}	λ_{s4}
C_1	.8057	.8249	.7525	.8350
C_2	−.2849	−.4136	.4756	.3485
C_3	.4169	−.3439	−.2910	.2602
C_4	−.3097	.1736	−.3506	.3371

The correlations among the four oblique factors are obtained as before and are presented in Table 11.9. The complete oblique solution, including both structure and pattern, for the twenty-four tests is given in Table 11.10. As a final check on the solution, the contributions of factors are presented in Table 11.11. The grand total agrees with the total original communality (11.383). The values in the diagonal of this table indicate the almost level contributions of the four oblique factors.

TABLE 11.9

INTERCORRELATIONS OF FACTORS

	γ_1	γ_2	γ_3	γ_4
γ_1......	1.000			
γ_2......	.585	1.000		
γ_3......	.458	.463	1.000	
γ_4......	.578	.514	.600	1.000

Since the structure and pattern are distinct in an oblique solution, the question arises as to how to employ these matrices in the naming of the factors. All the elements of the structure are generally different from zero because the factors are correlated. This may be seen geometrically from the fact that the vectors of the variables usually have appreciable projections on all the reference axes. This is true even if a particular vector lies directly on one of the reference axes. Thus it appears that the structure is not very useful for the naming of factors. On the other hand, when a vector lies on one of the reference axes, its end point has zero coordinates with respect to the remaining axes. Thus the points representing the variables of a subset (lying close to and determining one of the oblique axes) have large coordinates with respect to this axis and small coordinates with respect to the remaining reference axes. The oblique factor pattern, consisting of such coordinates, thus approximates the uni-factor form and furnishes a basis for clearly identifying the factors. In the case of composite variables

TABLE 11.10[a]

OBLIQUE SOLUTION FOR TWENTY-FOUR PSYCHOLOGICAL TESTS

Test j	STRUCTURE				PATTERN			
	$r_{j\gamma_1}$	$r_{j\gamma_2}$	$r_{j\gamma_3}$	$r_{j\gamma_4}$	Spatial Relations γ_1	Verbal γ_2	Speed γ_3	Memory γ_4
1......	.725	.403	.403	.461	**.703**	−.068	.091	.035
2......	.462	.261	.210	.278	**.462**	−.018	−.009	.025
3......	.564	.326	.195	.296	**.595**	.020	−.081	−.010
4......	.587	.378	.263	.316	**.578**	.067	−.002	−.051
5......	.449	.815	.419	.398	−.044	**.827**	.092	−.057
6......	.454	.811	.336	.440	−.045	**.828**	−.077	.086
7......	.440	.855	.371	.348	−.051	**.931**	.040	−.125
8......	.552	.681	.457	.414	.219	**.516**	.164	−.076
9......	.452	.847	.274	.459	−.076	**.903**	−.204	.161
10......	.133	.295	.718	.404	−**.316**	.081	**.779**	.078
11......	.278	.366	.700	.538	−.180	.066	**.606**	.245
12......	.345	.234	.715	.360	.138	−.152	**.794**	−.118
13......	.536	.412	.689	.392	**.350**	.014	**.645**	−.204
14......	.203	.338	.328	.534	−.237	.176	.011	**.575**
15......	.258	.261	.251	.527	−.068	.033	−.097	**.608**
16......	.501	.310	.316	.567	**.307**	−.080	−.069	**.471**
17......	.236	.305	.379	.657	−.237	.047	.008	**.765**
18......	.434	.251	.460	.653	.145	−.191	.128	**.592**
19......	.348	.296	.323	.492	.082	.021	.026	**.418**
20......	.595	.533	.339	.485	**.373**	.250	−.050	.171
21......	.538	.391	.543	.505	**.321**	−.014	**.324**	.133
22......	.549	.535	.299	.541	.259	.279	−.151	**.339**
23......	.693	.573	.445	.514	**.489**	.212	.079	.075
24......	.422	.528	.609	.539	−.014	.266	**.387**	.178
	Reduced Structure				Reduced Pattern			
u_1......	.823	.481	.377	.475	**.824**	.000	.001	−.002
u_2......	.557	.951	.441	.489	.001	**.949**	.005	−.002
u_3......	.411	.415	.897	.538	−.001	.003	**.899**	−.002
u_4......	.502	.446	.522	.869	−.000	−.002	.002	**.869**

[a] Based upon the centroid solution of Table 8.2.

TABLE 11.11

TOTAL CONTRIBUTIONS OF FACTORS

	γ_1	γ_2	γ_3	γ_4
γ_1.........	2.517	....	....	....
γ_2.........	.023	3.696	....	....
γ_3.........	.110	−.023	2.438	....
γ_4.........	−.052	.266	−.010	2.416

Grand total = 11.381

the resulting reduced structure and pattern bring out the above relationships more clearly inasmuch as the points representing these composites lie exactly on the reference axes.

In the factor patterns of Tables 11.6 and 11.10 the coefficients exceeding three-tenths have been printed in bold-face type to facilitate the naming of factors. It will be observed that in both of these patterns there are a large number of insignificant entries. From the descriptions of the variables, given in Appendix **B.1,** the names of the factors indicated in these tables are justified.

It may be noted that in the reduced oblique factor patterns all the entries are zero, within errors of rounding, except those in the principal diagonal. This follows from the fact that the oblique reference axes are passed through the points representing the composite variables. Thus, the reduced uni-factor pattern from Table 11.10 may be written in the form

$$(11.28) \qquad \begin{cases} u_1 = .824\gamma_1 \\ u_2 = \qquad\quad .949\gamma_2 \\ u_3 = \qquad\qquad\qquad .899\gamma_3 \\ u_4 = \qquad\qquad\qquad\qquad .869\gamma_4 \,. \end{cases}$$

The reduced oblique pattern for the thirteen variables may be written in a similar manner and agrees with the first three of equations (11.28) to within five points in the last decimal place.

The general stability of an oblique uni-factor solution, upon the reduction of the number of variables, can be observed from the patterns of Tables 11.6 and 11.10. For the thirteen tests which are common to these two patterns, the corresponding factor weights are quite similar. The discrepancies between the insignificant coefficients are of lesser importance than those between the large weights. For the latter set the differences are all less than one-tenth except for the two values of b_{31}. The two patterns may then be considered as essentially the same for the common portions. This agreement may also be observed in the factor structures and is evidenced most clearly in the reduced structures and patterns. Hence the composite variables may be taken as the best direct measures of the oblique factors determined in either solution.

2. SOLUTIONS BASED UPON INITIAL BI-FACTOR PATTERNS

In order to make it possible to compare oblique solutions for the same variables when based upon different initial patterns, the next two examples also will employ the psychological variables but will be based upon the bi-factor patterns of Tables 6.12 and 6.8. In transforming a bi-factor pattern to an oblique solution, the number of factors is frequently reduced by one. This is due to the fact that the bi-factor solution, in order to exhibit the great simplicity of form, sometimes must involve one more than the minimum number of factors possible for an equally adequate solution of some other type. The bi-factor pattern can be tested for its rank, say m, when it contains m or $m + 1$ factors. Then a reduced bi-factor pattern, involving m composite variables, can be calculated. The rank of this reduced pattern is also equal to m. The composite variables may be con-

TABLE 11.12

REDUCED BI-FACTOR PATTERNS

For Thirteen Psychological Tests						For Twenty-four Psychological Tests							
Variable	B_0	B_1	B_2	B_3	$D(Ou_j)$	Variable	B_0	B_1	B_2	B_3	B_4	B_5	$D(Ou_j)$
u_1	.6268	.5332	......	......	.8229	u_1	.6367	.5505	......	......	......	......	.8417
u_2	.7323	......	.6080	......	.9518	u_2	.6822	......	.6749	......	......	......	.9596
u_3	.5265	......	......	.7286	.8989	u_3	.6003	......	......	.6838	......	......	.9099
						u_4	.6626	......	......	......	.4398	.3141	.8551
						u_5	.9137	......	......	......	......	......	.9137

TABLE 11.13

DIRECTION COSINES

	For Thirteen Variables				For Twenty-four Variables				
	λ_{s1}	λ_{s2}	λ_{s3}		λ_{s1}	λ_{s2}	λ_{s3}	λ_{s4}	λ_{s5}
B_0	.7617	.7694	.5857	B_0	.7564	.7109	.6597	.7749	1.0000
B_1	.6480	0	0	B_1	.6540	0	0	0	0
B_2	0	.6388	0	B_2	0	.7033	0	0	0
B_3	0	0	.8105	B_3	0	0	.7515	0	0
				B_4	0	0	0	.5143	0
				B_5	0	0	0	0	.3673

sidered as m points in the original bi-factor space. It can be shown then that these m points are contained in a space of m dimensions which also contains the origin. Hence a transformation from the bi-factor coordinate system to a new oblique reference system of m dimensions can be accomplished.

The bi-factor patterns of Tables 6.12 and 6.8 can be shown to be (approximately) of rank three and five, respectively. The composite variables (11.25) are employed, and the reduced patterns of Table 11.12 are obtained. The same notation is used throughout the parallel development, but the reader should have no difficulty distinguishing the two examples. Denoting the oblique reference axes by β's, their direction cosines with respect to the bi-factor reference systems are given in Table 11.13. Then the correlations among the factors can be calculated and are presented in Table 11.14.

TABLE 11.14

INTERCORRELATIONS OF FACTORS

	For Thirteen Variables				For Twenty-four Variables				
	β_1	β_2	β_3		β_1	β_2	β_3	β_4	β_5
β_1.......	1.000	......	......	β_1.....	1.000	......	......	......	......
β_2.......	.586	1.000	......	β_2.....	.538	1.000	......	......	......
β_3.......	.446	.451	1.000	β_3.....	.499	.469	1.000	......	......
				β_4.....	.586	.551	.511	1.000	......
				β_5.....	.756	.711	.660	.775	1.000

TABLE 11.15[a]

OBLIQUE SOLUTION FOR THIRTEEN PSYCHOLOGICAL TESTS

Test j	Structure			Pattern			Commu-nality h_j^2
	$r_{j\beta_1}$	$r_{j\beta_2}$	$r_{j\beta_3}$	Spatial β_1	Verbal β_2	Speed β_3	
1........	.743	.472	.360	**.704**	.049	.024	.555
2........	.450	.261	.199	**.453**	−.005	−.001	.199
3........	.589	.284	.216	**.654**	−.082	−.039	.353
4........	.558	.354	.269	**.530**	.036	.016	.313
5........	.498	.802	.383	.038	**.771**	.019	.644
6........	.460	.801	.354	−.012	**.809**	−.005	.640
7........	.440	.857	.339	−.084	**.924**	−.040	.741
8........	.547	.703	.421	.182	**.555**	.090	.527
9........	.405	.849	.312	−.124	**.950**	−.062	.737
10........	.186	.188	.713	−.110	−.115	**.814**	.539
11........	.322	.325	.669	.021	.019	**.651**	.449
12........	.264	.266	.722	−.047	−.053	**.767**	.527
13........	.491	.495	.725	.141	.142	**.598**	.573
	Reduced Structure			Reduced Pattern			
u_1........	.823	.482	.367	**.823**	.000	.000	.677
u_2........	.558	.952	.429	.001	**.951**	−.001	.904
u_3........	.401	.405	.899	.001	−.001	**.899**	.808

[a] Based upon the bi-factor solution of Table 6.12.

The complete oblique solution for the thirteen tests is given in Table 11.15. Although based upon a bi-factor pattern involving four factors, there are only three oblique factors in this solution. The implication of this is that a solution which fits the data about as well as the bi-factor pattern of Table 6.12 can be made in terms of one fewer, but correlated, factors. Geometrically, the thirteen points representing the variables are approximated by a three-space in the oblique solution, whereas they are contained in a four-space in the bi-factor solution. Hence the communalities as given by the former solution are slightly less than those given by the latter. This may be noted from the last columns of Tables 11.15 and 6.12. The total contributions of the three oblique factors are indicated in Table 11.16, where the grand total is also given. This number, of course, falls short of the total original bi-factor communality (6.936), because the common-factor space is smaller. The difference (0.136) is so small, however, that the greater simplicity of having only three factors in the solution is well worth the sacrifice.

TABLE 11.16

TOTAL CONTRIBUTIONS OF FACTORS

	β_1	β_2	β_3
β_1......	1.501	....	....
β_2......	− .049	3.360	....
β_3......	.000	− .061	2.049

Grand total = 6.800

The oblique solution for the set of twenty-four psychological tests is presented in Table 11.17. Here, again, there is one fewer of the oblique factors than bi-factors upon which the solution is based. The communalities reproduced by the oblique solution are then slightly smaller than those from the bi-factor solution. These communalities are not calculated for the individual variables, but the total contributions of the factors are given in Table 11.18. The grand total of the contributions accounts for 96 per cent of the total bi-factor communality.

As in the case of the two oblique solutions based upon the centroid patterns, there is excellent agreement for the thirteen variables common to the solutions of Tables 11.15 and 11.17. Furthermore, the oblique solutions of Tables 11.6 and 11.15 for the set of thirteen variables are in harmony; and this is true also for the two solutions of the set of twenty-four variables. The oblique factors identified in any one of these solutions are practically identical with those of any of the others. Thus, there is evidence that an oblique solution is more or less invariant regardless of the particular form of the initial solution. What is important in order that the oblique solution shall be "almost unique," however, is that there be clearly defined subsets of variables.

TABLE 11.17[a]
OBLIQUE SOLUTION FOR TWENTY-FOUR PSYCHOLOGICAL TESTS

Test	STRUCTURE					PATTERN				
j	$r_{j\beta_1}$	$r_{j\beta_2}$	$r_{j\beta_3}$	$r_{j\beta_4}$	$r_{j\beta_5}$	Spatial β_1	Verbal β_2	Speed β_3	Memory β_4	Deduction β_5
1.....	.762	.419	.389	.456	.589	**.740**	.001	.001	− .001	.028
2.....	.456	.254	.236	.277	.357	**.434**	.001	− .001	.001	.028
3.....	.617	.285	.265	.311	.401	**.730**	− .003	− .001	− .000	− .147
4.....	.558	.329	.305	.359	.463	**.484**	− .001	− .002	− .002	.102
5.....	.440	.817	.384	.451	.582	− .001	**.814**	− .001	− .002	.006
6.....	.435	.802	.379	.446	.575	− .000	**.795**	− .002	.000	.011
7.....	.404	.878	.352	.414	.534	− .002	**1.006**	− .003	− .002	− .175
8.....	.472	.707	.412	.484	.624	.002	**.533**	− .000	.000	.243
9.....	.424	.840	.369	.434	.560	.001	**.894**	− .001	.003	− .079
10.....	.293	.276	.702	.301	.388	.002	.001	**.793**	.003	− .141
11.....	.394	.370	.703	.404	.521	.002	− .000	**.636**	.004	.096
12.....	.306	.287	.749	.313	.404	.001	− .001	**.853**	− .001	− .158
13.....	.436	.409	.709	.446	.576	.002	− .002	**.582**	− .000	.192
14.....	.293	.276	.256	.581	.388	.001	.000	.002	**.701**	− .158
15.....	.265	.250	.232	.517	.351	− .001	− .001	.002	**.613**	− .124
16.....	.375	.353	.327	.566	.496	.003	.002	.001	**.457**	.136
17.....	.319	.300	.278	.694	.422	.001	− .000	.002	**.920**	− .294
18.....	.390	.366	.340	.571	.515	.002	− .001	.001	**.429**	.181
19.....	.334	.314	.292	.445	.442	.000	− .001	− .000	.257	.243
20.....	.487	.458	.425	.499	.644	.000	.000	.000	.000	**.644**
21.....	.488	.459	.426	.500	.645	.001	.000	.000	.000	**.644**
22.....	.487	.458	.425	.499	.644	.000	.000	.000	.000	**.644**
23.....	.555	.522	.484	.569	.734	− .001	− .001	− .003	− .002	**.740**
24.....	.539	.506	.470	.552	.712	− .000	− .002	− .001	− .003	**.718**

	Reduced Structure					Reduced Pattern				
u_1.....	.842	.453	.420	.493	.637	**.842**	.000	.000	.000	.000
u_2.....	.516	.960	.450	.529	.682	− .001	**.958**	.000	.002	.000
u_3.....	.454	.427	.910	.465	.600	.000	− .000	**.909**	.000	.000
u_4.....	.501	.471	.437	.855	.663	− .002	.001	− .001	**.851**	.006
u_5.....	.691	.650	.603	.708	.914	− .002	− .002	− .003	− .002	**.921**

[a] Based upon the bi-factor solution of Table 6.8.

TABLE 11.18
TOTAL CONTRIBUTIONS OF FACTORS

	β_1	β_2	β_3	β_4	β_5
β_1.......	1.503	....	....	....	....
β_2.......	− .003	3.390	....	....	....
β_3.......	.003	− .007	2.100	....	....
β_4.......	.002	− .001	.010	2.173	....
β_5.......	− .036	− .150	− .102	− .401	2.765

Grand total = 11.246

11.5. *Illustration of Inapplicability of an Oblique Solution*

Now an illustration will be given in which an oblique solution is not suitable. Such a situation arises when there is no evidence of clearly defined clusters either by the method of *B*-coefficients or by inspection of a preliminary orthogonal pattern. The example of eight political variables of **7.5** is employed for this purpose. The principal-factor pattern of Table 7.9 is reproduced in Table 11.19 for convenience.

Although all the variables do not fall into distinct clusters, two subsets can be selected by inspection of the principal-factor pattern. It may be ob-

TABLE 11.19

INITIAL PRINCIPAL-FACTOR PATTERN AND FINAL OBLIQUE
SOLUTION FOR EIGHT POLITICAL VARIABLES

| VARIABLE | PRINCIPAL-FACTOR PATTERN | | OBLIQUE SOLUTION | | | |
| | | | Structure | | Pattern | |
	P_1	P_2	$r_{j\pi_1}$	$r_{j\pi_2}$	π_1	π_2
1............	.69	−.28	.74	−.57	.76	.03
2............	.88	−.48	.99	−.69	1.16	.22
3............	.87	−.17	.87	−.78	.68	−.24
4............	−.88	−.09	−.79	.87	−.29	.64
5............	.28	.65	.03	−.46	−.85	−1.13
6............	.89	.01	.83	−.85	.42	−.52
7............	−.66	−.56	−.42	−.80	.53	1.21
8............	−.96	−.15	−.84	.96	−.24	.77

served that the groups (1, 2, 3) and (4, 7, 8) are in the fourth and third quadrants, respectively. The eight variables are plotted in Figure 11.4, in which the grouping is verified geometrically. It is also evident from this figure that the clusters are not well defined in terms of the entire set of variables. Passing axes through the composite points determined by the above groups, the oblique factor solution is obtained by the procedure of **11.3** and is presented in Table 11.19.

The oblique factor pattern does not approach the uni-factor form of solution found in the preceding examples. Instead of being involved in distinct groups of variables, the factors are of the bipolar type. The interpretation is no simpler than in the case of the original principal-factor pattern and has the added complexity of correlated factors. Furthermore, the total direct contributions of the two oblique factors are 3.707 and 4.121, respectively, indicating level variances. Thus, while the essential principal-factor form is retained by the oblique solution, the important property of decreasing contributions of factors has been lost. Thus for the present example an oblique solution is evidently not desirable.

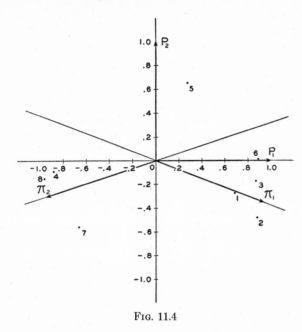

Fig. 11.4

From the foregoing examples it is evident that the usefulness of the oblique form of solution depends upon the design of the set of variables. When the variables can be clearly grouped by the method of B-coefficients or from any preliminary orthogonal pattern, it is to be expected that an oblique solution of the uni-factor form can be obtained. Moreover, such a solution is independent of the particular initial pattern and is practically unique once distinct clusters of variables are determined.

PART IV

ESTIMATION OF FACTORS AND RELATION-
SHIPS BETWEEN FACTORS

CHAPTER XII

ESTIMATION OF FACTORS

12.1. *Introduction*

There are two basic problems with which factor analysis is concerned. The first of these deals with the methods for obtaining the linear resolution of a set of variables in terms of hypothetical factors. The preceding chapters were primarily devoted to the solution of this problem, the results being the preferred solutions. The second problem is concerned with the description of the factors in terms of the observed variables and is the subject matter of the present chapter.

Since the total number of factors (both common and unique) exceeds the number of variables, the value of any particular factor for a given individual cannot be obtained by direct solution but can only be estimated from the observed values of the variables. The best prediction, in the least-square sense, is that obtained by the ordinary regression method. In **12.2** the linear regression of any factor on the n observed variables is obtained by the usual method. This is followed by an approximative method, which employs composite variables, in order to reduce the laborious task of the complete regression method. A method is presented in **12.4** which is superior to either of the preceding because it is more rapid and gives just as accurate results as the complete estimation method. This method, in effect, replaces the observed correlations of variables by those reproduced (or computed) from the factor pattern.

Two other methods, which at present do not seem to be as practical as the preceding ones, are also given. In **12.5** a regression method is presented in which the sum of the squares of the unique factors is minimized. This method produces estimates of factors which are usually quite different from those given by any of the other methods. The final method for describing the factors in terms of the variables involves the mathematical solution of a set of equations rather than the statistical estimation by regression. Hence the factors themselves instead of estimates of them are obtained. Unfortunately, however, this solution is in terms of "ideal" variables (not the observed ones) and therefore cannot be employed in a practical situation.

In order to simplify the development of the following sections, it will be convenient to formulate the essential concepts of the previous chapters in matrix notation. Let it be assumed that a set of n variables has been analyzed in terms of m common factors $(F_1, F_2, \ldots, F_m)$ and n unique factors

$(U_1, U_2, \ldots, U_n)$ as given by (2.16). Such a factor pattern may be written in the form of a matrix equation as follows:

(12.1) $$Z = MF,$$

where the column vectors

(12.2) $$\begin{cases} Z = \{z_1 \quad z_2 \ldots z_n\} \\ F = \{F_1 \quad F_2 \ldots F_m \quad U_1 \quad U_2 \ldots U_n\} \end{cases}$$

represent the variables* and factors, respectively, and M is the complete pattern matrix,

(12.3) $$M = \begin{Vmatrix} a_{11} & a_{12} & \ldots & a_{1m} & a_1 & 0 & \ldots & 0 \\ a_{21} & a_{22} & \ldots & a_{2m} & 0 & a_2 & \ldots & 0 \\ \cdot & \cdot & \cdot & \cdot & \cdot & \cdot & \cdot & \cdot \\ a_{n1} & a_{n2} & \ldots & a_{nm} & 0 & 0 & \ldots & a_n \end{Vmatrix}.$$

If the matrix of coefficients of the common factors is represented by A and the diagonal matrix of unique-factor coefficients is denoted by U, then M may be written as the composite of these matrices, i.e.,

(12.4) $$M = \|A \quad U\|.$$

It will be assumed that the unique factors are uncorrelated among themselves and with all common factors, but, unless stated to the contrary, the common factors may be correlated.

It was shown in **2.4** that when the common factors are uncorrelated the correlation of a variable with a factor is given by the corresponding coefficient in the factor pattern. Hence, for the orthogonal case the factor structure is identical with the matrix M. If the factors are correlated, however, this is no longer true. In that case the factor structure may be defined by

(12.5) $$S = \|T \quad U\| = \begin{Vmatrix} t_{11} & t_{12} & \ldots & t_{1m} & a_1 & 0 & \ldots & 0 \\ t_{21} & t_{22} & \ldots & t_{2m} & 0 & a_2 & \ldots & 0 \\ \cdot & \cdot & \cdot & \cdot & \cdot & \cdot & \cdot & \cdot \\ t_{n1} & t_{n2} & \ldots & t_{nm} & 0 & 0 & \ldots & a_n \end{Vmatrix},$$

where $t_{js} = r_{z_j F_s}$ and $a_j = r_{z_j U_j}$.

The notations here introduced will be used throughout the chapter. Additional definitions will be made, as needed, in the course of the development of the various procedures.

---

* Strictly speaking, of course, the variables should be designated by primes on the z's.

12.2. *Complete Estimation Method*

The rectilinear prediction of any common factor F_s involves the determination of the coefficients in the regression equation

$$(12.6) \qquad \bar{F}_s = \beta_{s1}z_1 + \beta_{s2}z_2 + \ldots + \beta_{sj}z_j + \ldots + \beta_{sn}z_n$$

$$(s = 1, 2, \ldots, m),$$

where the $(n-1)$ secondary subscripts have been omitted from the conventional notation for regression coefficients. A similar equation can be written for any one of the unique factors by employing it in place of F_s in equation (12.6). By the general theory of multivariate regression, it can be shown that the normal equations for the determination of the β's in (12.6) may be written as follows:

$$(12.7) \qquad \begin{cases} \beta_{s1} + r_{12}\beta_{s2} + \ldots + r_{1n}\beta_{sn} = t_{1s}, \\ r_{21}\beta_{s1} + \beta_{s2} + \ldots + r_{2n}\beta_{sn} = t_{2s}, \\ \cdot \quad \cdot \quad \cdot \quad \cdot \quad \cdot \quad \cdot \quad \cdot \quad \cdot \quad \cdot \\ r_{n1}\beta_{s1} + r_{n2}\beta_{s2} + \ldots + \beta_{sn} = t_{ns}. \end{cases}$$

Thus any factor F_s can be estimated when the correlations (t_{js}) of the variables with this factor and the observed correlations (r_{jk}) among the variables themselves are known. Of course, if a unique factor U_j is being estimated, then all the correlations of this factor with the variables are zero, except for the correlation with z_j which is equal to a_j.

The solution of equations (12.7) can be simply obtained by the determinantal method (Cramer's rule). To this end, define the matrix $\mathbf{D}$ of intercorrelations of variables bordered by their correlations with the factor F_s, as follows:

$$(12.8) \qquad \mathbf{D} = \begin{Vmatrix} 1 & t_{1s} & t_{2s} & \ldots & t_{ns} \\ t_{1s} & 1 & r_{12} & \ldots & r_{1n} \\ t_{2s} & r_{21} & 1 & \ldots & r_{2n} \\ \cdot & \cdot & \cdot & \cdot & \cdot \\ t_{ns} & r_{n1} & r_{n2} & \ldots & 1 \end{Vmatrix}.$$

Then the regression coefficient of any variable z_j in the estimation of F_s is given by

$$(12.9) \qquad \beta_{sj} = -\frac{D_{js}}{D_{ss}} \qquad (j = 1, 2, \ldots, n),$$

where D_{ss} is the minor of the first element and D_{js} is the cofactor of t_{js} in $\mathbf{D}$. It should be noted that D_{ss} is merely the determinant R of observed correlations and that the determinants D_{js} can be expressed in terms of the co-factors of the original correlation matrix $\mathbf{R}$. Thus the values (12.9) may be written explicitly in the form

$$(12.10) \qquad \beta_{sj} = \frac{1}{R} [t_{1s}R_{1j} + t_{2s}R_{2j} + \ldots + t_{ns}R_{nj}] ,$$

where R_{kj} is the cofactor of r_{kj} in $\mathbf{R}$.

The regression equation (12.6) for F_s may then be written as follows:

$$(12.11) \qquad \bar{F}_s = \mathbf{t}_s'\mathbf{R}^{-1}\mathbf{Z} ,$$

where $\mathbf{t}_s$ is the column vector $\{t_{1s}\ t_{2s}\ \ldots\ t_{ns}\}$ taken from column s of the factor structure $\mathbf{S}$. In particular, if F_s is one of the unique factors, say U_j, this equation becomes

$$(12.12) \qquad \bar{U}_j = \|0\ \ 0\ \ \ldots\ \ a_j\ \ \ldots\ \ 0\|\mathbf{R}^{-1}\mathbf{Z} ,$$

or, in expanded form,

$$(12.13) \qquad \bar{U}_j = \frac{a_j}{R} [R_{1j}z_1 + R_{2j}z_2 + \ldots + R_{nj}z_n] .$$

If in equation (12.11), s takes on the values $1, 2, \ldots, m$, the results can be expressed in a matrix equation as follows:

$$(12.14) \qquad \bar{\mathbf{f}} = \mathbf{T}'\mathbf{R}^{-1}\mathbf{Z} ,$$

where $\bar{\mathbf{f}}$ is the column vector $\{\bar{F}_1\ \bar{F}_2\ \ldots\ \bar{F}_m\}$ of common-factor estimates. More generally, if the range of s in (12.11) extends over the unique factors as well as the common factors, then the matrix equation for the prediction of the entire set of factors becomes

$$(12.15) \qquad \bar{\mathbf{F}} = \mathbf{S}'\mathbf{R}^{-1}\mathbf{Z} ,$$

where $\bar{\mathbf{F}}$ is the column vector of all the factor estimates. Furthermore, this equation represents the estimates for *all* the individuals if $\mathbf{Z}$ is regarded as the matrix of all the values of the set of variables.

An entire set of factors, whether orthogonal or oblique, can be estimated by means of equation (12.15). When the factors are uncorrelated, however, the elements of $\mathbf{M}$ are equal to the corresponding elements of $\mathbf{S}$, i.e., the pattern and structure coincide. Then equation (12.15) may be written in the form

$$(12.16) \qquad \bar{\mathbf{F}} = \mathbf{M}'\mathbf{R}^{-1}\mathbf{Z} \qquad \text{(uncorrelated factors)} .$$

If the factors are correlated, equation (12.16) obviously does not apply. Then the distinction between a pattern and structure must be clearly made.

It is possible to write a formula for the prediction of correlated factors which explicitly employs the pattern matrix $\mathbf{M}$. Let the matrix of correlations among the common factors be denoted by

$$(12.17) \qquad \phi = \begin{Vmatrix} 1 & r_{F_1 F_2} & \cdots & r_{F_1 F_m} \\ r_{F_2 F_1} & 1 & \cdots & r_{F_2 F_m} \\ \cdot & \cdot & \cdots & \cdot \\ r_{F_m F_1} & r_{F_m F_2} & \cdots & 1 \end{Vmatrix}$$

so that the matrix of correlations among all the factors is

$$(12.18) \qquad \Phi = \begin{Vmatrix} \phi & O \\ O & I \end{Vmatrix} .$$

The relationship between a factor pattern and a structure is

$$(12.19) \qquad S = M\Phi ,$$

which is proved in Appendix **B.11**. Substituting this expression into equation (12.15), the latter becomes

$$(12.20) \qquad \overline{F} = \Phi M' R^{-1} Z ,$$

upon recalling that Φ is a symmetric matrix. This equation reduces to (12.16) when all the factors are uncorrelated.

Since the unique factors are of minor interest in factor analysis, it is convenient to write a formula for the prediction of the common factors employing the pattern matrix $\mathbf{A}$. Substituting

$$(12.21) \qquad T = A\phi ,$$

which relation is shown in Appendix **B.11**, into equation (12.14), this becomes

$$(12.22) \qquad \overline{f} = \phi A' R^{-1} Z .$$

In case the common factors are uncorrelated, this equation reduces to

$$(12.23) \qquad \overline{f} = A' R^{-1} Z \qquad \text{(uncorrelated factors)} .$$

In the preceding formulas the pattern values are employed instead of the structure values.

A measure of the accuracy of estimation of a factor F_s by means of equation (12.6) is given by the coefficient of multiple correlation, which is designated by R_s. Several important and useful formulas involving R_s will next be developed. The normal equations for the regression equation (12.6) may be written in the condensed form

$$(12.24) \qquad \Sigma[F_{si} - \bar{F}_{si}]z_{ji} = 0 \qquad (j = 1, 2, \ldots, n),$$

where the summation extends over the N observations of each variable. It will be understood, in the following, that Σ means "sum for i from $i = 1$ to $i = N$," although the i is omitted. Since the set of residuals $(F_s - \bar{F}_s)$ is orthogonal to each of the n sets of numbers z_j, it is orthogonal to any linear combination of these z_j. In particular, the set $\bar{F}_s$ is such a linear combination, and hence

$$(12.25) \qquad \Sigma[F_s - \bar{F}_s]\bar{F}_s = 0.$$

This may be written

$$\Sigma F_s \bar{F}_s = \Sigma \bar{F}_s^2,$$

which, upon dividing through by N, reduces to

$$(12.26) \qquad \sigma_{\bar{F}_s} r_{F_s \bar{F}_s} = \sigma_{\bar{F}_s}^2.$$

The coefficient of multiple correlation of F_s in terms of $z_1, z_2, \ldots, z_n$ is defined to be the simple correlation coefficient of F_s and $\bar{F}_s$. The expression (12.26) may finally be written in the form

$$(12.27) \qquad R_s = r_{F_s \bar{F}_s} = \sigma_{\bar{F}_s}.$$

This formula shows that the standard deviation of the factor estimates is equal to the coefficient of multiple correlation.

A simple formula for the calculation of R_s may be given now. Multiply both sides of (12.6) by F_s and sum for the N individuals, obtaining

$$\Sigma F_s \bar{F}_s = \beta_{s1}\Sigma z_1 F_s + \beta_{s2}\Sigma z_2 F_s + \ldots + \beta_{sn}\Sigma z_n F_s.$$

Upon dividing by N, this equation becomes

$$\sigma_{\bar{F}_s} r_{F_s \bar{F}_s} = \beta_{s1} t_{1s} + \beta_{s2} t_{2s} + \ldots + \beta_{sn} t_{ns}.$$

Then, according to (12.27),

$$(12.28) \qquad R_s^2 = \beta_{s1} t_{1s} + \beta_{s2} t_{2s} + \ldots + \beta_{sn} t_{ns}.$$

This is the simplest formula for the computation of the multiple correlation coefficient.

Another formula for the calculation of R_s can readily be obtained. Multiply the first of the normal equations (12.7) by β_{s1}, the second by β_{s2}, etc., thus obtaining

$$(12.29) \quad \begin{cases} \beta_{s1}t_{1s} = \beta_{s1}^2 + \beta_{s1}\beta_{s2}r_{12} + \ldots + \beta_{s1}\beta_{sn}r_{1n}, \\ \beta_{s2}t_{2s} = \beta_{s2}\beta_{s1}r_{21} + \beta_{s2}^2 + \ldots + \beta_{s2}\beta_{sn}r_{2n}, \\ \cdot \quad \cdot \quad \cdot \quad \cdot \quad \cdot \quad \cdot \quad \cdot \quad \cdot \quad \cdot \quad \cdot \quad \cdots \quad \cdot \quad \cdot \quad \cdot \quad \cdot \\ \beta_{sn}t_{ns} = \beta_{sn}\beta_{s1}r_{n1} + \beta_{sn}\beta_{s2}r_{n2} + \ldots + \beta_{sn}^2. \end{cases}$$

Adding these equations, and employing (12.28), there results

$$(12.30) \qquad R_s^2 = \sum_{j=1}^n \beta_{sj}^2 + 2\sum_{j<k=1}^n \beta_{sj}\beta_{sk}r_{jk}.$$

This formula, although not so simple as (12.28) for computing R_s, illustrates an important property. Any product term $\beta_{sj}t_{js}$ in (12.28) measures the *total* (*direct* and *indirect*) contribution of the corresponding variable X_j to R_s^2, or the importance of that variable as a "determiner" of F_s. The resolution of the total contribution of any variable into its direct and indirect effect upon F_s is indicated in (12.29). Thus, while $\beta_{s1}t_{1s}$ represents the total portion of R_s^2 which is due to X_1, the right-hand member of the first of equations (12.29) shows that this is composed of the direct contribution (β_{s1}^2) of X_1 and of the indirect contribution $(\beta_{s1}\beta_{sk}r_{1k})$ of X_1 through its correlations with each of the other variables X_k ($k = 2, 3, \ldots, n$). It may be noted that the indirect or joint contribution of any two variables is distributed equally between them.

While the determinantal method for the calculation of the regression coefficients, given by formula (12.9), has some undisputed theoretical advantages, a more economical procedure is desired, especially when dealing with a large number of variables. Gauss's method of substitution, which is described in Appendix **G.1**, is employed for this purpose. The latter method produces a routine scheme for the evaluation of the β's and also furnishes a complete check on the arithmetical work. Two illustrations of the complete estimation of factors are presented in **G.4**. These illustrations are for the sets of principal factors and oblique factors for the eight physical variables.

The values of the regression coefficients in the equations for the prediction of the oblique factors γ_1 (Lankiness) and γ_2 (Stockiness) are given in Table G.5. The equations may be written explicitly as follows:

$$(12.31) \quad \begin{cases} \bar{\gamma}_{1i} = .275z_{1i} + .391z_{2i} + .203z_{3i} + .158z_{4i} + .043z_{5i} \\ \qquad\qquad\qquad - .009z_{6i} - .005z_{7i} - .002z_{8i}, \\ \bar{\gamma}_{2i} = -.048z_{1i} + .135z_{2i} - .072z_{3i} + .026z_{4i} + .606z_{5i} \\ \qquad\qquad\qquad + .208z_{6i} + .073z_{7i} + .163z_{8i}. \end{cases}$$

The values of these factors for a particular individual i are obtained by substituting the appropriate standardized values in the above equations. The subscript i has been included in these equations to indicate clearly that values are substituted for the variables in order to get particular estimates

TABLE 12.1

VALUES OF EIGHT PHYSICAL VARIABLES FOR TWO GIRLS

VARIABLE	CASE 1		CASE 2	
	X_{j1}	z_{j1}	X_{j2}	z_{j2}
1. Height	63.98 in.	0.01	66.34 in.	1.14
2. Arm span	63.19 in.	−0.42	66.89 in.	1.06
3. Length of forearm	16.89 in.	−0.31	17.99 in.	1.33
4. Length of lower leg	19.09 in.	−0.62	20.71 in.	1.27
5. Weight	149.25 lb.	1.98	125.5 lb.	0.41
6. Bitrochanteric diameter	13.15 in.	1.33	12.44 in.	0.26
7. Chest girth	34.37 in.	1.65	32.52 in.	0.69
8. Chest width	10.87 in.	1.42	10.55 in.	0.94

TABLE 12.2

MEANS AND STANDARD DEVIATIONS OF EIGHT
PHYSICAL VARIABLES FOR 305
FIFTEEN-YEAR-OLD GIRLS

Variable j	Mean M_j	Standard Deviation σ_j
1. Height	63.96 in.	2.09 in.
2. Arm span	64.25 in.	2.50 in.
3. Length of forearm	17.10 in.	.67 in.
4. Length of lower leg	19.62 in.	.86 in.
5. Weight	119.22 lb.	15.19 lb.
6. Bitrochanteric diameter	12.27 in.	.66 in.
7. Chest girth	31.21 in.	1.91 in.
8. Chest width	9.92 in.	.67 in.

of the factors. In general, however, the secondary subscript is dropped for simplicity.

The prediction of the above factors will now be illustrated for two individuals whose measurements for the eight variables are given in Table 12.1. The original observations X_{ji} are changed to standardized values z_{ji} by application of formula (2.2). The means and standard deviations required for this change are given in Table 12.2. Upon substituting the values z_{ji} into equations (12.31), the resulting estimates become

Estimates for Case 1: $\bar{\gamma}_{11} = -0.26,$ $\bar{\gamma}_{21} = 1.78$;

Estimates for Case 2: $\bar{\gamma}_{12} = $ $1.21,$ $\bar{\gamma}_{22} = 0.53$.

It can be seen from the eight standardized values for each girl in Table 12.1 that the first is of the stocky type and the second is tall or lanky. While the original values reveal these facts, they can be indicated more simply by the above factor estimates. Although the estimated factors are not in standard form, their standard deviations (.980 and .962) are nearly the same, and so the estimated values are approximately comparable. The estimates for the first girl indicate clearly that she is almost two standard deviations above the mean in the factor "Stockiness" and slightly below the average in "Lankiness." The second girl is a less extreme type—being less lanky than the other girl is stocky and also being above average in "Stockiness."

In the foregoing illustrations standardized values were employed in the direct application of equations (12.31). The calculations of the standardized values for many variables for a large sample of individuals is laborious. The work can be greatly reduced by formally expressing the equations of estimation in terms of observed values by the use of formula (2.2). Thus, in general, an equation of the form (12.6) may be written as follows:

(12.32) $$\bar{F}_s = \frac{\beta_{s1}}{\sigma_1} X_1 + \frac{\beta_{s2}}{\sigma_2} X_2 + \ldots + \frac{\beta_{sn}}{\sigma_n} X_n - C ,$$

where

(12.33) $$C = \frac{\beta_{s1}}{\sigma_1} M_1 + \frac{\beta_{s2}}{\sigma_2} M_2 + \ldots + \frac{\beta_{sn}}{\sigma_n} M_n .$$

It should be noted that an estimated factor is not in standard form. Such a variable, however, has a mean of zero and a standard deviation which is equal to the coefficient of multiple correlation as shown by (12.27). For data which produce a high multiple correlation the estimated factor is almost in standard form.

The values of the factors estimated by equation (12.6), or (12.32), include both positive and negative numbers. If it is desired to eliminate the negative values, a transformation can be made to an arbitrary positive scale. This can be accomplished by standardizing the values $\bar{F}_{si}$ given by (12.32) and equating this variable to an arbitrary variable in standard form. Thus if the arbitrary variable Y is assigned a mean of 50 and standard deviation of 10, the required transformation can be written in the form

(12.34) $$\bar{Y}_s = \frac{10}{\sigma_{\bar{F}_s}} \bar{F}_s + 50 ,$$

which reduces to

$$(12.35) \qquad \bar{Y}_s = \frac{10}{R_s} \bar{F}_s + 50$$

upon substituting the multiple correlation coefficient for the standard deviation of the estimated factor according to (12.27). Such transformations have been found especially useful in comparing factor estimates from a battery of psychological tests.*

An illustration of the proportions of the variance of one of the above estimated factors due to the eight physical variables will now be given. The direct and indirect contributions of these variables on the prediction of the factor "Lankiness" are indicated in Table 12.3. Each entry in the table

TABLE 12.3

PROPORTIONS OF VARIANCE OF COMPUTED γ_1 DUE
TO THE INDEPENDENT VARIABLES

Variable	1	2	3	4	5	6	7	8	Total Contribution $\beta_{1j}t_{j1}$
1...........									.253
2...........	.182								.369
3...........	.090	.140							.184
4...........	.075	.102	.051						.141
5...........	.011	.013	.007	.006					.020
6...........	−.002	−.002	−.001	−.001	−.001				−.003
7...........	−.001	−.001	−.000	−.001	−.000	.000			−.002
8...........	−.000	−.001	−.000	−.000	−.000	.000	.000		−.001
Direct contribution........	.076	.153	.041	.025	.002	.000	.000	.000	
Indirect contribution......	.177	.216	.143	.116	.018	−.003	−.002	−.001	$R_1^2 = .961$

proper represents the total indirect contribution $(2\beta_{1j}\beta_{1k}r_{jk})$ of variables X_j and X_k. The total indirect contribution of any variable is equal to one-half of the sum in the row and column representing that variable and is given in the last row of the table. The direct contributions (β_{1j}^2) are given in the row preceding the last. The total contribution $(\beta_{1j}t_{j1})$ of each variable is presented in the last column of the table. Of course, the sum of the direct and indirect contributions of each variable must be equal to its total contribution. Finally, the sum of the entries in the last column (or last two rows) is equal to the square of the coefficient of multiple correlation.

* Karl J. Holzinger and Frances Swineford, *A Study in Factor Analysis*, 1939.

Although the complete estimation method has been developed and illustrated in the present section, it is not very practical. The general formula (12.15), or (12.20), involves the calculation of the inverse of an $n \times n$ matrix of correlations—a task which is very laborious as n becomes large. The present method, nevertheless, forms the basis for the simplified methods of the succeeding sections.

12.3. *Approximative Method*

Several approximations for the estimation of common factors have been proposed* in order to reduce the matrix whose inverse is required. Such approximative methods involve the grouping of certain variables into composites. The simplest procedure is as follows: Combine the respective subsets of variables which best measure the factors and employ formula (12.14) in which all the symbols now stand for the corresponding reduced matrices. The approximative method is best adapted to the case of many variables which fall into a relatively small number of distinct subgroups. In applying formula (12.14) to such an example including, say, m subgroups, the $m \times m$ matrix of intercorrelations among the composite variables is used in the place of **R**. Then the major portion of the calculations is greatly reduced. The effect of this procedure is to give all variables of a subgroup equal weight.

If it is desired to give varying weights to some of the individual variables, the preceding method can be modified slightly. For example, if the first four variables of a set are the best measures of the first common factor, they may be used individually, while all other variables are grouped into composites, for the estimation of this factor. The matrix whose inverse is required then consists of the intercorrelations of the first four variables and the $(m - 1)$ composite variables. When the second, and successive, factors are estimated, the corresponding variables which best measure them are retained, while all other variables are grouped into composites.

To illustrate the approximative method, the data of the eight physical variables are again employed. Grouping the variables as indicated in (11.10) and using the standard deviations of (11.11), the composite variables may be written as follows:

$$(12.36) \quad \begin{cases} u_1 = \dfrac{v_1}{\sigma_{v_1}} = \dfrac{z_1 + z_2 + z_3 + z_4}{3.7465}, \\[3mm] u_2 = \dfrac{v_2}{\sigma_{v_2}} = \dfrac{z_5 + z_6 + z_7 + z_8}{3.4117}. \end{cases}$$

* Harry H. Harman, "Systems of Regression Equations for the Estimation of Factors," *Journal of Educational Psychology*, 1938.

The correlation between these composites can be calculated by means of formula (2.42), yielding

$$(12.37) \qquad r_{v_1 v_2} = \frac{\displaystyle\sum_{j=1}^{4}\sum_{k=5}^{8} r_{jk}}{\sigma_{v_1}\sigma_{v_2}} = \frac{5.686}{12.782} = .4448 \,,$$

in which the correlations of the original variables are taken from Table 7.1. The estimation of the first oblique factor γ_1, for example, can be made from the regression equation

$$(12.38) \qquad \bar{\gamma}_1 = \beta_{11}u_1 + \beta_{12}u_2 \,.$$

The normal equations (12.7) for this case become

$$(12.39) \qquad \begin{cases} \beta_{11} + .4448\beta_{12} = .977 \,, \\ .4448\beta_{11} + \qquad \beta_{12} = .455 \,, \end{cases}$$

where the correlations t_{11} and t_{21} of the composite variables with γ_1 are taken from the reduced structure of Table 11.2. The solution of equations (12.39) are $\beta_{11} = .9656$, $\beta_{12} = .0255$, so that

$$(12.40) \qquad \bar{\gamma}_1 = .9656u_1 + .0255u_2 \,.$$

This equation cannot be used for the estimation of individual values of γ_1 unless the values of the composite variables are computed. Rather than do this, however, equation (12.40) can be written explicitly in terms of the original variables by employing the definitions (12.36). Substituting the expressions for u_1 and u_2 in (12.40), this equation becomes

$$(12.41) \qquad \bar{\gamma}_1 = .258(z_1 + z_2 + z_3 + z_4) + .007(z_5 + z_6 + z_7 + z_8) \,.$$

This equation illustrates the fact that all variables of a subgroup are given equal weight by the approximative method. For the two girls, considered before, the values of γ_1 given by (12.41) are $\bar{\gamma}_{11} = -.30$ and $\bar{\gamma}_{12} = 1.25$. The slight discrepancies between these values and those previously obtained are due to the grouping of the variables.

The preceding illustration is given so that direct comparison, for the same data, can be made with the complete estimation method. One would not, ordinarily, use the approximative method when only eight variables are involved. The next illustration is more adapted to the present method.

Consider the problem of estimating the common factors in the twenty-four variable problem of **6.10,** the bi-factor pattern for which is given in

Table 6.8. The approximative method might be used to advantage for an example of this type. For purposes of estimating any of the factors B_0, B_1, B_2, B_3, the variables measuring B_4 and B_5 may be grouped to form a single composite variable v_4 as indicated in (2.45), the effect being merely that variables 14 to 19 will be equally weighted. Of course, in estimating B_4 or B_5, these variables may be given varying weights. Then to estimate the factor B_1 (Spatial Relations), for example, the following regression equation is employed:

$$(12.42) \qquad \bar{B}_1 = \beta_{z_1} z_1 + \beta_{z_2} z_2 + \beta_{z_3} z_3 + \beta_{z_4} z_4 + \beta_{u_2} u_2 + \beta_{u_3} u_3 + \beta_{u_4} u_4 + \beta_{u_5} u_5 ,$$

where, for simplicity, a single subscript is placed on each β to indicate the variable to which it is attached. The β's can be computed by means of a routine scheme such as that indicated in Table G.5. The necessary statistics are the intercorrelations of the first four variables (in Table 2.2), the correlations of these with the four composite variables (in Table 2.5), the intercorrelations of the composites (in Table 2.4), and the correlations of the variables with the factor (in Table 6.8). The equation of estimation becomes

$$(12.43) \quad \left\{ \begin{array}{l} \bar{B}_1 = .468 z_1 + .157 z_2 + .426 z_3 + .182 z_4 \\ \qquad\qquad - .114 u_2 - .013 u_3 - .125 u_4 - .371 u_5 . \end{array} \right.$$

This equation can be written explicitly in terms of the twenty-four observed variables by replacing the standardized composite variables by the corresponding sum of original variables divided by the standard deviation of the sum, that is,

$$(12.44) \qquad u_s = \frac{v_s}{\sigma_{v_s}} = \frac{1}{\sigma_{v_s}} \Sigma(z_j; \ j \epsilon G_s, \ s = 1, 2, 3, 4, 5) ,$$

where the groups of variables are defined in (2.35) and the standard deviations are given in (2.46). Then,

$$(12.45) \quad \left\{ \begin{array}{l} \bar{B}_1 = .468 z_1 + .157 z_2 + .426 z_3 + .182 z_4 \\ \qquad\qquad - .027 (z_5 + z_6 + z_7 + z_8 + z_9) \\ \qquad\qquad - .004 (z_{10} + z_{11} + z_{12} + z_{13}) \\ \qquad\qquad - .032 (z_{14} + z_{15} + z_{16} + z_{17} + z_{18} + z_{19}) \\ \qquad\qquad - .100 (z_{20} + z_{21} + z_{22} + z_{23} + z_{24}) . \end{array} \right.$$

Of course, if it is desired, this equation may be written in terms of the observed variables X_j.

12.4. *Shortened Method*

Recently, a much-shortened method for the appraisal of factors has been developed.* This method, which is just as accurate as the complete estimation method, has the great advantage of replacing the nth order matrix of correlations by a matrix of order equal to the number of common factors. Since the number of such factors is relatively small compared to the number of variables, the labor of computing the reciprocal matrix is greatly reduced.

The matrix of reproduced correlations, with ones in the diagonal, can be expressed as follows:†

$$(12.46) \qquad\qquad \mathbf{R} = \mathbf{M\Phi M'}.$$

Substituting (12.4) for $\mathbf{M}$ and (12.18) for $\mathbf{\Phi}$ into this equation, it becomes

$$(12.47) \quad \mathbf{R} = \|\mathbf{A}\ \ \mathbf{U}\| \cdot \left\| \begin{matrix} \mathbf{\phi} & \mathbf{O} \\ \mathbf{O} & \mathbf{I} \end{matrix} \right\| \cdot \left\| \begin{matrix} \mathbf{A'} \\ \mathbf{U} \end{matrix} \right\| = \|\mathbf{A\phi}\ \ \mathbf{U}\| \cdot \left\| \begin{matrix} \mathbf{A'} \\ \mathbf{U} \end{matrix} \right\| = \mathbf{A\phi A'} + \mathbf{U}^2.$$

This relation is useful in simplifying formula (12.22) for the estimation of the m common factors. Premultiplying both sides of (12.47) by $\mathbf{A'U^{-2}}$ there arises‡

$$\mathbf{A'U^{-2}R} = \mathbf{A'U^{-2}(A\phi A' + U^2)} = (\mathbf{A'U^{-2}A\phi + I})\mathbf{A'},$$

---

* This method was first presented, for the case of uncorrelated factors, by Ledermann, "On a Shortened Method of Estimation of Mental Factors by Regression," *Psychometrika*, 1939. It was then generalized by Harman, "On the Rectilinear Prediction of Oblique Factors," *Psychometrika*, 1941.

† The proof of (12.46) can be made by the method indicated in Appen. **B.11.** The matrix of observed correlations is given by

$$(\text{i}) \qquad\qquad \mathbf{R} = \frac{1}{N}\,\mathbf{ZZ'},$$

and if $\mathbf{Z} = \mathbf{MF}$ is substituted into (i), the matrix of reproduced correlations, with ones in the diagonal, is obtained:

$$(\text{ii}) \qquad \mathbf{R} = \frac{1}{N}\,\mathbf{MFF'M'} = \mathbf{M}\left(\frac{1}{N}\mathbf{FF'}\right)\mathbf{M'} = \mathbf{M\Phi M'},$$

where the last equality follows from (B.41). In replacing observed by computed correlations, the tacit assumption is made that the residuals vanish. To avoid additional symbolism, $\mathbf{R}$ is employed for both matrices, but it should be clear when it is computed from the observed variables and when it is computed from the factor pattern.

‡ Throughout this and the following section it is tacitly assumed that none of the uniquenesses vanishes. For an excellent treatment of the contrary case see Guttman, "Multiple Rectilinear Prediction and the Resolution into Components," *Psychometrika*, 1940, § 17.

or, defining the following $m \times m$ matrix,

$$(12.48) \qquad \mathbf{K} = \mathbf{A'U^{-2}A\phi} \,,$$

this expression reduces to

$$(12.49) \qquad (\mathbf{I} + \mathbf{K})\mathbf{A'} = \mathbf{A'U^{-2}R} \,.$$

Now, premultiplying both members of this equation by $(\mathbf{I} + \mathbf{K})^{-1}$ and postmultiplying by $\mathbf{R}^{-1}$, it becomes

$$(12.50) \qquad \mathbf{A'R^{-1}} = (\mathbf{I} + \mathbf{K})^{-1}\mathbf{A'U^{-2}} \,.$$

Then, substituting (12.50) for $\mathbf{A'R^{-1}}$ in (12.22), there finally results

$$(12.51) \qquad \bar{\mathbf{f}} = \mathbf{\phi}(\mathbf{I} + \mathbf{K})^{-1}\mathbf{A'U^{-2}Z} \,.$$

Although this formula may appear to be more complex than (12.22), it is actually much simpler to apply. Aside from the inverse of the square of the diagonal matrix of unique-factor coefficients, which is obtainable without any effort, the only matrix whose inverse must be calculated is of order m.

To show how the common factors can be estimated by the shortened method, employing the procedure of Appendix G, it is convenient to write formula (12.51) in another form. Premultiply both sides of this equation by $[\mathbf{\phi}(\mathbf{I} + \mathbf{K})^{-1}]^{-1}$ to get

$$(12.52) \qquad (\mathbf{I} + \mathbf{K})\mathbf{\phi}^{-1}\bar{\mathbf{f}} = \mathbf{A'U^{-2}Z} \,.$$

It will be observed that the resulting matrix, on carrying through the multiplications, on each side of (12.52) is of order $m \times 1$. This matrix equation thus represents a system of m algebraic equations, obtained by setting the corresponding elements equal to each other. The matrices in the right-hand member of (12.52) are quite simple, but the expression on the left appears to be rather complex. This expression can be simplified, however, by substituting the definition of $\mathbf{K}$ from (12.48), producing

$$(12.53) \qquad (\mathbf{I} + \mathbf{K})\mathbf{\phi}^{-1} = (\mathbf{I} + \mathbf{A'U^{-2}A\phi})\mathbf{\phi}^{-1} = (\mathbf{\phi}^{-1} + \mathbf{A'U^{-2}A}) \,.$$

Finally, the system of m equations for the estimation of the common factors may be written in the form of the matrix equation

$$(12.54) \qquad \mathbf{L}\bar{\mathbf{f}} = \mathbf{A'U^{-2}Z} \,,$$

where

(12.55) $L = \phi^{-1} + J$ and $J = A'U^{-2}A$.

It can easily be shown that the premultiplier of $\bar{f}$ is a symmetric matrix,* so that the system of equations represented by (12.54) can be solved by the method outlined in Appendix G.1.

In case the common factors are uncorrelated, ϕ is the identity matrix, and formula (12.54) reduces to

(12.56) $(I + J)\bar{f} = A'U^{-2}Z$ (uncorrelated factors) .

The recommended procedure in applying formula (12.56) to a numerical problem is as follows: Divide each element of the jth row of A by a_j^2, for $j = 1$ to $j = n$; this gives the matrix $U^{-2}A$, which occurs as a factor in J and the inverse of which also occurs as a factor in the right-hand member of (12.56). Then multiply A by $U^{-2}A$, column by column,† which yields the $m \times m$ matrix J. Since J is a symmetric matrix, it is necessary to calculate only those elements which lie on and above (or below) the principal diagonal. Finally, add unity to each diagonal element of J to complete the determination of the m equations represented by (12.56). Then the solution for the common factors can be carried out by the method of Appendix G.4.

The procedure for estimating a set of correlated factors by means of (12.54) is quite similar to the preceding. After the matrix J is determined, it must be added to ϕ^{-1} instead of the identity matrix. The procedure for calculating the reciprocal of a matrix is given in Appendix G.5. When the set of equations represented by (12.54) is determined, the solution for the oblique common factors is obtained by the method of G.4.

To illustrate the shortened method, a set of correlated factors will be estimated, and hence the most complex formula can be applied. Again, the example of eight physical variables will be used so that comparison with the solution by the complete estimation method can be made. In estimating the factors γ_1 and γ_2 of the solution given in Table 11.2, it is first necessary to have the uniquenesses of the eight variables. Since this oblique solution is based upon the centroid pattern of Table 8.4, and since the commu-

---

* To prove that L is a symmetric matrix it is sufficient to show that the transpose of this matrix is equal to the matrix itself, namely,

$$L' = (\phi^{-1} + A'U^{-2}A)' = (\phi^{-1})' + (A)'(U^{-2})'(A')' = \phi^{-1} + A'U^{-2}A = L ,$$

since ϕ (and hence ϕ^{-1}) is symmetric, as is also the diagonal matrix U^{-2}.

† This is the same as the conventional row-by-column multiplication of A' by $U^{-2}A$.

nalities remain invariant, the uniquenesses can be obtained simply by subtracting the calculated communalities of Table 8.4 from unity. The matrix of coefficients of the common factors and the matrix of uniquenesses follow:

$$
A = \begin{Vmatrix}
.894 & .051 \\
.956 & -.027 \\
.932 & -.052 \\
.879 & .029 \\
.005 & .930 \\
-.025 & .825 \\
-.060 & .769 \\
.080 & .685
\end{Vmatrix}, \quad
U^2 = \begin{Vmatrix}
.154 & & & & & & & \\
& .111 & & & & & & \\
& & .175 & & & & & \\
& & & .202 & & & & \\
& & & & .132 & & & \\
& & & & & .339 & & \\
& & & & & & .450 & \\
& & & & & & & .471
\end{Vmatrix}.
$$

Dividing each element of the jth row of A by the element in the corresponding row of U^2, the following matrix is obtained:

$$
U^{-2}A = \begin{Vmatrix}
5.805 & .331 \\
8.613 & -.243 \\
5.326 & -.297 \\
4.351 & .144 \\
.038 & 7.045 \\
-.074 & 2.434 \\
-.133 & 1.709 \\
.170 & 1.454
\end{Vmatrix}.
$$

The matrix J can then be calculated upon the column-by-column multiplication of A by this matrix, namely,

$$
\text{(12.57)} \qquad J = A'U^{-2}A = \begin{Vmatrix} 22.236 & -.099 \\ -.099 & 10.913 \end{Vmatrix}.
$$

For the present example the matrix of correlations of the common factors is

$$
\phi = \begin{Vmatrix} 1.000 & .484 \\ .484 & 1.000 \end{Vmatrix},
$$

and the inverse of this matrix, calculated in Appendix G.5, is

$$
\text{(12.58)} \qquad \phi^{-1} = \begin{Vmatrix} 1.306 & -.632 \\ -.632 & 1.305 \end{Vmatrix}.
$$

The sum of the two matrices in (12.57) and (12.58) is given by

$$(12.59) \qquad L = \phi^{-1} + J = \begin{Vmatrix} 23.542 & -.731 \\ -.731 & 12.218 \end{Vmatrix}.$$

Completing the indicated multiplications in (12.54), this equation becomes

$$\begin{Vmatrix} 23.542\bar{\gamma}_1 - .731\bar{\gamma}_2 \\ -.731\bar{\gamma}_1 + 12.218\bar{\gamma}_2 \end{Vmatrix} = \begin{Vmatrix} 5.805z_1 + 8.613z_2 + \ldots + .170z_8 \\ .331z_1 - .243z_2 + \ldots + 1.454z_8 \end{Vmatrix},$$

or, upon equating the corresponding elements, the following pair of algebraic equations arise for the solution of $\bar{\gamma}_1$ and $\bar{\gamma}_2$:

$$(12.60) \quad \begin{cases} 23.542\bar{\gamma}_1 - .731\bar{\gamma}_2 = (5.805z_1 + 8.613z_2 + \ldots + .170z_8), \\ -.731\bar{\gamma}_1 + 12.218\bar{\gamma}_2 = (.331z_1 - .243z_2 + \ldots + 1.454z_8). \end{cases}$$

The set of equations (12.60) can be solved by the method of Appendix G, as indicated in Table 12.4. Then the equations for the estimation of γ_1 and

TABLE 12.4

SOLUTION OF (12.60) BY GAUSS'S METHOD OF SUBSTITUTION

COEFFICIENTS OF FACTORS		VARIABLE								CHECK
γ_1	γ_2	1	2	3	4	5	6	7	8	
		Forward Solution								
23.542	− .731	5.805	8.613	5.326	4.351	.038	− .074	− .133	.170	46.907
− 1.	.031	− .247	− .366	− .226	− .185	− .002	.003	.006	− .007	− 1.993
....	12.218	.331	− .243	− .297	.144	7.045	2.434	1.709	1.454	24.795
....	− .023	.180	.267	.165	.135	.001	− .002	− .004	.005	.724
....	12.195	.511	.024	− .132	.279	7.046	2.432	1.705	1.459	25.519
....	− 1.	− .042	− .002	.011	− .023	− .578	− .199	− .140	− .120	− 2.093
		Back Solution								
	$\beta_{2j}\ldots$	.042	.002	− .011	.023	.578	.199	.140	.120	....
	$\beta_{1j}\ldots$	.248	.366	.226	.184	.020	.003	− .002	.011	....

γ_2 may be written in full as follows:

$$(12.61) \quad \begin{cases} \bar{\gamma}_1 = .248z_1 + .366z_2 + .226z_3 + .184z_4 + .020z_5 \\ \qquad\qquad\qquad\qquad + .003z_6 - .002z_7 + .011z_8, \\ \bar{\gamma}_2 = .042z_1 + .002z_2 - .011z_3 + .023z_4 + .578z_5 \\ \qquad\qquad\qquad\qquad + .199z_6 + .140z_7 + .120z_8. \end{cases}$$

These equations agree very well with (12.31), the minor discrepancies being due to the fact that the correlations computed from the factor pattern are not exactly equal to the corresponding observed correlations. The coefficients of multiple correlation, $R_1 = .978$ and $R_2 = .958$, indicate that the equations (12.61) for the prediction of γ_1 and γ_2 are just as reliable as the equations (12.31), for which $R_1 = .980$ and $R_2 = .962$. For the two girls whose measurements on the eight physical variables are given in Table 12.1 the values of the factors, as estimated by (12.61), are

$$\bar{\gamma}_{11} = -0.28\,, \qquad \bar{\gamma}_{21} = 1.80\,,$$
$$\bar{\gamma}_{12} = 1.22\,, \qquad \bar{\gamma}_{22} = 0.56\,,$$

which are practically identical with the values previously obtained by the use of (12.31).

12.5. *Regression Method Employing an Alternative Principle*

Instead of the ordinary regression method for estimating factors, another method has been proposed by Bartlett.* Whereas in the previous methods the sum of the squares of the discrepancies between the true and estimated factors over the range of individuals is minimized, in the procedure now to be described the sum of the squares of the unique factors over the range of variables is minimized. This method is in harmony with Bartlett's principle that unique factors should be introduced only in order to explain discrepancies between observed values and postulated general or group factors. According to Thomson, "Bartlett's estimates and the regression estimates attain different ends, and it is agreed that each method is correct in the right place."†

Suppose there are just two common factors, so that the factor pattern may be written as follows:

$$(12.62) \qquad z_j = a_{j1}F_1 + a_{j2}F_2 + a_jU_j \qquad (j = 1, 2, \ldots, n)\,.$$

The explicit expression for the unique factor of any variable z_j is

$$(12.63) \qquad U_j = \frac{1}{a_j}\,(z_j - a_{j1}F_1 - a_{j2}F_2)\,,$$

and the sum of the squares of all such factors may be denoted by

$$(12.64) \qquad F(F_1, F_2) = \sum_{j=1}^{n} U_j^2 = \sum_{j=1}^{n} \frac{1}{a_j^2}\,(z_j - a_{j1}F_1 - a_{j2}F_2)^2\,.$$

---

* M. S. Bartlett, "The Statistical Conception of Mental Factors," *British Journal of Psychology*, 1937.

† G. H. Thomson, "Methods of Estimating Mental Factors," *Nature*, 1938, p. 246.

Then to minimize the sum of the squares of the unique factors over the range of variables, it is necessary that the partial derivatives of the function F with respect to F_1 and F_2 vanish, i.e.,

$$(12.65) \quad \begin{cases} \dfrac{\partial F}{\partial F_1} = 2\Sigma \dfrac{1}{a_j^2} (z_j - a_{j1}F_1 - a_{j2}F_2)a_{j1} = 0 , \\[2ex] \dfrac{\partial F}{\partial F_2} = 2\Sigma \dfrac{1}{a_j^2} (z_j - a_{j1}F_1 - a_{j2}F_2)a_{j2} = 0 , \end{cases}$$

where the summations extend from $j = 1$ to $j = n$. These equations may be put in the form

$$(12.66) \quad \begin{cases} \left(\sum \dfrac{a_{j1}^2}{a_j^2}\right) F_1' + \left(\sum \dfrac{a_{j1}a_{j2}}{a_j^2}\right) F_2' = \sum \dfrac{a_{j1}}{a_j^2} z_j , \\[2ex] \left(\sum \dfrac{a_{j2}a_{j1}}{a_j^2}\right) F_1' + \left(\sum \dfrac{a_{j2}^2}{a_j^2}\right) F_2' = \sum \dfrac{a_{j2}}{a_j^2} z_j , \end{cases}$$

where primes have been placed on the F's to distinguish these estimates of the factors from the true factors. These equations involve the two unknowns, F_1' and F_2', which may be determined in terms of the a's and z's, as follows:

$$(12.67) \qquad\qquad F_t' = \sum_{j=1}^{n} c_{tj} z_j \qquad\qquad (t = 1, 2) ,$$

where the c's can be evaluated from equations (12.66) by Gauss's method of substitution.

A set of equations of the type (12.66) can be written, more generally, in matrix form, as follows:

$$(12.68) \qquad\qquad \mathbf{J}\bar{\mathbf{f}} = \mathbf{A}'\mathbf{U}^{-2}\mathbf{Z} ,$$

in which the matrix $\mathbf{J}$ is defined by (12.55). Formula (12.68) can be applied to problems involving any number of common factors if it is desired to estimate them according to the principle of minimizing the unique factors. Although formula (12.68) is not a special case of formula (12.54), it may be noted that, if the term $\boldsymbol{\phi}^{-1}$ is dropped from the matrix $\mathbf{L}$ in (12.54), that formula becomes identical with (12.68). The computations required in the application of formula (12.68) are the same as that described for the shortened method, except that nothing is added to the matrix $\mathbf{J}$.

The estimates of the common factors by means of formula (12.68) are then an alternative solution to any of the regression estimates of the preceding sections. Bartlett pointed out that the principle of estimation adopted in this section does not completely agree with the solution that has usually been employed, although the difference does not affect the relative weights assigned to the variables in estimating a single general factor. When several common factors are involved, however, the discrepancy between equations (12.54) and (12.68) is even more serious. Bartlett states: "One point of view appears to have been to consider all the persons with different possible factorial make-ups that would give rise to the observed test scores of a particular person, whereas I have regarded the test scores as a sample of all the possible scores that might have arisen for that person according to the different values of specific [unique] factors he may happen to have."*

The present method will be applied to the estimation of the two oblique factors, γ_1 and γ_2, which have already been predicted by means of formulas (12.14) and (12.54). The matrix $\mathbf{J}$ for this problem is given in (12.57), and the transpose of the matrix $(\mathbf{A}'\mathbf{U}^{-2})$ is given immediately above it. Then the set of equations represented by (12.68) can be solved by the method of Appendix G, producing

$$(12.69) \quad \begin{cases} \gamma_1' = .261z_1 + .387z_2 + .240z_3 + .196z_4 + .005z_5 \\ \qquad\qquad\qquad\qquad - .002z_6 - .005z_7 + .008z_8 \,, \\ \gamma_2' = .033z_1 - .019z_2 - .025z_3 + .015z_4 + .646z_5 \\ \qquad\qquad\qquad\qquad + .223z_6 + .157z_7 + .133z_8 \,. \end{cases}$$

For the two girls previously considered the factor estimates by (12.69) are as follows:

$$\gamma_{11}' = -0.35\,, \qquad \gamma_{21}' = 2.03\;;$$
$$\gamma_{12}' = 1.28\,, \qquad \gamma_{22}' = 0.56\,.$$

The reliability of prediction by means of equations (12.69) can be judged by the appropriate standard error or multiple correlation coefficient. It should be noted, however, that formula (12.28) does not yield the required multiple correlation for the present method. If formula (12.28) is applied, the resulting "multiple correlation" will be found to be equal to unity. This follows from the fact that the common factors are estimated under the condition that the unique factors are minimized, and the uniqueness is the standard error of estimate in a pattern equation.

* *Op. cit.*

For the method discussed in this section the coefficient of multiple correlation is given by[†]

$$(12.70) \qquad R_s^2 = 1 - \frac{J_{ss}}{J} ,$$

where J_{ss} is the minor of the element in row and column s of J. In general, it can be shown[‡] that the multiple correlation coefficient can be computed from the formula

$$(12.71) \qquad R_s^2 = 1 - \frac{L_{ss}}{L} ,$$

where $\mathbf{L}$ is defined in (12.55) and L_{ss} is the minor of the element in row and column s of L.

The multiple correlations for the estimates (12.69) as given by (12.70) are

$$R_1 = \sqrt{1 - 10.913/242.652} = .977 ,$$
$$R_2 = \sqrt{1 - 22.236/242.652} = .953 .$$

These values are just about equal to those obtained for the estimates (12.31) and (12.61). It may then be concluded that, statistically, the different methods for estimating factors are equally good. The choice of the method of this section instead of one of the other (equivalent) methods must be made on the basis of the principle of prediction which is involved.

12.6. *Factors Expressed in Terms of Ideal Variables*

Before leaving the subject of estimation of factors, one more approach will be presented. The present method is designed only for the description of the common factors—the expressions for these factors being in terms of hypothetical rather than the observed variables, and so are not immediately applicable in practice.

The common-factor portion of a pattern is required and may be written in matrix form as follows:

$$(12.72) \qquad \mathbf{Z}^* = \mathbf{Af} ,$$

where $\mathbf{f}$ is the column vector $\{F_1 \ F_2 \ \dots \ F_m\}$ of common factors, and $\mathbf{Z}^*$ is the column vector $\{z_1'' \ z_2'' \ \dots \ z_n''\}$ of the statistical variables projected into

---

† See Bartlett, *ibid.*

‡ For the orthogonal case see Guttman, *op. cit.*, § 10, and Dwyer, "The Evaluation of Multiple and Partial Correlation Coefficients from the Factorial Matrix," *Psychometrika*, 1940, p. 229.

the common-factor space. To solve for the factors in terms of the hypothetical variables (z''_j), proceed as follows: Premultiply both sides of (12.72) by $\mathbf{A'}$, obtaining

$$(12.73) \qquad\qquad \mathbf{A'Z^*} = \mathbf{A'Af} .$$

Let

$$(12.74) \qquad\qquad \boldsymbol{\Delta} = \mathbf{A'A} ,$$

which is readily seen to be a symmetric matrix of order m. Finally, premultiply both sides of (12.73) by $\boldsymbol{\Delta}^{-1}$ to obtain the result

$$(12.75) \qquad\qquad \mathbf{f} = \boldsymbol{\Delta}^{-1}\mathbf{A'Z^*} .$$

This matrix equation gives the linear descriptions of the factors in terms of the variables z''_j which are involved in the matrix $\mathbf{Z^*}$.

To illustrate the present method, formula (12.75) will be applied to the example of eight physical variables. The matrix $\mathbf{A}$ of coefficients of the common factors γ_1 and γ_2 is given on page 281. The matrix $\boldsymbol{\Delta}$, calculated according to its definition (12.74), and the inverse of this matrix follow:

$$\boldsymbol{\Delta} = \left\|\begin{matrix} 3.365 & -.011 \\ -.011 & 2.613 \end{matrix}\right\|, \qquad \boldsymbol{\Delta}^{-1} = \left\|\begin{matrix} .297 & .001 \\ .001 & .383 \end{matrix}\right\| .$$

The inverse matrix may be computed by the method outlined in Appendix **G.5**, or, for the simple case of a second-order matrix, directly according to the definition of an inverse in Appendix A. The only calculation remaining is the multiplication of $\boldsymbol{\Delta}^{-1}$ by $\mathbf{A'}$. Then the expressions for the factors can be put in the form

$$(12.76) \quad \begin{cases} \gamma_1 = .266z''_1 + .284z''_2 + .277z''_3 + .261z''_4 + .002z''_5 \\ \qquad\qquad\qquad\qquad - .007z''_6 - .017z''_7 + .024z''_8 , \\ \gamma_2 = .020z''_1 - .009z''_2 - .019z''_3 + .012z''_4 + .356z''_5 \\ \qquad\qquad\qquad\qquad + .316z''_6 + .294z''_7 + .262z''_8 . \end{cases}$$

Equations (12.76) give the descriptions of the two oblique factors (not their estimates) in terms of the "common-factor portions" of the original variables. The values of the variables z''_j are not known, and hence (12.76) cannot be applied directly to obtain the values of the factors for the individuals. An approximation can be made, however—replacing each z''_j by z_j. When this is done, the estimates of the factors may be denoted by double primes. Thus, the estimates of γ_1 and γ_2 by (12.76), employing the values of the eight physical variables given in Table 12.1, become

$$\text{Estimates for Case 1: } \gamma_{11}'' = -.036\,, \qquad \gamma_{21}'' = 1.98\,;$$
$$\text{Estimates for Case 2: } \gamma_{12}'' = \quad 1.31\,, \qquad \gamma_{22}'' = 0.68\,.$$

The method of the present section can be applied in another situation with less misgiving than that involved in the foregoing example. When a factor analysis is made under the assumed composition of variables into common factors only,† then the investigator is justified in replacing the **Z*** matrix by the **Z** matrix throughout this section.

† This assumption implies the following linear expression for the approximation of any variable z_j instead of the expression (2.4):

$$z_j' = a_{j1}F_1 + a_{j2}F_2 + \ldots + a_{jm}F_m \qquad (j = 1, 2, \ldots, n)\,,$$

where $m \leq n$ and the prime is used to distinguish the theoretical from the observed variable. Under this assumption the analysis is carried to the point where there are no more statistically significant (common) factors.

CHAPTER XIII

RELATIONSHIPS BETWEEN DIFFERENT FACTOR SOLUTIONS

13.1. *Introduction*

The present chapter is designed to show the essential unity of factor analysis. Although the preferred solutions which yield the linear expressions of the variables in terms of factors have certain distinct characteristics, they can be transformed from one into another. The problem of relating two sets of factors, obtained by different methods of analysis, was first considered by the authors in 1937,* but the present treatment is somewhat more general.

In **13.2** the general procedure for transforming one solution into another is presented. This is followed in **13.3** by a numerical illustration, employing the bi-factor and oblique solutions of the set of thirteen psychological variables. Finally, in **13.4** the complete plan for obtaining a factor solution is outlined and should serve as a summary of the methods of factor analysis.

13.2. *Relationships among Factors*

In mathematics the reference system plays a very minor role; the particular configuration of points is of prime importance, and the coordinate system is of much lesser significance. Thus, if it is desired to describe an ellipse, i.e., get an algebraic equation for the ellipse, it is quite irrelevant whether rectangular Cartesian coordinates, nonrectangular Cartesian coordinates, or polar coordinates are employed. Furthermore, the particular orientation of axes is immaterial. With each change of the coordinate system, of course, the equation of the ellipse will generally change, but the fact remains that the equation in each case describes the ellipse with respect to the given reference system.

The object of factor analysis, on the other hand, is the selection of an appropriate frame of reference, the configuration of points representing the variables being of lesser significance. Then the indeterminacy of the factor problem is obvious. In selecting a particular reference system, the unit vectors along the coordinate axes represent the factors, and, since the reference system can be rotated about its origin in an infinitude of ways in the common-factor space, there arises an infinite number of factor systems for a given body of data.

---

* Holzinger and Harman, "Relationships between Factors Obtained from Certain Analyses," *Journal of Educational Psychology*, 1937, pp. 321–46.

The problem of relating two factorial solutions involves the determination of the relationships among the coordinates of the two systems. This may be accomplished by finding a matrix of transformation which carries the coordinates of one factor pattern into another. Thus, if the first factor pattern is denoted by $\mathbf{A}$ and the second factor pattern by $\mathbf{B}$, then the problem is to find a matrix $\mathbf{T}$ such that

$$(13.1) \qquad\qquad\qquad \mathbf{AT} = \mathbf{B} .$$

The matrix $\mathbf{A}$ represents the coordinates a_{js} of the n points with respect to one set of m common-factor axes, say $F_1, F_2, \ldots, F_m$; the matrix $\mathbf{B}$ represents the coordinates b_{js} of the points with respect to a new set of axes, say $K_1, K_2, \ldots, K_m$; while the matrix $\mathbf{T}$ represents the transformation of the coordinates in $\mathbf{A}$ to those in $\mathbf{B}$. The foregoing transformation implies that the number of axes in the two reference systems is the same. Actually, however, it is only required that the n points be contained in the same space of m dimensions, although the second reference system might employ a larger number of coordinate axes.

If the number of factors is equal to the number of variables then the solution for $\mathbf{T}$ is simply

$$(13.2) \qquad\qquad\qquad \mathbf{T} = \mathbf{A}^{-1}\mathbf{B} .$$

Since the number of factors is usually much smaller than the number of variables, however, the matrix $\mathbf{A}$ does not have an inverse and $\mathbf{T}$ cannot be calculated directly. It may be noted that, for any matrix $\mathbf{A}$,

$$(13.3) \qquad\qquad\qquad (\mathbf{A'A})^{-1}(\mathbf{A'A}) = \mathbf{I} ,$$

and hence, if both members of (13.1) are premultiplied by $(\mathbf{A'A})^{-1}\mathbf{A'}$, there results

$$(13.4) \qquad\qquad\qquad \mathbf{T} = (\mathbf{A'A})^{-1}\mathbf{A'B} .$$

This formula gives the desired matrix of transformation.

The distinction between the problem treated here and the transformations considered in Chapter X should be noted. In relating two solutions, the factor patterns ($\mathbf{A}$ and $\mathbf{B}$) are assumed to be known, and the matrix of transformation ($\mathbf{T}$) from one to the other must be determined. In obtaining a derived solution, as in Chapter X, only the initial pattern ($\mathbf{A}$) is given, and a matrix of transformation ($\mathbf{T}$) is built up to produce the desired final solution ($\mathbf{B}$).

The relationships among the *factors themselves* may also be obtained by means of the matrix $\mathbf{T}$. Without loss of generality the column vectors of the first and second sets of factors may be taken to be $\mathbf{F} = \{F_1\ F_2\ F_3\}$ and $\mathbf{K} = \{K_1\ K_2\ K_3\ K_4\}$, respectively. From the definitions of the two factor patterns, and their assumed equality, it follows that

(13.5)
$$\mathbf{AF} = \mathbf{BK}\,.$$

Premultiplying both sides of this equation by $(\mathbf{A'A})^{-1}\mathbf{A'}$, and again employing (13.3), there results

(13.6)
$$\mathbf{F} = (\mathbf{A'A})^{-1}\mathbf{A'BK}\,.$$

By making use of (13.4), this expression finally simplifies to

(13.7)
$$\mathbf{F} = \mathbf{TK}\,.$$

This is the matrix formulation of the relationships between the factors F_1, F_2, F_3 and K_1, K_2, K_3, K_4.

The important distinction between the relationships (13.1) and (13.7) can be exhibited clearly for the case of three factors in the first solution and four factors in the second. The matrix $\mathbf{T}$ may be represented by

(13.8)
$$\mathbf{T} = \begin{Vmatrix} c_1 & d_1 & e_1 & f_1 \\ c_2 & d_2 & e_2 & f_2 \\ c_3 & d_3 & e_3 & f_3 \end{Vmatrix}\,,$$

in which the c's, d's, e's, and f's are constants calculated by means of formula (13.4). From the matrix equation (13.1), four algebraic equations can be written for the expression of the coordinates of the second solution in terms of those of the first, as follows:

(13.9)
$$\begin{cases} c_1 a_{j1} + c_2 a_{j2} + c_3 a_{j3} = b_{j1}\,, \\ d_1 a_{j1} + d_2 a_{j2} + d_3 a_{j3} = b_{j2}\,, \\ e_1 a_{j1} + e_2 a_{j2} + e_3 a_{j3} = b_{j3}\,, \\ f_1 a_{j1} + f_2 a_{j2} + f_3 a_{j3} = b_{j4}\,, \end{cases} \qquad (j = 1, 2, \ldots, n)\,.$$

Similarly, from the matrix equation (13.7), three algebraic equations for the expression of the first set of factors in terms of the second set can be written as follows:

(13.10)
$$\begin{cases} F_1 = c_1 K_1 + d_1 K_2 + e_1 K_3 + f_1 K_4\,, \\ F_2 = c_2 K_1 + d_2 K_2 + e_2 K_3 + f_2 K_4\,, \\ F_3 = c_3 K_1 + d_3 K_2 + e_3 K_3 + f_3 K_4\,. \end{cases}$$

It may be noted that the transpose of the matrix of coefficients of (13.9) appears in (13.10). However, the variables in the former system are coordinates, while those in the latter are factors.

A system of equations of the type (13.9) gives the actual transformation of coordinates between the two factorial solutions. Thus the factor weights for any variable in one solution are expressed linearly in terms of the weights of the other solution. Equations (13.9) may also be used as a check on the calculation of the elements of T since the factor weights of both solutions are known.

An alternative way of expressing the relationship between two factorial solutions is afforded by a system of equations of the type (13.10). Since all factors are assumed to be in standard form, the variances of the F's can be simply calculated from (13.10) in terms of the variances of the K's. For example, if the K's are uncorrelated, $100c_1^2$ is the per cent contribution of the factor K_1 to the variance of F_1. Equations (13.10) might also be useful in estimating the factors F if the equations of estimation of the K's are known.

13.3. Numerical Illustration

A detailed numerical illustration of the procedures of the last section will now be given, employing the example of thirteen psychological tests. The relationships between the bi-factor solution of Table 6.12 and the oblique solution of Table 11.6 will be obtained. The matrix of coefficients of the bi-factor pattern will be denoted by B, while that of the oblique factor pattern will be denoted by A, in agreement with the general treatment of 13.2. For the convenience of the reader these matrices are repeated here:

$$
A =
\begin{Vmatrix}
.731 & -.089 & .142 \\
.441 & .004 & .004 \\
.721 & -.090 & -.142 \\
.508 & .090 & -.003 \\
-.058 & .801 & .087 \\
.037 & .809 & -.051 \\
-.068 & .901 & -.030 \\
.155 & .591 & .078 \\
-.068 & .919 & -.081 \\
-.385 & .164 & .809 \\
-.039 & .077 & .659 \\
.073 & -.177 & .773 \\
.351 & -.061 & .594
\end{Vmatrix}
\begin{matrix}
\gamma_1 & \gamma_2 & \gamma_3
\end{matrix}
,\qquad
B =
\begin{Vmatrix}
.614 & .425 & & \\
.339 & .296 & & \\
.369 & .475 & & \\
.460 & .320 & & \\
.654 & & .467 & \\
.604 & & .526 & \\
.578 & & .645 & \\
.718 & & .235 & \\
.532 & & .689 & \\
.244 & & & .703 \\
.423 & & & .520 \\
.346 & & & .641 \\
.644 & & & .429
\end{Vmatrix}
\begin{matrix}
B_0 & B_1 & B_2 & B_3
\end{matrix}
$$

The first problem is the determination of the matrix **T** which transforms **A** into **B**. This is given by formula (13.4). In applying this formula, the product **A'A** is first calculated. This may be done most simply by computing the sums of the squares of each column of **A** and the sums of the paired products of the columns two at a time, giving

$$\mathbf{A'A} = \begin{Vmatrix} 1.823 & - .232 & - .058 \\ - .232 & 3.394 & - .017 \\ - .058 & - .017 & 2.103 \end{Vmatrix}.$$

The next step involves the calculation of the inverse of the preceding matrix. The outline for the calculation of an inverse is given in Appendix

TABLE 13.1

FORWARD SOLUTION FOR CALCULATION OF $(\mathbf{A'A})^{-1}$

Line	γ_1	γ_2	γ_3	Identity Matrix		
1......	1.823	− .232	− .058	1	0	0
2......	−1.	.127	.032	− .549	0	0
3......		3.394	− .017	0	1	0
4......		− .029	− .007	.127	0	0
5......		3.365	− .024	.127	1	0
6......		−1.	.007	− .038	− .297	0
7......			2.103	0	0	1
8......			− .002	.032	0	0
9......			− .000	.001	.007	0
10......			2.101	.033	.007	1
11......			−1.	− .016	− .003	− .476

G.5, and the numerical details for the present case are exhibited in Table 13.1. The inverse matrix is obtained by means of the back solution, employing the values in lines 11, 6, and 2, as follows:

$$(\mathbf{A'A})^{-1} = \begin{Vmatrix} .554 & .038 & .016 \\ .038 & .297 & .003 \\ .016 & .003 & .476 \end{Vmatrix}.$$

The check column is omitted in Table 13.1 because of the check afforded by the property of the product of a matrix by its inverse being the identity matrix, namely,

$$(\mathbf{A'A})(\mathbf{A'A})^{-1} = \begin{Vmatrix} 1.000 & .000 & .001 \\ .000 & .999 & - .002 \\ .001 & -.001 & 1.000 \end{Vmatrix}.$$

After obtaining the inverse matrix it is postmultiplied by **A**, row by row,* which yields

$$(\mathbf{A'A})^{-1}\mathbf{A'} =$$

$$\begin{Vmatrix} .404 & .245 & .394 & .285 & -.000 & .050 & -.004 & .110 & -.004 & -.194 & -.008 & .046 & .202 \\ .002 & .018 & .001 & .046 & .236 & .242 & .265 & .182 & .270 & .037 & .023 & -.047 & -.003 \\ .079 & .009 & -.056 & .007 & .043 & -.021 & -.013 & .041 & -.037 & .379 & .313 & .369 & .288 \end{Vmatrix}.$$

Finally, upon postmultiplying this matrix by **B**, the desired matrix of transformation is obtained:

$$\mathbf{T} = (\mathbf{A'A})^{-1}\mathbf{A'B} = \begin{Vmatrix} .808 & .523 & .047 & -.024 \\ .757 & .021 & .637 & .007 \\ .590 & .012 & -.015 & .789 \end{Vmatrix}.$$

The actual rotation from the oblique coordinates to the bi-factor coordinates is given by

$$(13.11) \quad \begin{cases} b_{j0} = & .808a_{j1} + .757a_{j2} + .590a_{j3}, \\ b_{j1} = & .523a_{j1} + .021a_{j2} + .012a_{j3}, \\ b_{j2} = & .047a_{j1} + .637a_{j2} - .015a_{j3}, \\ b_{j3} = & -.024a_{j1} + .007a_{j2} + .789a_{j3}, \end{cases}$$

where the a's and b's are the coordinates in the matrices **A** and **B**, respectively. It is evident from these equations that the coefficients of the first bi-factor (general) are composed of fairly uniform portions of the corresponding coefficients of all three oblique factors. The coefficients of each of the remaining bi-factors are composed almost entirely of fractional parts of a single oblique factor coefficient.

Similarly, by means of the matrix **T**, the relationships among the factors may be exhibited as follows:

$$(13.12) \quad \begin{cases} \gamma_1 = .808B_0 + .523B_1 + .047B_2 - .024B_3, \\ \gamma_2 = .757B_0 + .021B_1 + .637B_2 + .007B_3, \\ \gamma_3 = .590B_0 + .012B_1 - .015B_2 + .789B_3. \end{cases}$$

From these equations it appears that each of the oblique factors consists of a substantial portion of the general factor and the corresponding group factor of the bi-factor solution. For example, the factors B_0 and B_2 con-

* This is equivalent to the conventional row-by-column multiplication $(\mathbf{A'A})^{-1}$ by $\mathbf{A'}$.

tribute 57 per cent and 41 per cent, respectively, to the unit variance of γ_2. It may be noted that the sum of the squares of the coefficients in the respective equations of (13.12) is not exactly unity. This discrepancy is due to the fact that the assumption of the equality of the two factor patterns is met only roughly. That is to say, the communalities and the correlations reproduced by the two solutions are not quite the same; or, in geometric terms, the two sets of coordinates do not define the same points precisely.

13.4. *Suggestions for Order of Analysis*

From the various methods of analysis presented throughout the text it is evident that the choice of a particular form of solution is somewhat arbitrary. In all cases, however, a certain routine of analysis must precede the final choice of solution. An effective outline which may be followed for all problems is given below. The first seven steps deal with the preliminaries, while the eighth step for any problem is to select a particular form of the final solution. Following the outline there will be a brief recapitulation of the bases for the choice of a preferred solution.

1. Formulate the problem.
2. Decide upon a set of variables relevant to this problem.
3. Calculate all the product-moment correlation coefficients. For most rigorous results the distributions of the variables should be investigated for normality and the correlations tested for linearity. Reliability coefficients may also be helpful in determining the adequacy of the variables as effective instruments of measurement.
4. By inspection, rearrange the variables into tentative subsets of highly interrelated variables.
5. If each variable in a subset has high positive correlations with all other variables in this group, and negative correlations with the remaining variables, reverse the scale of measurement for each of these variables and thus obtain positive correlations throughout.

6'. If all the correlations are essentially positive, the method of B-coefficients can be employed as an objective procedure for determining distinct subsets of variables. The number of groups roughly determines the rank of the correlation matrix.

6''. If, after the reflection of variables, there are still negative correlations, then the method of B-coefficients does not apply, and an approximation to the rank of the correlation matrix is not obtainable at this stage. Similarly, when a matrix contains positive correlations throughout but does not indicate distinct clusters of variables, then the rank cannot be approximated by the method of B-coefficients.

7′. Calculate complete estimates of the communalities of the variables, as described in **7.2**, by the direct methods when the rank is one or two, or by the bi-factor method for higher rank. Then obtain a centroid solution based upon these communalities.

7″. When complete estimates of the communalities are not available, some arbitrary choice of the communalities must be made. One of the simplest methods is to select the average of all the correlations for each variable as its communality. This gives rise to the averoid solution described in **8.4**.

8*a*. Calculate a bi-factor solution as the final form by the method described in Appendix C.

8*b*. Calculate a principal-factor solution as the final form. For a small number of variables this may be obtained directly, when the communalities are known, by the method of Appendix D. Otherwise, the principal-factor solution can be obtained by transformation from an initial solution as described in Chapter IX.

8*c*. Calculate a multiple-factor solution as the final form by the methods described in Chapter X.

8*d*. Calculate an oblique solution as the final form by the methods described in Chapter XI.

When the analyst has reached Step 8 in the foregoing outline, he will need to consider the bases for choice of one of the preferred forms of solution. As indicated throughout the book—especially in Chapters I, V, and XI—such a choice depends upon certain statistical criteria as well as upon the nature of the problem and the data. If the investigator starts with a theory in a given field, such as Spearman's theory of intelligence, then he might select the particular form of factor solution which would verify the theory. In another type of problem the variables may be of such a nature that the bipolar form of expression of the factors may appear most simple and clear to the analyst. An example of this is given by the solution of eight physical variables which is presented in Table 7.4. An eminent biologist selected the principal-factor form not only because it was the most statistically elegant solution but also because the bipolar nature of the factor "body type" was explicitly revealed. For other problems the chief aim may be to secure the greatest simplicity in the factorial solution. Usually this may be accomplished by the choice of an oblique factor pattern, as illustrated in Chapter XI. Certain data, however, such as the political variables analyzed in **11.5**, may yield an oblique solution which is no simpler than an orthogonal one. For such data, then, an orthogonal solution would be preferred. In other cases, also, if the investigator prefers a solution with uncorrelated factors, he would select the bi-factor form including a general factor, or the multiple-factor form involving group factors only.

It should be evident that in the choice of the form of solution the analyst must be guided both by the statistical criteria and by other considerations, such as theories in given fields and the nature of the data being analyzed. Since the interdependence of criteria and data will vary with the type of problem, the choice of the analyst will vary in different situations. Such variations, however, are due largely to the convenience of a particular form of solution for a given body of data and not to any essential uniqueness of that solution. The fact that all solutions for a given problem may be brought into relationship with one another indicates that in factor analysis, as in other branches of applied science, several equally satisfactory laws may be employed as expressions of the essential nature of the phenomena being studied.

APPENDIXES

APPENDIX A

FUNDAMENTALS OF MATRIX THEORY

It is the aim of this appendix to present in brief outline form the fundamental definitions and theorems on matrices.* First, however, a short review of determinants will be given.

1. Definition of a Determinant of Order 2

A sum of product terms, with alternating algebraic signs, frequently occurs in mathematical work and hence has been given a special notation. For example, the expression

$$ad - bc$$

is denoted by the symbol

$$\begin{vmatrix} a & b \\ c & d \end{vmatrix},$$

which is called a *determinant of the second order*, since it contains two rows and two columns.

2. Definition of a Determinant of Order 3

The symbol

$$\begin{vmatrix} a_1 & b_1 & c_1 \\ a_2 & b_2 & c_2 \\ a_3 & b_3 & c_3 \end{vmatrix}$$

is called a *determinant of the third order* and stands for

$$a_1 b_2 c_3 - a_1 b_3 c_2 + a_2 b_3 c_1 - a_2 b_1 c_3 + a_3 b_1 c_2 - a_3 b_2 c_1.$$

A method for obtaining the expanded form of a determinant will be described in **5** below.

The nine numbers $a_1, \ldots, c_3$ are called the *elements* of the determinant. In the symbol these elements lie in three (horizontal) *rows* and also in three

* For a detailed treatment see Bocher, *Introduction to Higher Algebra*, pp. 20–80; Dickson, *Modern Algebraic Theories*, pp. 39–63.

(vertical) *columns*. For example, a_3, b_3, c_3 are the elements of the third row, while the three b's are the elements of the second column. The diagonal from the upper left-hand corner to the lower right-hand corner is called the *principal diagonal*. In the third-order determinant the principal diagonal contains the elements a_1, b_2, c_3.

3. Definition of a Determinant of Order n

A determinant of general order n may be denoted by

$$A = \begin{vmatrix} a_{11} & a_{12} & \dots & a_{1n} \\ a_{21} & a_{22} & \dots & a_{2n} \\ . & . & \dots & . \\ a_{n1} & a_{n2} & \dots & a_{nn} \end{vmatrix},$$

where the n^2 elements are denoted by a's with two subscripts, the first representing the number of the row and the second the number of the column in which the element appears. By definition the determinant A shall stand for the sum of the $n!$ terms each of which is (apart from sign) the product of n elements, one and only one from each column, and one and only one from each row. The algebraic signs are determined most easily by the method of expanding the determinant which is explained in **5** below.

4. Minors and Cofactors

The determinant of order $n - 1$ obtained by striking out the row and column crossing at a given element of a determinant of order n is called the *minor* of that element. Thus, corresponding to the element a_{jk}, which stands in the jth row and the kth column of the determinant A, there exists the minor M_{jk} which is obtained upon crossing out the given row and column. Frequently there is occasion to consider not this minor M_{jk} but the *cofactor* A_{jk} of a_{jk} defined by

$$A_{jk} = (-1)^{j+k} M_{jk}.$$

The algebraic signs attached to the minors to obtain the corresponding cofactors are alternately $+$ and $-$, as indicated by the following diagram which is associated with the elements of a determinant:

$$
\begin{matrix}
+ & - & + & - \\
- & + & - & + \\
+ & - & + & - \\
- & + & - & +
\end{matrix}
$$

5. Expansion of a Determinant

Any determinant A may be expanded according to the elements of any row or any column, that is,

$$A = \sum_{k=1}^{n} a_{jk}A_{jk} \qquad (j = 1, 2, \ldots, n),$$

$$A = \sum_{j=1}^{n} a_{jk}A_{jk} \qquad (k = 1, 2, \ldots, n).$$

Thus, for the third-order determinant

$$A = \begin{vmatrix} a_{11} & a_{12} & a_{13} \\ a_{21} & a_{22} & a_{23} \\ a_{31} & a_{32} & a_{33} \end{vmatrix},$$

the expansion according to the elements of the second column becomes

$$\begin{aligned} A &= a_{12}A_{12} + a_{22}A_{22} + a_{32}A_{32} \\ &= -a_{12}M_{12} + a_{22}M_{22} - a_{32}M_{32} \\ &= -a_{12}(a_{21}a_{33} - a_{31}a_{23}) + a_{22}(a_{11}a_{33} - a_{31}a_{13}) - a_{32}(a_{11}a_{23} - a_{21}a_{13}), \end{aligned}$$

which, upon rearranging of terms, may be written as follows:

$$A = a_{11}a_{22}a_{33} + a_{12}a_{23}a_{31} + a_{13}a_{32}a_{21} - a_{13}a_{22}a_{31} - a_{23}a_{32}a_{11} - a_{33}a_{21}a_{12}.$$

By successive application of the method of expansion of a determinant according to the elements of some row or column, a determinant of any order eventually can be reduced to the explicit expansion of determinants of the second order.

6. Definition of a Matrix

A system of mn numbers a_{jk} arranged in a rectangular array of m rows and n columns is called an $m \times n$ *matrix*. If $m = n$, the array is called a square matrix of order n. A matrix will generally be represented as follows:

$$\mathbf{A} = \begin{Vmatrix} a_{11} & a_{12} & \cdots & a_{1n} \\ a_{21} & a_{22} & \cdots & a_{2n} \\ \cdot & \cdot & \cdots & \cdot \\ a_{m1} & a_{m2} & \cdots & a_{mn} \end{Vmatrix},$$

although parentheses are sometimes used instead of the double bars, or the matrix might be designated by its general element in the form $\|a_{jk}\|$ or

(a_{jk}). The notation here used, matrices being denoted by bold-face type, is systematically followed in the text.

Simple examples of one-rowed matrices are the notations $(x,\ y)$ and $(x,\ y,\ z)$ for points in a plane and in space, the elements of these matrices being the coordinates of the points. Similarly, the set of coordinates representing three points in a plane, when arranged in a definite order, form a matrix, e.g.,

$$\left\| \begin{array}{cc} x_1 & y_1 \\ x_2 & y_2 \\ x_3 & y_3 \end{array} \right\|.$$

7. Distinction between Matrices and Determinants

It should be noted that even when a matrix is square it is not a determinant. A determinant, whose elements are real numbers, represents a real number, while a matrix does not have a value in the ordinary sense. The difference between a square matrix and a determinant is clearly seen upon interchanging the rows and columns; the determinant has the same value, but the matrix is generally different from the original one.

8. Transpose of a Matrix

A matrix which is derived from another by interchanging the rows and columns is called the *transpose* of the original matrix. Thus, if

$$\mathbf{A} = \left\| \begin{array}{ccc} a_{11} & a_{12} & a_{13} \\ a_{21} & a_{22} & a_{23} \\ a_{31} & a_{32} & a_{33} \end{array} \right\|,$$

then the transpose of $\mathbf{A}$ is the matrix

$$\mathbf{A}' = \left\| \begin{array}{ccc} a_{11} & a_{21} & a_{31} \\ a_{12} & a_{22} & a_{32} \\ a_{13} & a_{23} & a_{33} \end{array} \right\|.$$

The prime notation for the transpose is followed throughout the text.

9. Determinants of a Matrix

Although square matrices and determinants are wholly different things, it is possible to form from the elements of a square matrix a determinant which is called the *determinant of the matrix*. The notation which is employed is bold-face type for the matrix and the corresponding italic type for the determinant of the matrix. Thus the determinant of a square matrix $\mathbf{A}$ is denoted by A. Other determinants, of lower order, can be formed from any rectangular matrix by striking out certain rows and columns. For many problems it is important to know the order of the highest nonvanishing determinant of a matrix.

10. Rank of a Matrix

A matrix $\mathbf{A}$ is said to be of *rank r* if it contains at least one r-rowed determinant which is not zero, whereas all determinants of $\mathbf{A}$ of order higher than r are zero.

By the rank of a determinant is meant the rank of its matrix.

11. Singular Matrix

A square matrix is said to be *singular* if its determinant is zero. Otherwise, it is called *nonsingular*.

12. Matrix Equations

Any two matrices $\mathbf{A}$ and $\mathbf{B}$ are said to be equal if and only if every element of $\mathbf{A}$ is equal to the corresponding element of $\mathbf{B}$. Thus, if $\mathbf{A} = (a_{jk})$ and $\mathbf{B} = (b_{jk})$ then the equation

$$\mathbf{A} = \mathbf{B}$$

implies that $a_{jk} = b_{jk}$ for every j and k. Thus it is evident that a single matrix equation stands for as many algebraic equations as there are elements in either of the matrices which are equated.

13. Symmetric Matrix

A matrix $\mathbf{A}$ is *symmetric* if and only if it is equal to its transpose $\mathbf{A}'$. In other words, the matrix $\mathbf{A} = (a_{jk})$ is symmetric in case it remains unaltered by the interchange of its rows and columns, i.e.,

$$a_{jk} = a_{kj} \qquad (j, k = 1, 2, \ldots, n).$$

The following is an example of a symmetric matrix:

$$\begin{Vmatrix} .78 & -.16 & .23 & .04 \\ -.16 & .59 & -.34 & -.21 \\ .23 & -.34 & .86 & .40 \\ .04 & -.21 & .40 & .65 \end{Vmatrix}.$$

14. Sum or Difference of Matrices

The sum (or difference) of two matrices each of m rows and n columns is defined to be an $m \times n$ matrix each of whose elements is the sum (or difference) of the corresponding elements of the given matrices. All the laws of ordinary algebra hold for the addition or subtraction of matrices.

15. Multiplication of Matrices

The element in the jth row and the kth column of the product of a matrix A with n columns by a matrix B with n rows is the sum of the products of the successive elements of the jth row of A by the corresponding elements of the kth column of B.

For example, if

$$A = \left\| \begin{matrix} a_{11} & a_{12} & a_{13} \\ a_{21} & a_{22} & a_{23} \end{matrix} \right\|, \qquad B = \left\| \begin{matrix} b_{11} & b_{12} \\ b_{21} & b_{22} \\ b_{31} & b_{32} \end{matrix} \right\|,$$

then the product C of these matrices is

$$C = A \cdot B = \left\| \begin{matrix} a_{11}b_{11} + a_{12}b_{21} + a_{13}b_{31} & a_{11}b_{12} + a_{12}b_{22} + a_{13}b_{32} \\ a_{21}b_{11} + a_{22}b_{21} + a_{23}b_{31} & a_{21}b_{12} + a_{22}b_{22} + a_{23}b_{32} \end{matrix} \right\|.$$

It should be noted that in this *row-by-column multiplication* of matrices the number of columns in the first matrix must be equal to the number of rows in the second. The product matrix then contains the number of rows of the first matrix and the number of columns of the second. Thus, in the example, the product of the 2×3 matrix by the 3×2 matrix is a 2×2 matrix. This may be conveniently noted by writing the order of each matrix as superscripts, namely,

$$A^{2 \times 3} \cdot B^{3 \times 2} = C^{2 \times 2}.$$

In general,

$$A^{m \times n} \cdot B^{n \times s} = C^{m \times s},$$

that is, the product of an $m \times n$ matrix by an $n \times s$ matrix is an $m \times s$ matrix.

Multiplication of matrices is not commutative in general, that is,

$$AB \neq BA.$$

Hence it is important to specify in what order matrices are multiplied. In the product AB the matrix B is said to be *premultiplied* by the matrix A, or A is *postmultiplied* by B.

16. Scalars

In order to distinguish the ordinary quantities of algebra (i.e., real and complex numbers) from matrices, the former are called *scalars* and will here be designated in italics. The product of a matrix **A** by a scalar k (k**A** or **A**k) is defined to be the matrix each of whose elements is k times the corresponding element of **A**. All the laws of ordinary algebra hold for the multiplication of matrices by scalars.

17. Diagonal and Scalar Matrices

A matrix in which the diagonal elements do not all vanish and all remaining elements are zero is called a *diagonal matrix*. A special instance of such a matrix is one in which all the elements of the diagonal are identical; it is then called a *scalar matrix*. If a scalar matrix

$$\mathbf{k} = \begin{Vmatrix} k & 0 & \dots & 0 \\ 0 & k & \dots & 0 \\ . & . & \dots & . \\ . & . & \dots & . \\ 0 & 0 & \dots & k \end{Vmatrix}$$

is premultiplied or postmultiplied by any matrix **A** of the same order as **k,** the following relationships become evident:

$$\mathbf{kA} = \mathbf{Ak} = k\mathbf{A} .$$

In particular, the matrix

$$\mathbf{I} = \begin{Vmatrix} 1 & 0 & \dots & 0 \\ 0 & 1 & \dots & 0 \\ . & . & \dots & . \\ . & . & \dots & . \\ 0 & 0 & \dots & 1 \end{Vmatrix}$$

is called the *identity matrix*, and it has the property that, if **A** is any matrix whatever,

$$\mathbf{IA} = \mathbf{AI} = \mathbf{A} .$$

It is evident that, in matrix algebra, all scalar matrices may be replaced by the corresponding scalars and, conversely, that all scalars may be considered as standing for the corresponding scalar matrices. The identity matrix **I** corresponds to unity in ordinary algebra, and hence in products of matrices the factor **I** may be suppressed.

18. Inverse Matrix

If a matrix

$$\mathbf{A} = \begin{Vmatrix} a_{11} & a_{12} & \cdots & a_{1n} \\ a_{21} & a_{22} & \cdots & a_{2n} \\ \cdot & \cdot & \cdots & \cdot \\ a_{n1} & a_{n2} & \cdots & a_{nn} \end{Vmatrix}$$

is nonsingular, i.e., $A \neq 0$, then there exists another matrix

$$\mathbf{A}^{-1} = \begin{Vmatrix} \dfrac{A_{11}}{A} & \dfrac{A_{21}}{A} & \cdots & \dfrac{A_{n1}}{A} \\ \dfrac{A_{12}}{A} & \dfrac{A_{22}}{A} & \cdots & \dfrac{A_{n2}}{A} \\ \cdot & \cdot & \cdots & \cdot \\ \dfrac{A_{1n}}{A} & \dfrac{A_{2n}}{A} & \cdots & \dfrac{A_{nn}}{A} \end{Vmatrix} = \frac{1}{A} \begin{Vmatrix} A_{11} & A_{21} & \cdots & A_{n1} \\ A_{12} & A_{22} & \cdots & A_{n2} \\ \cdot & \cdot & \cdots & \cdot \\ A_{1n} & A_{2n} & \cdots & A_{nn} \end{Vmatrix}$$

in which A_{kj} denote the cofactors of the elements of A. The matrix $\mathbf{A}^{-1}$ is called the *inverse* of $\mathbf{A}$ and is itself a nonsingular matrix which has the property

$$\mathbf{A}\mathbf{A}^{-1} = \mathbf{A}^{-1}\mathbf{A} = \mathbf{I} .$$

It should be noted that the rows and columns of cofactors in the inverse of a matrix are interchanged. In other words, when $1/A$ is factored out, the element A_{kj} in the jth row and kth column of the inverse of $\mathbf{A}$ is the cofactor of the element a_{kj} in the kth row and jth column of A.

19. Theorems on Transpose and Inverse of Products of Matrices

The transpose of a product of matrices is equal to the product of their transposes taken in reverse order. Thus,

$$(\mathbf{ABC})' = \mathbf{C}'\mathbf{B}'\mathbf{A}' .$$

The inverse of a product of matrices is the product of their inverses taken in reverse order. For example,

$$(\mathbf{ABC})^{-1} = \mathbf{C}^{-1}\mathbf{B}^{-1}\mathbf{A}^{-1} .$$

APPENDIX B

MISCELLANEOUS TOPICS AND PROOFS

B.1. *Brief Description of a Set of Twenty-four Psychological Tests*

To illustrate the factorial methods a numerical example is introduced in **2.8.** The variables from which the fundamental data (the correlations of Table 2.2) are obtained consists of twenty-four psychological tests which were given to $N = 145$ children of the Grant-White School of Forest Park, Illinois.* Copies of the tests are reproduced in the monograph by Holzinger and Swineford, so that only brief descriptions of them are given here.

1. *Visual Perception Test.* A nonlanguage multiple-choice test composed of items selected from Spearman's Visual Perception Test, Part III. Testing time: 19 minutes.

2. *Cubes.* A simplification of Brigham's test of spatial relations. Testing time: 8 minutes.

3. *Paper Form Board.* A revised multiple-choice test of spatial imagery, with dissected squares, triangles, hexagons, and trapezoids. Testing time: 8 minutes.

4. *Flags.* Adapted from a test by Thurstone. Requires visual imagery in two or three dimensions. Testing time: $5\frac{1}{2}$ minutes.

5. *General Information.* A multiple-choice test of a wide variety of simple scientific and social facts. Testing time: 18 minutes.

6. *Paragraph Comprehension.* Part III of Traxler Silent Reading Test, Form 1, for Grades VII–X. Comprehension measured by completion and multiple-choice questions. Testing time: 20 minutes.

7. *Sentence Completion.* A multiple-choice test in which "correct" answers reflect good judgment on the part of the subject. Testing time: 6 minutes.

8. *Word Classification.* Arranged by M. A. Wenger. Sets of five words one of which is to be indicated as not belonging with the other four. Testing time: 10 minutes.

9. *Word Meaning.* Part II of Traxler Silent Reading Test. A multiple-choice vocabulary test. Testing time: 14 minutes.

10. *Add.* Speed of adding pairs of one-digit numbers. Testing time: 2 minutes.

11. *Code.* A simple code of three characters is presented and exercise therein given to measure perceptual speed. Testing time: 2 minutes.

12. *Counting Groups of Dots.* Four to seven dots, arranged in random patterns, to be counted by the subject. A test of perceptual speed. Testing time: 4 minutes.

13. *Straight and Curved Capitals.* A series of capital letters. The subject is required to distinguish between those composed of straight lines only and those containing curved lines. A test of perceptual speed. Testing time: 3 minutes.

* K. J. Holzinger and F. Swineford, *A Study in Factor Analysis*, 1939.

14. *Word Recognition.* Twenty-five four-letter words are studied for three minutes. These words are then to be checked from memory on a hundred-word list. Testing time: 5 minutes. (Score includes two forms.)

15. *Number Recognition.* Similar to Test 14. Fifteen three-digit numbers.

16. *Figure Recognition.* Similar to Test 14. Fifteen geometric designs.

17. *Object-Number.* Twenty pairs of names of familiar objects and two-digit numbers are studied for three minutes. The words only are then presented to the subject, who is required to supply the proper numbers. Testing time: 5 minutes. (Score includes two forms.)

18. *Number-Figure.* Similar to Test 17. Ten pairs of numbers and geometric figures.

19. *Figure-Word.* Similar to Test 17. Ten pairs of geometric figures and words studied for one minute.

20. *Deduction.* Logical deduction test using the symbols) and (and the letters A, B, C, and D. Testing time: 24 minutes.

21. *Numerical Puzzles.* A numerical deduction test, the object being to supply four numbers which will produce four given answers employing the operations of addition, multiplication, or division. Testing time: 14 minutes.

22. *Problem Reasoning.* A reasoning test in completion form. Each problem lists the steps in obtaining a required amount of water using two or three vessels of given capacity. Testing time: 14 minutes.

23. *Series Completion.* From a series of five numbers the subject is supposed to deduce the rule of procedure from one number to the next, and thus supply the sixth number in the series. Testing time: 14 minutes.

24. *Woody-McCall Mixed Fundamentals: Form I.* A series of 35 arithmetic problems, graduated for difficulty, is included. Testing time: 20 minutes.

It should be noted that Tests 3 and 4 are Tests 25 and 26 of *A Study in Factor Analysis*, while Tests 3 and 4 of that monograph have not been used in the present study. This change has been made as a consequence of the findings in the other study. It was found that the original Tests 3 and 4 were too difficult for the group of children in the sample and hence yielded smaller reliability coefficients than the revised forms 25 and 26 (which are called here Tests 3 and 4).

B.2. *Factor Patterns as Classical Regression Equations*

It will be shown here that any equation of a factor pattern may be considered as a classical regression equation, where the dependent variable is the observed variable and the independent variables are the hypothetical factors. The formal expression for such an equation is

(B.1) $$z_j = \beta_{j1}F_1 + \beta_{j2}F_2 + \ldots + \beta_{jm}F_m + \beta_j U_j$$
$$(j = 1, 2, \ldots, n),$$

where the subscripts on β are so arranged that the position of any regression coefficient is uniquely determined. Thus, for the coefficients β_{js}, the first subscript j indicates that z_j is the dependent variable, and the second subscript s ($s = 1, 2, \ldots, m$) shows the factor F_s to which the coefficient is attached. The regression coefficient attached to the unique factor U_j is distinguished merely by one subscript. Of course, (B.1) cannot be obtained by the ordinary methods of solution for a regression equation because the factors are not observed variables. It will be shown, however, that a pattern produced by a factor analysis consists of equations of the form (B.1).

The formal expressions for the coefficients in (B.1) may be written, although the factors are not observed variables. The correlations among the variables involved in (B.1) may be given a symbolic representation even though they may not be obtainable by experiment. Let the matrix of intercorrelations of factors, bordered by the correlations of any variable z_j with the factors, be denoted by Δ. Then

$$
\Delta = \begin{Vmatrix}
1 & r_{z_jF_1} & r_{z_jF_2} & r_{z_jF_3} & \cdots & r_{z_jF_m} & r_{z_jU_j} \\
r_{F_1z_j} & 1 & r_{F_1F_2} & r_{F_1F_3} & \cdots & r_{F_1F_m} & 0 \\
r_{F_2z_j} & r_{F_2F_1} & 1 & r_{F_2F_3} & \cdots & r_{F_2F_m} & 0 \\
r_{F_3z_j} & r_{F_3F_1} & r_{F_3F_2} & 1 & \cdots & r_{F_3F_m} & 0 \\
\cdot & \cdot & \cdot & \cdot & \cdots & \cdot & \cdot \\
r_{F_mz_j} & r_{F_mF_1} & r_{F_mF_2} & r_{F_mF_3} & \cdots & 1 & 0 \\
r_{U_jz_j} & 0 & 0 & 0 & \cdots & 0 & 1
\end{Vmatrix},
$$

since the unique factors are assumed to be uncorrelated with the common factors.

Let Δ_{11} be the minor of the element in the first row and column, Δ_j the cofactor of the element $r_{z_jU_j}$, and Δ_{js} the cofactor of the element $r_{z_jF_s}$ ($s = 1, 2, \ldots, m$). Then the regression coefficients in the linear equation for z_j are given by*

(B.2)
$$
\beta_{js} = -\frac{\Delta_{js}}{\Delta_{11}}
$$

and

(B.3)
$$
\beta_j = -\frac{\Delta_j}{\Delta_{11}}.
$$

* Karl J. Holzinger, *Statistical Methods for Students in Education*, p. 313.

The last expression can be simplified by inserting the value $\Delta_j = -r_{z_j U_j}\Delta_{11}$. It then becomes

$$\beta_j = r_{z_j U_j}$$

or, on applying formula (2.18),

(B.4) $$\beta_j = a_j.$$

The algebraic solution, by determinants, for the coefficients a_{js} of the factor pattern,

(2.4^{bis}) $$z_j = a_{j1}F_1 + a_{j2}F_2 + \ldots + a_{jm}F_m + a_j U_j,$$

by means of equations (2.17) is*

(2.19^{bis}) $$a_{js} = \frac{A_{js}}{A} \qquad (j = 1, 2, \ldots, n;\ s = 1, 2, \ldots, m).$$

Now A is precisely the determinant Δ_{11}, and A_{js} is readily seen to be $-\Delta_{js}$. Hence

(B.5) $$\beta_{js} = a_{js}.$$

Formulas (B.5) and (B.4) show that the equations (2.16) of a factor pattern are exactly of the form of the classical regression equation (B.1).

It will next be shown that the equations of a factor pattern, considered as regression equations, include the errors of estimate. In other words, the multiple correlation between the dependent variable z_j and the independent variables $F_1, F_2, \ldots, F_m, U_j$ is unity. The standard error of estimate of the variable z_j from the regression equation (B.1) is given by†

(B.6) $$S_j = \sqrt{\frac{\Delta}{\Delta_{11}}}.$$

Expanding the determinant Δ according to the elements of the last column, equation (B.6) may be written

$$S_j^2 = \frac{\Delta}{\Delta_{11}} = \frac{-r_{z_j U_j}^2\Delta_{11} + (\Delta_{11} + r_{z_j F_1}\Delta_{j1} + r_{z_j F_2}\Delta_{j2} + \ldots + r_{z_j F_m}\Delta_{jm})}{\Delta_{11}},$$

which simplifies to

(B.7) $$S_j^2 = 1 - (r_{z_j F_1}\beta_{j1} + r_{z_j F_2}\beta_{j2} + \ldots + r_{z_j F_m}\beta_{jm}) - a_j^2$$

upon substituting the values from (B.2) and $r_{z_j U_j} = a_j$.

---

* See p. 16. † Holzinger, *op. cit.*

In (B.5) the relationship $\beta_{js} = a_{js}$ was deduced, and for uncorrelated factors $r_{z_jF_s} = a_{js}$ as shown in (2.20). Putting these values into (B.7), it reduces to

$$(B.8) \quad S_j^2 = 1 - (a_{j1}^2 + a_{j2}^2 + \ldots + a_{jm}^2) - a_j^2 = 1 - h_j^2 - a_j^2 = 0 ,$$

where h_j^2 is the communality of variable j, and the last equality follows from the fact that the communality and uniqueness sum to the total unit variance of a variable. The last equation shows that, in predicting a variable z_j from the independent variables $F_1, F_2, \ldots, F_m, U_j$, there is no error of estimate. A factor analysis usually produces the values of a_{js} so that the communality h_j^2 is determined. The coefficient of the unique factor U_j is then obtained merely from the relation,

$$a_j = \sqrt{1 - h_j^2} ,$$

to bring the total variance of the variable up to unity. Thus any equation of a factor pattern may be thought of as a classical regression equation with the error of estimate given by the coefficient of the unique factor.

B.3. *Indeterminateness of Factor Solutions*

It is a well-known proposition that the factor problem is indeterminate in the sense that, given a matrix of correlations of a set of variables, the coefficients of a factor pattern are not uniquely determined. That is, systems of orthogonal, or uncorrelated, factors F_j may be chosen, *consistent with the observed correlations*, in an infinity of ways. Perhaps the clearest demonstration of this theorem was given by Hotelling,* and that is the form that will be employed here.

For simplicity of proof it will be assumed that the factor pattern contains as many factors as variables. Without specializing the type of factors (e.g., into common and unique), the pattern may be written

$$(B.9) \quad z_j = a_{j1}F_1 + a_{j2}F_2 + \ldots + a_{jn}F_n \qquad (j = 1, 2, \ldots, n) ,$$

where the factors are normally distributed having zero correlations and in standard form, that is, zero means and unit variances.† The condition that the means shall be zero is expressed by

$$(B.10) \quad M_{F_s} = \frac{\Sigma F_s}{N} = 0 ,$$

* Harold Hotelling, "Analysis of a Complex of Statistical Variables," *Journal of Educational Psychology*, 1933, Sec. 1.

† It will be assumed here that these properties, which are postulated for an infinite population, also hold for a sample of N observations.

where the summation is taken over N values. The properties of zero correlations and unit variances are expressed in the single statement

(B.11) $$\frac{\Sigma F_s F_t}{N} = \delta_{st} ,$$

where δ_{st} is the Kronecker delta, which is equal to unity if $s = t$ and equal to zero if $s \neq t$.

Now the correlation between variables z_j and z_k, equal to unity if $j = k$, is given by

(B.12) $$r_{jk} = \frac{\Sigma z_j z_k}{N} ,$$

where the summation is over the N values of the variables z_j and z_k. Substituting the value of z_j from (B.9) and a similar expression for z_k into (B.12), and making use of the conditions (B.11), equation (B.12) becomes

(B.13) $$r_{jk} = \sum_{s=1}^{n} a_{js} a_{ks} \qquad (j, k = 1, 2, \ldots , n) .$$

The indices j and k take on n^2 values together,* but since $r_{jk} = r_{kj}$ the number of equations (B.13) is only

$$n^2 - \binom{n}{2} = n^2 - \tfrac{1}{2}n(n - 1) = \tfrac{1}{2}n(n + 1) .$$

This number of equations is insufficient for uniquely determining the n^2 quantities a_{js} when the correlations are given. The difference between the number of unknowns and the number of conditions is

$$n^2 - \tfrac{1}{2}n(n + 1) = \tfrac{1}{2}n(n - 1) .$$

This suggests that it should be possible to express all the coefficients in terms of $\tfrac{1}{2}n(n - 1)$ of them, or generally, in terms of $\tfrac{1}{2}n(n - 1)$ other parameters. Thus systems of uncorrelated factors F may be chosen, consistently with the observed correlations, in $\tfrac{1}{2}n(n - 1)$ ways. This result may also be interpreted geometrically. In a space of n dimensions there are $\tfrac{1}{2}n(n - 1)$ degrees of freedom of a rigid rotation. Thus after a set of n factors is selected there are $\tfrac{1}{2}n(n - 1)$ degrees of freedom of a rigid rotation of this set into another set of factors.

One assumption made on the nature of the factors F has not been brought

* It is here assumed that the diagonal values of the correlation matrix are unity.

explicitly into the proof. That assumption is that the factors are normally distributed. It is because of this condition that no additional equations for determining the a_{js}'s could be obtained from the moments of higher order, or of other parameters of the population. For the z_j's, being linear combinations of normally distributed factors, have a multivariate normal distribution; and every parameter of such a distribution is a function of the means, standard deviations, and correlations.* Thus all the available information is embodied in the equations (B.13), and these being fewer in number than the coefficients a_{js}, the indeterminacy exists.

B.4. *Basic Axioms for Euclidean Geometry*

The most fundamental axioms are those of incidence or connection. They may be listed as follows for three-dimensional space:

1. Any two distinct points uniquely determine a straight line.
2. If P_1 and P_2 are distinct points, there is at least one point not on the straight line P_1P_2.
3. Any three noncollinear points determine a plane.
4. If two distinct points P_1, P_2 both belong to a plane π, every point of the straight line P_1P_2 belongs to π.
5. If P_1, P_2, P_3 are noncollinear points, there is at least one point not on the plane $P_1P_2P_3$.
6. If two planes have a point P_1 in common, they have a second point P_2 in common, and hence the line P_1P_2 in common.

Axioms 2 and 5 postulate the existence of a two- and three-dimensional space, respectively. If Axiom 6 is assumed, it limits space to three dimensions. On the other hand, if at least one point not in this region is postulated, then a four-dimensional region is obtained.

There is some difficulty in determining all the elements of space by means of the preceding axioms; for, while Axiom 1 postulates that two distinct points determine a line, there is no axiom guaranteeing that two distinct lines in a plane determine a point. This, of course, is not true in the Euclidean plane since parallel lines have no point in common. To simplify the geometric discussion, therefore, the following *projective axiom* will be assumed:

7. Any two distinct straight lines in a plane uniquely determine a point.

This axiom extends a Euclidean to a projective plane. The advantage of working in a projective space is that most theorems are greatly simplified by not having to treat the special cases of parallel elements.

* Yule and Kendall, *An Introduction to the Theory of Statistics*, 1937, Chap. XIV, Sec. 28.

B.5. *Proof of Theorem 3.1*

For purposes of reference, the theorem is here repeated: *If m is the rank of the matrix*

$$\|x_{ji}\| = \begin{Vmatrix} x_{11} & x_{12} & x_{13} & \ldots & x_{1N} \\ x_{21} & x_{22} & x_{23} & \ldots & x_{2N} \\ x_{31} & x_{32} & x_{33} & \ldots & x_{3N} \\ \cdot & \cdot & \cdot & \ldots & \cdot \cdot \\ x_{n1} & x_{n2} & x_{n3} & \ldots & x_{nN} \end{Vmatrix},$$

the points $P_1, P_2, \ldots, P_n$ are all dependent upon m of them, which are themselves independent.

The proof of this theorem may be split into two parts. First consider the case where $n \leqq N$. By hypothesis the matrix $\|x_{ji}\|$ is of rank m, so that without loss of generality it may be assumed that the determinant

$$D = \begin{vmatrix} x_{11} & x_{12} & \ldots & x_{1m} \\ x_{21} & x_{22} & \ldots & x_{2m} \\ \cdot & \cdot & \ldots & \cdot \cdot \\ x_{m1} & x_{m2} & \ldots & x_{mm} \end{vmatrix}$$

is different from zero. If $m = n$ the set of equations

$$\sum_{k=1}^{n} x_{kj} t_k = 0 \qquad\qquad (j = 1, 2, \ldots, n)$$

have the unique solution $t_1 = t_2 = \ldots = t_n = 0$, since $D \neq 0$. Then, according to the definition (3.2), the points $P_1, P_2, \ldots, P_n$ are linearly independent. If $m < n$ the points $P_1, P_2, \ldots, P_m$ may be shown to be independent by the preceding argument. This establishes the last part of the theorem.

Now it remains to be shown that all n points are dependent upon these. Let $D_{1i}, D_{2i}, \ldots, D_{mi}$ be the cofactors of $x_{1i}, x_{2i}, \ldots, x_{mi}$ in the matrix

$$\begin{Vmatrix} x_{11} & x_{12} & \ldots & x_{1m} & x_{1i} \\ x_{21} & x_{22} & \ldots & x_{2m} & x_{2i} \\ \cdot & \cdot & \ldots & \cdot & \cdot \\ x_{m1} & x_{m2} & \ldots & x_{mm} & x_{mi} \\ x_{p1} & x_{p2} & \ldots & x_{pm} & x_{pi} \end{Vmatrix},$$

where $p = m + 1, \ldots, n$ and i is arbitrary. The determinant of this matrix, when expanded according to the elements of the last column, becomes

(B.14) $\qquad x_{1i}D_{1i} + x_{2i}D_{2i} + \ldots + x_{mi}D_{mi} + x_{pi}D$.

This expression vanishes, for, if $i \leq m$, two columns then have equal elements; and, if $i > m$, it vanishes, since the rank of $\|x_{ji}\|$ is m and every $(m + 1)$-order minor vanishes. The solution for x_{pi} from the expression (B.14) set equal to zero is

(B.15) $\qquad x_{pi} = \sum_{q=1}^{m} t_q x_{qi} \qquad (p = m + 1, \ldots, n)$,

where the constants

$$t_q = - \frac{D_{qi}}{D}$$

do not depend on the elements $x_{1i}, x_{2i}, \ldots, x_{mi}, x_{pi}$. It follows from definition (3.1) that the points P_p, whose coordinates are given in (B.15), are linearly dependent on the points $P_1, P_2, \ldots, P_m$, which are themselves independent.

If $n > N$, consider the points P_j: $(x_{j1}, x_{j2}, \ldots, x_{jN}, 0, \ldots, 0)$ in the space of n dimensions. Then the foregoing argument can be applied to obtain the relation (B.15), and thus the theorem is established for all values of n.

B.6. *Proof of Theorem 3.4*

The product of the matrix $\|z_{ji}\|$ of standardized values by its transpose is equal to the correlation matrix $\|r_{jk}\|$ multiplied by N^2, as shown in equation (3.44). Since the theorem is concerned only with the ranks of the matrices, the non-zero factor N^2 is irrelevant to it. The product of the two matrices might be represented by $\|r^*_{jk}\| = \|Nr_{jk}\|$ to be absolutely rigorous, but for simplicity $\|r^*_{jk}\|$ will be written $\|r_{jk}\|$. With this clearly in mind, the theorem may be restated as follows: If m is the rank of the matrix $\|z_{ji}\|$, and if $\|z_{ik}\|$ is its transpose, then the rank μ of $\|r_{jk}\| = \|z_{ji}\| \cdot \|z_{ik}\|$ is equal to m.

The proof consists of two parts: first, to show that $\mu \leq m$ and, second, that $m \leq \mu$. That the rank of the product of any two matrices cannot exceed the rank of either factor is a well-known theorem.† The remainder of

† See, e.g., L. E. Dickson, *Modern Algebraic Theories*, p. 51.

the proof is concerned with showing that $m \leqq \mu$ for the product of a matrix by its transpose.

Let

$$\|z_{pq}\| = \begin{Vmatrix} z_{11} & z_{12} & \cdots & z_{1m} \\ z_{21} & z_{22} & \cdots & z_{2m} \\ \cdot & \cdot & \cdot & \cdots & \cdot & \cdot \\ z_{m1} & z_{m2} & \cdots & z_{mm} \end{Vmatrix}$$

be a minor of $\|z_{ji}\|$ whose rows form a *maximal linearly independent* set of rows of $\|z_{ji}\|$. By this is meant that the rows of $\|z_{pq}\|$ are linearly independent and every minor of which $\|z_{pq}\|$ is a proper minor has its rows linearly dependent. Then the rank of $\|z_{ji}\|$ is the number, m, of vectors (or rows) in this set.

The product of $\|z_{pq}\|$ by its transpose, $\|z_{qs}\|$, may be represented by

$$\|r_{ps}\| = \|z_{pq}\| \cdot \|z_{qs}\| \,,$$

where $\|r_{ps}\|$ is an m-order minor of $\|r_{jk}\|$. Now, if*

(B.16)
$$\begin{Vmatrix} r_{11} & r_{12} & \cdots & r_{1m} \\ r_{21} & r_{22} & \cdots & r_{2m} \\ \cdot & \cdot & \cdot & \cdots & \cdot & \cdot \\ r_{m1} & r_{m2} & \cdots & r_{mm} \end{Vmatrix} \cdot \begin{Vmatrix} z_1 \\ z_2 \\ \cdot \\ \cdot \\ z_m \end{Vmatrix} = 0 \,,$$

then, premultiplying by $\|z_1\ z_2 \ldots z_m\|$, this expression becomes

(B.17)
$$\left\{ \begin{aligned} 0 &= \|z_1 z_2 \ldots z_m\| \cdot \|r_{ps}\| \cdot \begin{Vmatrix} z_1 \\ z_2 \\ \cdot \\ \cdot \\ \cdot \\ z_m \end{Vmatrix} \\ &= \|z_1 z_2 \ldots z_m\| \cdot \|z_{pq}\| \cdot \|z_{qs}\| \cdot \begin{Vmatrix} z_1 \\ z_2 \\ \cdot \\ \cdot \\ \cdot \\ z_m \end{Vmatrix} \cdot \end{aligned} \right.$$

* This condition is equivalent to (3.2), and if it implies that $z_1 = z_2 = \ldots = z_m = 0$, then the columns of the correlation matrix are linearly independent.

Let the product of the last two matrices be represented by the column vector $\{y_q\}$, as follows:

$$
\begin{Vmatrix} y_1 \\ y_2 \\ \cdot \\ \cdot \\ \cdot \\ y_m \end{Vmatrix} = \|z_{qs}\| \cdot \begin{Vmatrix} z_1 \\ z_2 \\ \cdot \\ \cdot \\ \cdot \\ z_m \end{Vmatrix},
$$

then the transpose of $\{y_q\}$ is

$$
\|y_q\| = \|y_1\, y_2 \dots y_m\| = \|z_1\, z_2 \dots z_m\| \cdot \|z_{pq}\| .
$$

Equation (B.17) may now be put in the form

$$
0 = \|y_q\| \cdot \{y_q\} = \|y_1\, y_2 \dots y_m\| \cdot \begin{Vmatrix} y_1 \\ y_2 \\ \cdot \\ \cdot \\ \cdot \\ y_m \end{Vmatrix} = \sum_{q=1}^{m} y_q^2 .
$$

In order for a sum of positive numbers to be zero, each element must be zero, and therefore $\|y_q\|$ is a zero vector. Then

$$
\|y_q\| = \|z_1\, z_2 \dots z_m\| \cdot \|z_{pq}\| = 0 ,
$$

and, since the rows of $\|z_{pq}\|$ are linearly independent, it follows from the definition (3.2) that $z_1 = z_2 = \dots = z_m = 0$, that is, the vector $\|z_1\, z_2 \dots z_m\|$ is a zero vector. It has thus been shown that the condition (B.16) implies that $z_1 = z_2 = \dots = z_m = 0$, and hence according to (3.2) the columns of $\|r_{ps}\|$ are linearly independent. Then the matrix $\|r_{ps}\|$ is nonsingular, and its rank μ is at least equal to its order, m. Now that $\mu \geq m$ and, as has been pointed out, $\mu \leq m$, it therefore follows that $\mu = m$. The rank of the product of a matrix by its transpose has thus been shown to be equal to the common rank of either factor.

B.7. *Standard Error of a Function in Terms of the Standard Errors of Its Variables*

Let $f(x_1, x_2, \dots, x_n)$ be a function of the n variables $x_1, x_2, \dots, x_n$ and let $f_i = \partial f/\partial x_i$, $\sigma_i = \sigma_{x_i}$, $r_{jk} = r_{x_j x_k}$. Then the total differential is given by

$$
df = f_1 dx_1 + f_2 dx_2 + \dots + f_n dx_n .
$$

Squaring this expression and taking the mean value over the population produces

$$\sigma_f^2 = f_1^2\sigma_1^2 + f_2^2\sigma_2^2 + \ldots + f_n^2\sigma_n^2 + 2(f_1f_2\sigma_1\sigma_2r_{12}$$
$$+ f_1f_3\sigma_1\sigma_3r_{13} + \ldots + f_1f_n\sigma_1\sigma_nr_{1n} + f_2f_3\sigma_2\sigma_3r_{23}$$
$$+ \ldots + f_2f_n\sigma_2\sigma_nr_{2n} + \ldots + f_{n-1}f_n\sigma_{n-1}\sigma_nr_{n-1,n}),$$

$$= \sum_{j=1}^{n} f_j^2\sigma_j^2 + 2\sum_{j<k=1}^{n} f_jf_k\sigma_j\sigma_kr_{jk},$$

(B.18)
$$\sigma_f^2 = \sum_{j=1}^{n}\sum_{k=1}^{n} f_jf_k\sigma_j\sigma_kr_{jk},$$

since $r_{jj} = 1$ and $r_{jk} = r_{kj}$.

For the particular case in which the variables $x_1, x_2, \ldots, x_n$ are statistically independent (i.e., uncorrelated), formula (B.18) reduces to

(B.19)
$$\sigma_f^2 = \sum_{j=1}^{n} f_j^2\sigma_j^2 .$$

A very important special case of (B.18) occurs when f is a function of a single variable x. Then

(B.20)
$$\sigma_{f(x)}^2 = \left(\frac{df}{dx}\right)^2\sigma_x^2 .$$

This states that the mean square error of a function of x is equal to the mean square error of x multiplied by the square of the derivative of the function with respect to x. It is this theorem which is employed in obtaining (6.25) or (6.26).

B.8. *Mean Value of Certain Ratios*

The mean value of a nonlinear function of two or more variables can, in general, only be expressed in terms of the means, standard deviations, and correlations of the original variables to a first approximation. Thus, let it be required to find the mean value of the ratio ab/c^3 in terms of these statistics for a, b, and c. The determination of the other four expressions in (6.28) follows a similar pattern to the one which will be treated in detail here. To save space, therefore, their derivations will not be given.

Denoting the mean over $\nu = \binom{n-1}{2}$ values by scoring, it is required to find an expression for $\Sigma(r_{ej}r_{ek}/r_{jk}^3; \; j < k, \; j,k \neq e, \; j,k = 1, 2, \ldots, n) /\nu$, or employing the definitions (6.19),

(B.21)
$$\overline{\left(\frac{ab}{c^3}\right)} = \frac{1}{\nu}\sum \frac{ab}{c^3},$$

where the summation extends over the ν values of the ratio. Let α, β, and γ stand for the respective deviates of a, b, and c from their means, that is,

$$\alpha = a - \bar{a}, \qquad \beta = b - \bar{b}, \qquad \gamma = c - \bar{c}.$$

Then (B.21) may be expressed as follows:

$$\overline{\left(\frac{ab}{c^3}\right)} = \frac{1}{\nu}\sum \frac{\bar{a}\bar{b}}{\bar{c}^3}\left(1 + \frac{\alpha}{\bar{a}}\right)\left(1 + \frac{\beta}{\bar{b}}\right)\left(1 + \frac{\gamma}{\bar{c}}\right)^{-3}.$$

Now expand the last bracket by the binomial theorem, dropping third and higher degree terms. To this approximation, the formula becomes

$$\overline{\left(\frac{ab}{c^3}\right)} = \frac{\bar{a}\bar{b}}{\bar{c}^3}\frac{1}{\nu}\sum\left(1 + \frac{\alpha}{\bar{a}} + \frac{\beta}{\bar{b}} + \frac{\alpha\beta}{\bar{a}\bar{b}}\right)\left(1 - 3\frac{\gamma}{\bar{c}} + 6\frac{\gamma^2}{\bar{c}^2}\right).$$

This may be expanded, again keeping only terms to the second degree, as follows:

$$\overline{\left(\frac{ab}{c^3}\right)} = \frac{\bar{a}\bar{b}}{\bar{c}^3}\frac{1}{\nu}\left(\nu + \frac{1}{\bar{a}}\Sigma\alpha + \frac{1}{\bar{b}}\Sigma\beta + \frac{1}{\bar{a}\bar{b}}\Sigma\alpha\beta\right.$$
$$\left. - \frac{3}{\bar{c}}\Sigma\gamma - \frac{3}{\bar{a}\bar{c}}\Sigma\alpha\gamma - \frac{3}{\bar{b}\bar{c}}\Sigma\beta\gamma + \frac{6}{\bar{c}^2}\Sigma\gamma^2\right).$$

Employing the definitions of the standard deviation and the correlation coefficient for these variables, the mean of the required ratio finally reduces to

(B.22)
$$\overline{\left(\frac{ab}{c^3}\right)} = \frac{\bar{a}\bar{b}}{\bar{c}^3}\left(1 + \frac{\sigma_a\sigma_b r_{ab}}{\bar{a}\bar{b}} - \frac{3\sigma_a\sigma_c r_{ac}}{\bar{a}\bar{c}} - \frac{3\sigma_b\sigma_c r_{bc}}{\bar{b}\bar{c}} + \frac{6\sigma_c^2}{\bar{c}^2}\right).$$

The last of equations (6.28) is precisely (B.22). The means of the other ratios in (6.28) can be obtained in a manner similar to that which is used here for ab/c^3. It must be remembered that in the derivation of the formulas (6.28) it was assumed that $\alpha/\bar{a}$, $\beta/\bar{b}$, $\gamma/\bar{c}$ are so small, in each case, that powers higher than the second can be neglected.

B.9. *Derivation of the Principal-Factor Method*

The first stage of the principal-factor method involves the selection of the first-factor coefficients a_{j1} so as to make the sum of the contributions of that factor to the total communality a maximum. This sum is given by

$$(7.3^{\text{bis}}) \qquad A_1 = a_{11}^2 + a_{21}^2 + \ldots + a_{n1}^2 \,,$$

and the coefficients a_{j1} must be chosen so as to make A_1 a maximum under the conditions

$$(7.4^{\text{bis}}) \qquad r_{jk} = \sum_{t=1}^{m} a_{jt} a_{kt} \qquad (j, k = 1, 2, \ldots, n) \,,$$

where r_{jj} is the communality h_j^2 of variable z_j.

In order to maximize a function of n variables when the variables are connected by an arbitrary number of auxiliary equations, the method of Lagrange multipliers* is particularly well adapted. This method will be employed to maximize A_1, which is a function of the n variables a_{j1}, under the $\frac{1}{2}n(n+1)$ conditions (7.4) among all the coefficients a_{jt}. Let

$$(B.23) \qquad 2T = A_1 - \sum_{j,k=1}^{n} \mu_{jk} r_{jk} = A_1 - \sum_{j,k=1}^{n} \sum_{t=1}^{m} \mu_{jk} a_{jt} a_{kt} \,,$$

where $\mu_{jk} (= \mu_{kj})$ are the Lagrange multipliers. Then set the partial derivative of this new function T with respect to any one of the n variables a_{j1} equal to zero, namely,

$$(B.24) \qquad \frac{\partial T}{\partial a_{j1}} = a_{j1} - \sum_{k=1}^{n} \mu_{jk} a_{k1} = 0 \,,$$

and similarly put the partial derivative with respect to any of the other coefficients a_{jt} ($t \neq 1$) equal to zero, that is,

$$(B.25) \qquad \frac{\partial T}{\partial a_{jt}} = - \sum_{k=1}^{n} \mu_{jk} a_{kt} = 0 \qquad (t \neq 1) \,.$$

The two sets of equations (B.24) and (B.25) may be combined as follows:

$$(B.26) \qquad \frac{\partial T}{\partial a_{jt}} = \delta_{1t} a_{j1} - \sum_{k=1}^{n} \mu_{jk} a_{kt} = 0 \qquad (t = 1, 2, \ldots, m) \,,$$

where $\delta_{1t} = 1$ if $t = 1$ and $\delta_{1t} = 0$ if $t \neq 1$.

* See, e.g., William F. Osgood, *Advanced Calculus*, 1932, pp. 180–85.

Multiply (B.26) by a_{j1} and sum with respect to j, obtaining*

(B.27)
$$\delta_{1t} \sum_{j=1}^{n} a_{j1}^2 - \sum_{j=1}^{n} \sum_{k=1}^{n} \mu_{jk} a_{j1} a_{kt} = 0 .$$

Now, the expression $\sum_{j=1}^{n} \mu_{jk} a_{j1}$ is equal to a_{k1} according to (B.24), and,

setting $\sum_{j=1}^{n} a_{j1}^2 = \lambda_1$, equation (B.27) may be written as follows:

(B.28)
$$\delta_{1t} \lambda_1 - \sum_{k=1}^{n} a_{k1} a_{kt} = 0 .$$

Upon multiplying (B.28) by a_{jt} and summing for t, this equation becomes

(B.29)
$$a_{j1} \lambda_1 - \sum_{k=1}^{n} a_{k1} \left(\sum_{t=1}^{m} a_{jt} a_{kt} \right) = 0 ,$$

or, by using (7.4),

(B.30)
$$\sum_{k=1}^{n} r_{jk} a_{k1} - \lambda_1 a_{j1} = 0 .$$

The expression (B.30) represents n equations, one for each value of j. Writing these equations explicitly, there results

(B.31)
$$\begin{cases} (h_1^2 - \lambda_1) a_{11} + r_{12} a_{21} + r_{13} a_{31} + \ldots + r_{1n} a_{n1} = 0 , \\ r_{21} a_{11} + (h_2^2 - \lambda_1) a_{21} + r_{23} a_{31} + \ldots + r_{2n} a_{n1} = 0 , \\ r_{31} a_{11} + r_{32} a_{21} + (h_3^2 - \lambda_1) a_{31} + \ldots + r_{3n} a_{n1} = 0 , \\ \cdots \cdots \cdots \cdots \cdots \cdots \cdots \cdots \cdots \\ r_{n1} a_{11} + r_{n2} a_{21} + r_{n3} a_{31} + \ldots + (h_n^2 - \lambda_1) a_{n1} = 0 . \end{cases}$$

These equations furnish the basis for the solution of the unknown coefficients a_{j1}. The remaining description of the method is presented in **7.3**.

B.10. *Direction Cosines of Oblique Reference Axes*

One stage in the process of obtaining an oblique factor solution involves the calculation of the direction cosines of these reference vectors with re-

* This procedure was suggested by M. A. Girshick, "Principal Components," *Journal of the American Statistical Association*, 1936, pp. 519–28.

spect to the original orthogonal reference system. In **11.3** two methods were suggested for the determination of such direction cosines. One method is based upon averages of points representing the variables, and the other depends upon composite variables. It will now be shown that these two approaches lead to identical values of the direction cosines.

For simplicity, let there be two initial orthogonal factors, F_1 and F_2, and eight variables consisting of two subgroups. Let the composite variables of these subsets be defined by

$$v_1 = z_1 + z_2 + z_3 + z_4,$$
$$v_2 = z_5 + z_6 + z_7 + z_8.$$

Then the coordinates of the point representing the first of these variables are given by

$$(B.32) \qquad P_1 : \left(r_{v_1 F_1} = \frac{1}{\sigma_{v_1}} \sum_{j=1}^{4} r_{jF_1}, \qquad r_{v_1 F_2} = \frac{1}{\sigma_{v_1}} \sum_{j=1}^{4} r_{jF_2} \right),$$

and a similar expression is possible for the second variable. The distance of this point from the origin is

$$(B.33) \qquad D(OP_1) = \sqrt{r_{v_1 F_1}^2 + r_{v_1 F_2}^2},$$

and the direction cosines of the line from the origin through this point are

$$(B.34) \qquad \lambda_{11} = \frac{r_{v_1 F_1}}{D(OP_1)} \quad \text{and} \quad \lambda_{21} = \frac{r_{v_1 F_2}}{D(OP_1)}.$$

Instead of employing the composite variable, the centroid of the first subgroup may be obtained, as follows:

$$(B.35) \qquad Q_1 : \left(\frac{1}{4} \sum_{j=1}^{4} r_{jF_1}, \qquad \frac{1}{4} \sum_{j=1}^{4} r_{jF_2} \right).$$

Now it may be noted from (B.32) that

$$\sum_{j=1}^{4} r_{jF_1} = \sigma_{v_1} r_{v_1 F_1}, \qquad \sum_{j=1}^{4} r_{jF_2} = \sigma_{v_1} r_{v_1 F_2},$$

and hence the distance of the point Q_1 from the origin is

$$(B.36) \qquad D(OQ_1) = \tfrac{1}{4}\sigma_{v_1} \sqrt{r_{v_1 F_1}^2 + r_{v_1 F_2}^2} = \tfrac{1}{4}\sigma_{v_1} D(OP_1).$$

Then the direction cosines of the line OQ_1 are given by

$$(B.37) \quad \frac{\frac{1}{4}\sigma_{v_1} r_{v_1 F_1}}{\frac{1}{4}\sigma_{v_1} D(OP_1)} = \frac{r_{v_1 F_1}}{D(OP_1)} = \lambda_{11} \quad \text{and} \quad \frac{\frac{1}{4}\sigma_{v_1} r_{v_1 F_2}}{\frac{1}{4}\sigma_{v_1} D(OP_1)} = \frac{r_{v_1 F_2}}{D(OP_1)} = \lambda_{21}.$$

From (B.34) and (B.37) it is evident that either the method of composite variables or the method of averages yields the same values of the direction cosines of the axis passing through the first cluster of points. Similar results can, of course, be obtained for the axis through the second cluster of points, and the method can readily be generalized to any number of variables in the subgroups and any number of factors.

B.11. *Matrix Formulation of the Relation between a Pattern and a Structure*

In matrix notation a factor pattern expressing the N values of each of the n variables in terms of the factors may be written in the form:

$$(B.38) \quad \mathbf{Z} = \mathbf{MF},$$

where

$$\mathbf{Z} = \begin{Vmatrix} z_{11} & z_{12} & \cdots & z_{1N} \\ z_{21} & z_{22} & \cdots & z_{2N} \\ \cdot & \cdot & \cdots & \cdot \\ z_{n1} & z_{n2} & \cdots & z_{nN} \end{Vmatrix} \qquad \mathbf{F} = \begin{Vmatrix} F_{11} & F_{12} & \cdots & F_{1N} \\ \cdot & \cdot & \cdots & \cdot \\ F_{m1} & F_{m2} & \cdots & F_{mN} \\ U_{11} & U_{12} & \cdots & U_{1N} \\ \cdot & \cdot & \cdots & \cdot \\ U_{n1} & U_{n2} & \cdots & U_{nN} \end{Vmatrix},$$

and $\mathbf{M}$ is the complete pattern matrix,

$$\mathbf{M} = \begin{Vmatrix} a_{11} & a_{12} & \cdots & a_{1m} & a_1 & 0 & \cdots & 0 \\ a_{21} & a_{22} & \cdots & a_{2m} & 0 & a_2 & \cdots & 0 \\ \cdot & \cdot & \cdots & \cdot & \cdot & \cdot & \cdots & \cdot \\ a_{n1} & a_{n2} & \cdots & a_{nm} & 0 & 0 & \cdots & a_n \end{Vmatrix}.$$

Postmultiplying both sides of (B.38) by $\mathbf{F}'$, and multiplying by the scalar $1/N$, this equation becomes

$$(B.39) \quad \frac{1}{N} \mathbf{ZF}' = \mathbf{M} \left(\frac{1}{N} \mathbf{FF}' \right).$$

The expression in the left-hand member of equation (B.39) can easily be shown to be the factor structure

$$(B.40) \quad \mathbf{S} = \frac{1}{N} \mathbf{ZF'} = \begin{Vmatrix} t_{11} & t_{12} & \ldots & t_{1m} & a_1 & 0 & \ldots & 0 \\ t_{21} & t_{22} & \ldots & t_{2m} & 0 & a_2 & \ldots & 0 \\ \cdot & \cdot & & \cdot & \cdot & \cdot & & \cdot \\ t_{n1} & t_{n2} & \ldots & t_{nm} & 0 & 0 & \ldots & a_n \end{Vmatrix},$$

where $t_{js} = r_{z_j F_s}$, and $a_j = r_{z_j U_j}$ according to (2.18). The expression in the right-hand member of (B.39) can also be simplified by means of the relation

$$\frac{1}{N} \mathbf{FF'} = \frac{1}{N} \begin{Vmatrix} \Sigma F_{1i}^2 & \ldots & \Sigma F_{1i} F_{mi} & \Sigma F_{1i} U_{1i} & \ldots & \Sigma F_{1i} U_{ni} \\ \cdot & & \cdot & \cdot & & \cdot \\ \Sigma F_{mi} F_{1i} & \ldots & \Sigma F_{mi}^2 & \Sigma F_{mi} U_{1i} & \ldots & \Sigma F_{mi} U_{ni} \\ \Sigma U_{1i} F_{1i} & \ldots & \Sigma U_{1i} F_{mi} & \Sigma U_{1i}^2 & \ldots & \Sigma U_{1i} U_{ni} \\ \cdot & & \cdot & \cdot & & \cdot \\ \Sigma U_{ni} F_{1i} & \ldots & \Sigma U_{ni} F_{mi} & \Sigma U_{ni} U_{1i} & \ldots & \Sigma U_{ni}^2 \end{Vmatrix}.$$

Since all factors are in standard form, each element in this matrix represents a coefficient of correlation multiplied by N. Hence, the preceding expression is equal to the matrix of correlations among the factors, namely,

$$(B.41) \quad \frac{1}{N} \mathbf{FF'} = \mathbf{\Phi} = \begin{Vmatrix} \phi & \mathbf{O} \\ \mathbf{O} & \mathbf{I} \end{Vmatrix},$$

where the matrix of correlations among the common factors is given by

$$\phi = \begin{Vmatrix} 1 & r_{F_1 F_2} & \ldots & r_{F_1 F_m} \\ r_{F_2 F_1} & 1 & \ldots & r_{F_2 F_m} \\ \cdot & \cdot & & \cdot \\ r_{F_m F_1} & r_{F_m F_2} & \ldots & 1 \end{Vmatrix}.$$

Now, substituting (B.40) and (B.41) into (B.39), the latter reduces to

$$(B.42) \quad \mathbf{S} = \mathbf{M\Phi},$$

which states that a factor structure is equal to the pattern matrix post-multiplied by the matrix of intercorrelations among all the factors. This relationship shows clearly that if the factors are uncorrelated (i.e., $\mathbf{\Phi}$ is the identity matrix) then the elements of the structure are equal to the corresponding elements of the pattern. The explicit expression for the pattern matrix can be obtained from (B.42) by postmultiplying both sides by Φ^{-1}. The result is

(B.43) $$M = S\Phi^{-1}.$$

Sometimes it is convenient to have the relationship between a pattern and structure for the common-factor portion only. If f is used to represent the matrix of common factors, A the matrix of common-factor coefficients, and T the common-factor portion of the structure, then by analysis similar to the preceding it can be shown that

(B.44) $$T = A\phi.$$

This relationship between the common-factor portions of the pattern and structure is analogous to that for the complete solution.

APPENDIX C

OUTLINE FOR COMPUTATION OF A BI-FACTOR PATTERN

A bi-factor solution can be obtained from a given matrix of correlations by the following calculations. This is the method developed in **6.4** and reduced to a routine procedure. For concreteness the method will be described in relation to the computation of the pattern for the data of **2.8**. The detailed procedure is presented as a series of steps.*

1. Determine the grouping of variables by the method of B-coefficients, as developed in **2.7**, for the given matrix of correlations. The method of computing B-coefficients is completely exhibited in **2.9** and will not be repeated here. For the given data, the B-coefficients are computed in Table 2.3, and the groups of variables indicated in (2.35).

2. Arrange the matrix of correlations so that the variables constituting a group are together. Of course, only the correlations below the principal diagonal need be written because the matrix is symmetric. The variables in Table 2.2 have been arranged according to their respective groups. It may be convenient, but not at all necessary, to renumber the variables at this stage from 1 to n. In the present example the variables are already numbered consecutively from 1 to 24 when they are arranged by groups.

3. As a result of the B-coefficient analysis, there are postulated six factors, viz., the general factor and five group factors, one for each group of variables. This hypothesis may be changed if the ensuing analysis indicates necessary modifications.

4. In the following analysis it is assumed that the matrix of correlations contains only essentially positive entries. This condition has always been found to be met with psychological data; but high negative correlations might occur for different variables. If there are one or two negative correlations which are insignificantly different from zero, they may be set equal to zero for purposes of computing the general-factor coefficients. On the other hand, when an observed matrix includes significantly high negative correlations, the variables producing these values may be changed in direction in an attempt to reduce the matrix to essentially positive correlations. In the example there is one negative correlation, namely, $r_{3,10} = -.075$, which is insignificant, being only nine-tenths of its standard error. Hence a value of zero is used for this correlation in the following step.

5. To obtain the general-factor coefficients, formula (6.14) is used. The component parts of this formula will be calculated piecemeal, however, to clarify the procedure. First, add all the correlations of any variable s ($s \epsilon G_i$)

---

* The essential steps in this outline are based upon those of Miss Frances Swineford given in *Student Manual of Factor Analysis*.

with each variable j of a group G_u ($u \neq i$, $u = 1, 2, \ldots, 5$). This sum may be written

$$\sum_{j \epsilon G_u} r_{sj} \, ,$$

where s is a fixed variable in G_i, and G_u is any other group. The number of such sums for n variables and m groups is

$$\sum_{i=1}^{m} (n - p_i) = mn - n = n(m - 1) \, ,$$

where p_i is the number of variables in the group G_i. In the example there are $24(5 - 1) = 96$ such sums. These sums are obtained from Table 2.2 and are presented in Table C.1. Looking down the G_1 column, the first entry is

$$\sum_{j \epsilon G_1} r_{5j} = r_{51} + r_{52} + r_{53} + r_{54} = 1.080 \, .$$

Similarly, any other entry represents the sum of the correlations of the variable in the stub with all the variables in the group indicated at the head of the column.

TABLE C.1

SUMS OF CORRELATIONS FOR VARIABLES WITH GROUPS

		G_1	G_2	G_3	G_4	G_5
G_1	1....	....	1.618	1.227	1.591	1.903
	2....	....	1.028	.591	.878	1.389
	3....	....	1.304	.552	1.205	1.298
	4....	....	1.605	.696	1.090	1.651
G_2	5....	1.080	....	1.214	1.357	2.012
	6....	1.164	....	.960	1.525	1.948
	7....	1.019	....	1.004	1.201	2.003
	8....	1.262	....	1.251	1.502	2.035
	9....	1.030	....	.843	1.506	2.123
G_3	10....	.272	1.215	....	1.246	1.531
	11....	.659	1.509	....	1.906	1.568
	12....	.759	.875	....	1.160	1.558
	13....	1.376	1.673	....	1.395	1.685
G_4	14....	.471	1.320	.848	....	1.274
	15....	.561	1.075	.706	....	1.171
	16....	1.271	1.196	.838	....	1.641
	17....	.545	1.238	1.123	....	1.321
	18....	1.085	1.047	1.339	....	1.652
	19....	.831	1.215	.853	....	1.517
G_5	20....	1.293	2.157	.862	1.692	....
	21....	1.189	1.523	1.584	1.624	....
	22....	1.275	2.063	.936	1.704	....
	23....	1.540	2.276	1.245	1.720	....
	24....	.944	2.102	1.715	1.836	....

6. Using the values below the diagonal of Table C.1, compute the following intergroup sums:

$$\sum_{s\epsilon G_i} \sum_{j\epsilon G_u} r_{sj} \, ,$$

that is, the sums of all the correlations of the variables of one group with those of any other group. There are evidently $\binom{m}{2} = m(m-1)/2$ such sums for m groups. For the example the ten sums appear in Table C.2. The first entry is

$$\sum_{s\epsilon G_2} \left(\sum_{j\epsilon G_1} r_{sj} \right) = 1.080 + 1.164 + 1.019 + 1.262 + 1.030 = 5.555 \, ,$$

while any of the others is similarly obtained. The sum in the parentheses was obtained for each s, in step **5**, and now the summation is taken for s varying over a specified group. The values above the diagonal in Table C.1 should be used to check the entries of Table C.2, but the sums need not be written twice in the latter table. For example, the first entry in Table C.2 could also be obtained as follows:

$$\sum_{s\epsilon G_1} \left(\sum_{j\epsilon G_2} r_{sj} \right) = 1.618 + 1.028 + 1.304 + 1.605 = 5.555 \, .$$

Thus a check on all the additions is provided.

TABLE C.2

SUMS OF INTERGROUP CORRELATIONS AND DENOMINATORS
FOR GENERAL-FACTOR COEFFICIENTS

	G_1	G_2	G_3	G_4	G_5	
G_1.........						
G_2.........	5.555					
G_3.........	3.066	5.272				
G_4.........	4.764	7.091	5.707			
G_5.........	6.241	10.121	6.342	8.576		
Total...	19.626	28.039	20.387	26.138	31.280	$2S = 125.470$ $S = 62.735$
Denominator	43.109	34.696	42.348	36.597	31.455	$3S = 188.205$

7. It will be noted from (6.14) that the denominator for the calculation of the general-factor coefficient for variable z_s is the sum of all intergroup correlations exclusive of the group which includes z_s. The denominators for all variables of a group are therefore alike.

8. Add the entries in the row and column corresponding to each group in Table C.2 and record the sum in the "Total" row. Thus, for the group G_4, say, the Total is obtained as follows:

$$4.764 + 7.091 + 5.707 + 8.576 = 26.138 .$$

9. The sum of the "Total" row should then equal twice the sum, S, of the entries in Table C.2. In the example the sum of the entries is $S = 62.735$, and the sum of the "Total" row is 125.470, or $2S$, completing the check.

10. Subtract from S each Total in turn, entering the difference in the "Denominator" row. For example, the denominator for the calculation of the general-factor coefficient for any variable in G_1 is

$$62.735 - 19.626 = 43.109 .$$

11. There is another computational check available at this point. Each Denominator is obtained by subtracting a Total from S. Hence, if there are m groups, the sum of the "Denominator" row is equal to mS minus the sum of the "Total" row. Since the sum of the "Total" row is always twice the sum of the entries in the table, it follows that the sum of the "Denominator" row must be $(m - 2)S$. In the example, the sum of the "Denominator" row is 188.205, which checks with $(5 - 2)S$.

12. Tables C.1 and C.2 may now be employed to get the general-factor (B_0) coefficients. Each a_{s0}^2, or $r_{z_s B_0}^2$, is a fraction whose numerator is the sum of the $\binom{m-1}{2} = \binom{4}{2} = 6$ products by pairs of the $m - 1 = 5 - 1 = 4$ entries in row s of Table C.1, and whose denominator is the Denominator in the column of Table C.2 for that group which includes variable z_s.

13. The calculation of the numerator of a_{s0}^2, when there are five or more groups, may be shortened with the aid of an additional table. It will be noted that the first entry in a given row of Table C.1 is to be multiplied by each of the remaining entries in turn. Construct Table C.3 so that the first entry in any row is the sum of the $m - 2 = 3$ entries beyond the first entry of the corresponding row of Table C.1. Similarly, the second entry in a row of Table C.3 is the sum of the $m - 3 = 2$ remaining entries in the corresponding row of Table C.1. The other entries of Table C.3 are obtained in like manner, the final value for each row being the same as that in Table C.1. The total number of entries in each row of Table C.3 is one less than that in Table C.1.

14. The columns of Table C.3 are so headed, and the entries recorded, that the sum of the products of the entries for variable z_s in Table C.1 by the corresponding entries in Table C.3 gives the numerator of a_{s0}^2. Table C.3

may then be folded for each row and placed over Table C.1 so that corresponding entries are directly under one another. The sums of the products of these corresponding entries give the desired numerators.

TABLE C.3

FOR THE CALCULATION OF THE NUMERATORS FOR
GENERAL-FACTOR COEFFICIENTS

		G_1	G_2	G_3	G_4
G_1	1......	....	4.721	3.494	1.903
	2......	....	2.858	2.267	1.389
	3......	....	3.055	2.503	1.298
	4......	....	3.437	2.741	1.651
G_2	5......	4.583	....	3.369	2.012
	6......	4.433	....	3.473	1.948
	7......	4.208	....	3.204	2.003
	8......	4.788	....	3.537	2.035
	9......	4.472	....	3.629	2.123
G_3	10......	3.992	2.777	....	1.531
	11......	4.983	3.474	....	1.568
	12......	3.593	2.718	....	1.558
	13......	4.753	3.080	....	1.685
G_4	14......	3.442	2.122	1.274	....
	15......	2.952	1.877	1.171	....
	16......	3.675	2.479	1.641	....
	17......	3.682	2.444	1.321	....
	18......	4.038	2.991	1.652	....
	19......	3.585	2.370	1.517	....
G_5	20......	4.711	2.554	1.692	....
	21......	4.731	3.208	1.624	....
	22......	4.703	2.640	1.704	....
	23......	5.241	2.965	1.720	....
	24......	5.653	3.551	1.836	....

15. When working on a calculating machine, these numerators need not be copied down but can be directly divided by the denominators, which are given in Table C.2, to get the squares of the coefficients. For example,

$$a_{40}^2 = \frac{1.605(3.437) + .696(2.741) + 1.090(1.651)}{43.109} = .21396 .$$

Record the squares of the coefficients in Table C.4.

16. Without the short cuts described in this outline, each a_{s0}^2 of the example if computed directly by formula (6.14) would involve 121, 134, or 149 products in the numerator and the sum of an equal number of correlations in the denominator, depending on whether the variable z_s is included in a group of 6, 5, or 4 variables, respectively. The method described in step **12** reduces the large number of products for each numerator to 6, while the method of step **13** reduces this number to 3. Of course, a certain amount of time is required in obtaining the sums of Tables C.1 and C.3, but the eventual saving of time is tremendous for a large number of groups.

17. The general-factor coefficients are the square roots of the values calculated in step **15**. These coefficients also appear in Table C.4. In practice, these coefficients need not be written down in this table but can be put directly in the final factor pattern shown in Table 6.8.

TABLE C.4

GENERAL-FACTOR COEFFICIENTS

Test s	a_{s0}^2	a_{s0}	Test s	a_{s0}^2	a_{s0}
1.......	.34687	.589	13......	.33162	.576
2.......	.12752	.357	14......	.15036	.388
3.......	.16074	.401	15......	.12298	.351
4.......	.21396	.463	16......	.24622	.496
5.......	.33923	.582	17......	.17804	.422
6.......	.33044	.575	18......	.26573	.515
7.......	.28563	.534	19......	.19544	.442
8.......	.38978	.624	20......	.41516	.644
9.......	.31308	.560	21......	.41594	.645
10.......	.15036	.388	22......	.41448	.644
11.......	.27191	.521	23......	.53921	.734
12.......	.16323	.404	24......	.50705	.712

18. Now the general-factor residuals must be obtained, and then the group-factor coefficients can be calculated. To facilitate the calculation of these residuals, a table of products of general-factor coefficients may be prepared. This table of $a_{j0}a_{k0}$ is presented in Table C.5 for the given data. A convenient procedure for the calculation of the elements of Table C.5 is to proceed by columns, as follows: multiply $a_{10} = .589$ by every other a_{k0} ($k = 2, 3, \ldots, 24$), in turn, to obtain the first column of values of Table C.5; then multiply $a_{20} = .357$ by all remaining a_{k0} ($k = 3, 4, \ldots, 24$) to get the second column of values of Table C.5; and so forth for all remaining columns.

19. Subtract the values in Table C.5 from the corresponding entries of Table 2.2 to get the general-factor residuals. Record these residuals below the principal diagonal in Table C.6 (the meaning of the values above the principal diagonal will be clarified in step **28**). Thus the general-factor residual for variables 1 and 2 is

$$\dot{r}_{12} = r_{12} - a_{10}a_{20} = .318 - .210 = .108 .$$

The correlation $r_{12} = .318$ comes from Table 2.2 while the product $a_{10}a_{20} = .210$ comes from Table C.5, and the difference .108 is the residual $\dot{r}_{12}$ which is entered in Table C.6.

TABLE C.5

PRODUCTS OF GENERAL-FACTOR COEFFICIENTS: $a_{jo}a_{ko}$

	1	2	3	4	5	6	7	8	9	10	11	12	13	14	15	16	17	18	19	20	21	22	23	24
1																								
2	.210																							
3	.236	.143																						
4	.273	.165	.186																					
5	.343	.208	.233	.269																				
6	.339	.205	.231	.266	.335																			
7	.315	.191	.214	.247	.311	.307																		
8	.368	.223	.250	.289	.363	.359	.333																	
9	.330	.200	.225	.259	.326	.322	.299	.349																
10	.229	.139	.156	.180	.226	.223	.207	.242	.217															
11	.307	.186	.209	.241	.303	.300	.278	.325	.292	.202														
12	.238	.144	.162	.187	.235	.232	.216	.252	.226	.157	.210													
13	.339	.206	.231	.267	.335	.331	.308	.359	.323	.223	.300	.233												
14	.229	.139	.156	.180	.226	.223	.207	.242	.217	.151	.202	.157	.223											
15	.207	.125	.141	.163	.204	.202	.187	.219	.197	.136	.183	.142	.202	.136										
16	.292	.177	.199	.230	.289	.285	.265	.310	.278	.192	.258	.200	.286	.192	.174									
17	.249	.151	.169	.195	.246	.243	.225	.263	.236	.164	.220	.170	.243	.164	.148	.209								
18	.303	.184	.207	.238	.300	.296	.275	.321	.288	.200	.268	.208	.297	.200	.181	.255	.217							
19	.260	.158	.177	.205	.257	.254	.236	.276	.248	.171	.230	.179	.255	.171	.155	.219	.187	.228						
20	.379	.230	.258	.298	.375	.370	.344	.402	.361	.250	.336	.260	.371	.250	.226	.319	.272	.332	.285					
21	.380	.230	.259	.299	.375	.371	.344	.402	.361	.250	.336	.261	.372	.250	.226	.320	.272	.332	.285	.415				
22	.379	.230	.258	.298	.375	.370	.344	.402	.361	.250	.336	.260	.371	.250	.226	.319	.272	.332	.285	.415	.415			
23	.432	.262	.294	.340	.427	.422	.392	.458	.411	.285	.382	.297	.423	.285	.258	.364	.310	.378	.324	.473	.473	.473		
24	.419	.254	.286	.330	.414	.409	.380	.444	.399	.276	.371	.288	.410	.276	.250	.353	.300	.367	.315	.459	.459	.459	.523	

TABLE C.6

RESIDUAL CORRELATIONS[a]

k ＼ j	1	2	3	4	5	6	7	8	9	10	11	12	13	14	15	16	17	18	19	20	21	22	23	24
1		−.030	−.065	.042																				
2	−.108		.037	.025																				
3	.167	*.174*		−.033																				
4	.195	*.065*	*.119*																					
5	−.022	.077	.014	.042		.034	.061	.000	.037															
6	−.004	.029	.037	.061	*.287*		.019	−.042	.041															
7	−.011	−.034	.009	.088	*.345*	*.415*		.020	−.059															
8	−.036	−.066	.132	.102	*.215*	*.168*	*.286*		.053															
9	−.004	−.005	.041	.066	*.397*	*.392*	*.386*	*.183*																
10	−.113	−.082	−.231	−.081	.085	.020	.039	.043	.047		−.002	.047	.075											
11	.001	−.036	−.118	−.131	.041	.053	.046	.025	−.012	*.282*		−.089	.026											
12	.076	.001	.022	.027	.020	−.137	.035	.019	−.113	*.428*	*.218*		−.002											
13	.150	.033	.090	.060	.009	−.022	.037	.036	−.043	*.185*	*.235*	*.279*												
14	−.104	.036	.021	.114	.054	.069	.029	.010	.043	.021	.148	.026	.028		−.025	.028	.020							
15	.031	.006	.076	.036	.025	.049	−.015	.044	.051	.018	.057	.031	.063	*.234*		.017	.025							
16	.122	.095	.064	.092	.102	.006	−.085	−.014	.036	.068	.056	.081	.005	*.220*	*.151*		.012							
17	−.073	−.146	.008	.008	.038	.030	−.003	.008	.038	.125	.142	.108	.049	*.177*	*.197*	*.115*		.000	.000					
18	.065	.071	.004	.013	.037	.129	−.116	.071	.080	.117	.082	.141	.026	.001	.153	.089	*.231*		.000					
19	.010	.046	.135	−.068	.067	.003	−.010	.002	.026	.019	.060	.069	.008	.035	.037	.039	*.137*	*.130*						
20	−.014	.062	.039	.041	.023	.065	.107	.025	.085	.077	.134	−.014	.130	.052	.046	.069	.010	.031	.118					
21	−.011	.076	.094	.050	.057	.108	−.030	−.040	.095	.155	.063	−.094	−.053	.067	.006	.028	−.099	.025	.046	.002				
22	.034	.002	−.008	.082	.066	.016	.052	−.045	.122	−.090	.032	−.067	−.092	−.007	.020	.036	.001	.015	.057	.048	.041			
23	.042	−.086	.089	−.005	.008	.009	.013	−.043	.093	−.023	.131	−.053	−.041	−.043	−.002	−.004	−.023	−.106	.021	.036	.022	.030		
24	.137	.043	−.083	−.082	.006	.024	.057	.056	.025	*.255*	.041	.126	−.052	.028	.085	.091	.026	.038	.059	.093	.011	.084	.089	

[a] The values in italics are not final; they are factored further, and the final residuals corresponding to them appear above the principal diagonal.

335

20. A check on the subtractions involved in the calculations of the residuals is provided by means of the table of products. The general-factor residual for any two variables z_j and z_k is given by

$$\dot{r}_{jk} = r_{jk} - a_{j0}a_{k0} ,$$

and the sum of all such residuals for j fixed and all $k > j$ is

$$\sum_{k=j+1}^{n} \dot{r}_{jk} = \sum_{k=j+1}^{n} r_{jk} - \sum_{k=j+1}^{n} a_{j0}a_{k0} .$$

In other words, the sum of the entries below the principal diagonal of any column, j, in Table C.6 is equal to the difference between the corresponding sums in Tables 2.2 and C.5. Record these sums in Table C.7 and check that the sums obtained from Table C.6 are actually the required differences of sums from the other tables.

TABLE C.7

CHECK ON CALCULATION OF RESIDUALS

Test j	$\sum_{k=j+1}^{24} r_{jk}$	$\sum_{k=j+1}^{24} a_{j0}a_{k0}$	$\sum_{k=j+1}^{24} \dot{r}_{jk}$	Test j	$\sum_{k=j+1}^{24} r_{jk}$	$\sum_{k=j+1}^{24} a_{j0}a_{k0}$	$\sum_{k=j+1}^{24} \dot{r}_{jk}$
1........	7.528	7.056	.472	13.......	3.080	3.453	−.373
2........	4.433	4.150	.283	14.......	2.804	2.174	.630
3........	4.589	4.501	.088	15.......	2.367	1.844	.523
4........	5.042	4.981	.061	16.......	2.567	2.358	.209
5........	7.162	5.922	1.240	17.......	2.093	1.830	.263
6........	6.396	5.519	.877	18.......	2.010	1.969	.041
7........	5.512	4.840	.672	19.......	1.517	1.494	.023
8........	5.320	5.266	.054	20.......	1.751	1.762	−.011
9........	4.472	4.415	.057	21.......	1.273	1.347	−.074
10........	4.254	2.907	1.347	22.......	.878	.932	−.054
11........	4.437	3.632	.805	23.......	.434	.523	−.089
12........	3.230	2.655	.575	24.......	....	....	....

21. If the grouping of variables is reasonable, the general-factor residual correlations of Table C.6 will all tend to be insignificant except those within the groups. Thus for G_1, the intercorrelations are consistently positive and in general greater in value than the remaining correlations with the G_1 variables, while the residual correlations of the variables in G_1 with the others are all insignificant. The same is true for G_2 and G_4. The group G_3 also has this property with one exception—the value $\dot{r}_{10,24} = .255$ is significantly different from zero (shown in **6.10**). The group G_5, however, contains a number of negative residual correlations and very small positive ones, clearly indicating that no additional factor is required for these variables. The general-factor residuals among the variables of G_5 are insignificant and may be considered as final residuals.

If the analysis of the table of general factor residuals indicates numerous revisions of the original plan, it may be expected that the general-factor coefficients will change somewhat. A more accurate solution may then be obtained by recalculating the general-factor coefficients from the revised plan. In the present example the modifications are so slight that such a procedure is not deemed necessary.

22. To obtain the group-factor coefficients, formula (6.16) is used. The coefficients of B_1 are calculated in Table C.8, where all the triads are put

TABLE C.8

CALCULATION OF THE COEFFICIENTS OF B_1

TEST 1		TEST 2		TEST 3		TEST 4	
jk	t_{jk}	jk	t_{jk}	jk	t_{jk}	jk	t_{jk}
23.........	.1037	13........	.1125	12........	.2691	12........	.1174
24.........	.3240	14........	.0360	14........	.1019	13........	.1390
34.........	.2737	34........	.0950	24........	.3186	23........	.0445
a_{11}^2.........	.2338	a_{21}^2........	.0812	a_{31}^2........	.2299	a_{41}^2........	.1003
a_{11}.........	.484	a_{21}........	.285	a_{31}........	.479	a_{41}........	.317

down explicitly, the average obtained in each case, and the square root extracted. The number of variables in G_1 is $p_1 = 4$, so that there are just $\binom{3}{2} = 3$ triads for the calculation of each coefficient. Thus, the first coefficient is obtained as follows:

$$a_{11}^2 = \tfrac{1}{3}(t_{23} + t_{24} + t_{34})$$

$$= \frac{1}{3}\left(\frac{.108 \times .167}{.174} + \frac{.108 \times .195}{.065} + \frac{.167 \times .195}{.119}\right)$$

$$= \tfrac{1}{3}(.1037 + .3240 + .2737)$$

$$= \frac{.7014}{3} = .2338 ,$$

and

$$a_{11} = \sqrt{.2338} = .484 .$$

23. The coefficients of B_2 and B_3 are computed in a similar manner in Tables C.9 and C.10. In the calculation of the B_2 coefficients, there are $\binom{5-1}{2} = 6$ triads in each case, whereas for each of the B_3 coefficients there are again only 3 triads since there are 4 variables in G_3. The significant general-factor residual between Tests 10 and 24 will be treated in step **26**.

TABLE C.9

CALCULATION OF THE COEFFICIENTS OF B_2

TEST 5		TEST 6		TEST 7		TEST 8		TEST 9	
jk	t_{jk}	jk	t_{jk}	jk	t_{jk}	jk	t_{jk}	jk	t_{jk}
67......	.2386	57.....	.3452	56.....	.4989	56.....	.1259	56.....	.5422
68......	.3673	58.....	.2243	58.....	.4589	57.....	.1782	57.....	.4442
69......	.2907	59.....	.2834	59.....	.3354	59.....	.2090	58.....	.3379
78......	.2594	78.....	.2438	68.....	.7065	67.....	.1158	67.....	.3646
79......	.3548	79.....	.4215	69.....	.4086	69.....	.0784	68.....	.4270
89......	.4664	89.....	.3599	89.....	.6033	79.....	.1356	78.....	.2470
a_{52}^2......	.3295	a_{62}^2.....	.3130	a_{72}^2.....	.5019	a_{82}^2.....	.1405	a_{92}^2.....	.3938
a_{52}......	.574	a_{62}.....	.559	a_{72}.....	.708	a_{82}.....	.375	a_{92}.....	.628

TABLE C.10

CALCULATION OF THE COEFFICIENTS OF B_3

TEST 10		TEST 11		TEST 12		TEST 13	
jk	t_{jk}	jk	t_{jk}	jk	t_{jk}	jk	t_{jk}
11, 12.....	.5537	10, 12.....	.1436	10, 11.....	.3309	10, 11.....	.1542
11, 13.....	.2220	10, 13.....	.3582	10, 13.....	.6455	10, 12.....	.1206
12, 13......	.2838	12, 13.....	.1836	11, 13.....	.2588	11, 12.....	.3008
$a_{10,3}^2$.......	.3532	$a_{11,3}^2$.......	.2285	$a_{12,3}^2$.......	.4117	$a_{13,3}^2$.......	.1918
$a_{10,3}$.......	.594	$a_{11,3}$.......	.478	$a_{12,3}$.......	.642	$a_{13,3}$.......	.438

24. It will be noted that the values of the triads for the calculation of any one of the preceding group-factor coefficients are fairly constant, i.e., they satisfy (statistically) the conditions for one common factor. If the triads are written out for the calculation of $a_{14,4}$ from all the tests of G_4, it will be found that they vary from

$$t_{18,19} = \frac{\dot{r}_{18,14}\dot{r}_{19,14}}{\dot{r}_{18,19}} = \frac{.001 \times .035}{.130} = .0003$$

to

$$t_{15,16} = \frac{\dot{r}_{15,14}\dot{r}_{16,14}}{\dot{r}_{15,16}} = \frac{.234 \times .220}{.151} = .3409 ,$$

with five triads nearly zero and the other five significantly different. Clearly, the six variables of G_4 do not measure a single factor, and the original pattern plan must be modified for these tests.

25. By various procedures in **6.10**, it is shown that the revised plan may be formulated as follows: Tests 14 to 17 involve a single factor, say B_4, and

TABLE C.11

CALCULATION OF THE COEFFICIENTS OF B_4

TEST 14		TEST 15		TEST 16		TEST 17	
jk	t_{jk}	jk	t_{jk}	jk	t_{jk}	jk	t_{jk}
15, 16.....	.3409	14, 16.....	.1606	14, 15.....	.1420	14, 15.....	.1490
15, 17.....	.2102	14, 17.....	.2604	14, 17.....	.1429	14, 16.....	.0925
16, 17.....	.3386	16, 17.....	.2587	15, 17.....	.0881	15, 16.....	.1500
$a_{14,4}^2$.......	.2966	$a_{15,4}^2$.......	.2266	$a_{16,4}^2$.......	.1243	$a_{17,4}^2$.......	.1305
$a_{14,4}$.......	.545	$a_{15,4}$.......	.476	$a_{16,4}$.......	.353	$a_{17,4}$.......	.361

Tests 17 to 19 involve another factor, say B_5, so that Test 17 is of complexity 3 while the other tests are still of complexity 2. The coefficients of B_4 are then calculated in Table C.11. Since there are just three tests that measure B_5, each of their coefficients is given by one triad. Thus

$$a_{17,5} = \sqrt{t_{18,19}} = \sqrt{\frac{.231 \times .137}{.130}} = \sqrt{.2434} = .493 \ ,$$

$$a_{18,5} = \sqrt{t_{17,19}} = \sqrt{\frac{.231 \times .130}{.137}} = \sqrt{.2192} = .468 \ ,$$

$$a_{19,5} = \sqrt{t_{17,18}} = \sqrt{\frac{.137 \times .130}{.231}} = \sqrt{.0771} = .278 \ .$$

26. Another modification of the original pattern plan involves the significant general-factor residual $\dot{r}_{10,24} = .255$ between two variables which were not together in the initial grouping. A doublet is postulated for the two tests, and its coefficients, according to (6.50), are taken to be

$$d_{10,1} = d_{24,1} = \sqrt{.255 - .117} = \sqrt{.138} = .371 \ .$$

27. The group-factor coefficients, the doublet coefficients, and the general-factor weights may now be entered in Table 6.8 to give the final factor pattern.

28. The final residuals can now be obtained by means of the formula

$$\bar{r}_{jk} = \dot{r}_{jk} - a_{ju}a_{ku} \ .$$

If the variables z_j and z_k do not measure the same group factor, then their general-factor residual is the final residual. On the other hand, if variables j and k involve the same group factor, then the product of their group-factor coefficients must be subtracted from their general-factor residual to obtain the final residual. For example, Tests 1 and 5 are in different groups, and, therefore, their general-factor residual, $-.022$, is the final residual. Tests 6 and 9, however, involve the same group factor, and their final residual is not .392 but

$$\bar{r}_{69} = .392 - .559(.628) = .041 \ .$$

Record the final residuals for the variables that involve a common factor, beyond the general, above the principal diagonal of Table C.6.

TABLE C.12

FREQUENCY DISTRIBUTION OF FINAL RESIDUALS

Value of Residual	Frequency	Value of Residual	Frequency
.150— .169.......	3	−.130——.111.......	8
.130— .149.......	5	−.150——.131.......	6
.110— .129.......	6	−.170——.151.......	....
.090— .109.......	8	−.190——.171.......	....
.070— .089.......	12	−.210——.191.......	....
.050— .069.......	25	−.230——.211.......	....
.030— .049.......	33	−.250——.231.......	1
.010— .029.......	30		
−.010— .009.......	39	Total...........	276
−.030——.011.......	29		
−.050——.031.......	29	Mean...........	−.0004
−.070——.051.......	15		
−.090——.071.......	17	Standard deviation....	.0655
−.110——.091.......	10		

29. According to the methods of Chapter VI, the factor pattern of Table 6.8 is a valid description of the twenty-four psychological variables, and the factorization has been carried to the proper stage as judged by the various statistical tests. The degree of factorization represented by this pattern is also in agreement with the more crude criteria for "when to stop factoring" which have hitherto been followed in factorial analyses, namely, that the communality of a variable should not exceed its reliability and that the standard deviation of the final residuals should be of just about the same magnitude as the standard error of a zero correlation in a sample of equal size. In Table 6.11 it is shown that the first of these standards is met, while Table C.12 gives the frequency distribution of the final residuals of Table C.6. Since the standard deviation (.0655) of the final residuals is less than the standard error (.0830) of a zero correlation, the second standard is also satisfied.

30. The variance of each variable which is not accounted for by the common factors can easily be deduced by the formulas of **2.3.** In Table 6.11 the communality and uniqueness of each variable is presented, and then the coefficients of the unique factors are obtained. These are given in Table 6.8 along with the common-factor coefficients. Each row of this factor pattern then completely expresses a variable as a linear function of the factors.

APPENDIX D

OUTLINE FOR COMPUTATION OF A PRINCIPAL-FACTOR PATTERN

A principal-factor pattern can be procured for any matrix of correlations by the iterative method of **7.4.** The form of the numerical calculations is exhibited in the following steps, in which the method is applied to the example of eight physical variables introduced in **7.5.**

1. Determine the best possible estimates of the communalities for the given set of variables. This problem is considered in detail in **4.6** and in **7.2,** and will not be repeated here. For the illustrative example, the choice of communalities is discussed in **7.5.**

2. Insert the estimates of the communalities in the principal diagonal of the correlation matrix and fill in the complete matrix. It has usually been suggested that only the lower-left half of a matrix of correlations be written, since such a matrix is symmetric, and the correlations of any variable with all the others can be determined from this portion. In the present method of analysis, however, it will be found more convenient to write the symmetric matrix in full in order to facilitate the squaring of the matrix. The correlation matrix **R** for the given data is presented in Table D.1.

TABLE D.1
CORRELATION MATRIX: **R**

	1	2	3	4	5	6	7	8	S_j	$a_{j1}^{(1)}$
1	.854	.846	.805	.859	.473	.398	.301	.382	4.918	1.000
2	.846	.897	.881	.826	.376	.326	.277	.415	4.844	.985
3	.805	.881	.833	.801	.380	.319	.237	.345	4.601	.936
4	.859	.826	.801	.783	.436	.329	.327	.365	4.726	.961
5	.473	.376	.380	.436	.870	.762	.730	.629	4.656	.947
6	.398	.326	.319	.329	.762	.687	.583	.577	3.981	.809
7	.301	.277	.237	.327	.730	.583	.521	.539	3.515	.715
8	.382	.415	.345	.365	.629	.577	.539	.579	3.831	.779

3. Obtain the sums of the rows (or columns) of **R**. For any variable j this sum is

$$S_j = \sum_{k=1}^{n} r_{jk},$$

in which the estimate of the communality h_j^2 is used for r_{jj}. For the example, $n = 8$ and the sums are given in the column alongside the matrix of correlations in Table D.1.

342

4. To determine the first-factor coefficients, take as the set of trial values the numbers $a_{j1}^{(1)}$, which are the quotients of S_j by the largest (absolute) sum. It should be noted that these numbers will not be used immediately in equations like (7.12), but it is convenient to refer to them as trial values. The numbers $a_{j1}^{(1)}$ ($j = 1, 2, \ldots, 8$) for the example, which are obtained by dividing the numbers S_j by 4.918, are also given in Table D.1. It may be found more convenient, especially if the number of variables is great, to obtain the reciprocal of the largest S_j and to multiply all the sums by it.

5. Square the matrix of correlations. Any element, off the diagonal, of the resulting matrix $\mathbf{R}^2$ is the sum of all the products of corresponding elements in two columns of $\mathbf{R}$. The diagonal elements are merely the sums of the squares of the elements in the corresponding columns of $\mathbf{R}$. Thus, the element in the jth row and the kth column of $\mathbf{R}^2$ is given by

$$\sum_{v=1}^{n} r_{vj} r_{vk} \qquad (j, k = 1, 2, \ldots, n) .$$

The matrix $\mathbf{R}^2$ for the given data is presented in Table D.2. The entry in

TABLE D.2

SQUARE OF CORRELATION MATRIX: $\mathbf{R}^2$

	1	2	3	4	5	6	7	8	$S_j^{(2)}$	$T_j^{(2)}$	$a_{j1}^{(2)}$
1	3.450	3.450	3.301	3.325	2.577	2.185	1.903	2.179	22.370	22.370	1.0000
2	3.450	3.475	3.322	3.333	2.471	2.093	1.815	2.115	22.074	22.075	.9868
3	3.301	3.322	3.181	3.188	2.341	1.983	1.718	2.003	21.037	21.039	.9405
4	3.325	3.333	3.188	3.213	2.461	2.084	1.810	2.085	21.499	21.499	.9611
5	2.577	2.471	2.341	2.461	2.966	2.550	2.278	2.372	20.016	20.016	.8948
6	2.185	2.093	1.983	2.084	2.550	2.200	1.965	2.041	17.101	17.102	.7645
7	1.903	1.815	1.718	1.810	2.278	1.965	1.765	1.820	15.074	15.074	.6739
8	2.179	2.115	2.003	2.085	2.372	2.041	1.820	1.925	16.540	16.540	.7394

the second row and third column is given by

$$\sum_{v=1}^{8} r_{v2} r_{v3} = .846(.805) + .897(.881) + .881(.833) + .826(.801)$$
$$+ .376(.380) + .326(.319) + .277(.237) + .415(.345) = 3.322 ,$$

while any of the others is obtained similarly. Of course, only the diagonal elements and the entries above (or below) the diagonal need to be calculated because the square of a symmetric matrix is also symmetric. The complete matrix is written, however, for convenience of further squaring.

6. A check is available on the squaring process. Compute the product of

R by the column of values S_j of Table D.1. The result is the column of values $T_j^{(2)}$ of Table D.2. These values are given by the following formula:

$$T_j^{(2)} = \sum_{v=1}^{8} r_{vj}S_v \qquad (j = 1, 2, \ldots, 8),$$

so that the first entry, for example, is

$$T_1^{(2)} = \sum_{v=1}^{8} r_{v1}S_v = .854(4.918) + .846(4.844) + \ldots + .382(3.831) = 22.370.$$

Now, add the rows of $\mathbf{R}^2$ and denote the respective sums by $S_j^{(2)}$. Corresponding values of $S_j^{(2)}$ and $T_j^{(2)}$ should agree except for errors of rounding.

7. Take as the next set of trial values the numbers $a_{j1}^{(2)}$, which are the quotients of $T_j^{(2)}$ by the largest check sum $T_j^{(2)}$. Every number $T_j^{(2)}$ is divided by 22.370 in Table D.2 in obtaining the trial values $a_{j1}^{(2)}$.

TABLE D.3

FOURTH POWER OF CORRELATION MATRIX: $\mathbf{R}^4$

	1	2	3	4	5	6	7	8	$S_j^{(4)}$	$T_j^{(4)}$	$a_{j1}^{(4)}$
1	65.54	64.94	61.95	63.06	56.04	47.80	42.00	46.59	447.92	447.93	1.0000
2	64.94	64.38	61.41	62.49	55.27	47.13	41.41	45.98	443.01	443.02	.9890
3	61.95	61.41	58.59	59.61	52.67	44.91	39.45	43.82	422.41	422.43	.9431
4	63.06	62.49	59.61	60.67	53.86	45.93	40.36	44.78	430.76	430.76	.9617
5	56.04	55.27	52.67	53.86	50.40	43.06	37.97	41.61	390.88	390.90	.8727
6	47.80	47.13	44.91	45.93	43.06	36.80	32.45	35.55	333.63	333.64	.7448
7	42.00	41.41	39.45	40.36	37.97	32.45	28.62	31.33	293.59	293.60	.6555
8	46.59	45.98	43.82	44.78	41.61	35.55	31.33	34.39	324.05	324.05	.7234

8. Compare the trial values $a_{j1}^{(2)}$ with the corresponding $a_{j1}^{(1)}$ of the first set. When there is no appreciable variation between two successive sets of trial values, then the squaring process has been carried far enough. This is the scheme for determining the number of times a matrix should be squared. In the present case the values $a_{j1}^{(2)}$ differ sufficiently from the corresponding $a_{j1}^{(1)}$ (see Table D.5) so that the need for further squaring is disclosed. The standard recommended is to obtain agreement between successive trial values to within five units in the last decimal place desired in the final results. Here it is planned to retain three decimal places for the factor coefficients, the same as in the original correlations. Hence the absolute values of the discrepancies between trial values should be less than .005.

9. Square the matrix of correlations a sufficient number of times to make the successive sets of trial values approximately equal. In calculating the various powers of **R,** always determine the check column T_j first. Thus for the eth power of $\mathbf{R}$, the column of values $T_j^{(e)}$ can be calculated from $\mathbf{R}^{e/2}$ and $S_j^{(e/2)}$ before the elements of $\mathbf{R}^e$ are obtained. Then the values of $a_{j1}^{(e)}$ may be computed and if they agree with the values $a_{j1}^{(e/2)}$, the calculation of the elements of $\mathbf{R}^e$ is obviated.

In the illustrative example, the values $T_j^{(4)}$ are obtained from $\mathbf{R}^2$ and $S_j^{(2)}$, and the $a_{j1}^{(4)}$ are calculated. These values are not close enough to the corresponding $a_{j1}^{(2)}$ and so the elements of $\mathbf{R}^4$ are computed in Table D.3. Next, the values of $T_j^{(8)}$ are determined in Table D.4. Since the maximum

TABLE D.4

EIGHTH POWER OF CORRELATION MATRIX: $\mathbf{R}^8$

	1	2	3	4	5	6	7	8	$S_j^{(8)}$	$T_j^{(8)}$	$a_{j1}^{(8)}$
1	.....	.....	.....	.....	.....	.....	.....	.....	.....	176738	1.0000
2	.....	.....	.....	.....	.....	.....	.....	.....	.....	174853	.9893
3	.....	.....	.....	.....	.....	.....	.....	.....	.....	166733	.9434
4	.....	.....	.....	.....	.....	.....	.....	.....	.....	169980	.9618
5	.....	.....	.....	.....	.....	.....	.....	.....	.....	153733	.8698
6	.....	.....	.....	.....	.....	.....	.....	.....	.....	131201	.7423
7	.....	.....	.....	.....	.....	.....	.....	.....	.....	115430	.6531
8	.....	.....	.....	.....	.....	.....	.....	.....	.....	127505	.7214

difference between $a_{j1}^{(8)}$ and $a_{j1}^{(4)}$ is only three thousandths, this agreement is sufficiently close. It is therefore not necessary to calculate the entries of $\mathbf{R}^8$. The differences between successive a determinations are summarized in Table D.5.

TABLE D.5

DIFFERENCES BETWEEN SUCCESSIVE
TRIAL VALUES

Variable j	$a_{j1}^{(2)} - a_{j1}^{(1)}$	$a_{j1}^{(4)} - a_{j1}^{(2)}$	$a_{j1}^{(8)} - a_{j1}^{(4)}$
1............	.000	.0000	.0000
2............	.002	.0022	.0003
3............	.005	.0026	.0003
4............	.000	.0006	.0001
5............	−.052	−.0221	−.0029
6............	−.044	−.0197	−.0025
7............	−.041	−.0190	−.0024
8............	−.040	−.0160	−.0020

10. Employ the last set of trial values as the arbitrary numbers a_{j1} in the equation

$$(7.12^{\text{bis}}) \qquad a_{j1}' = \sum_{k=1}^{n} r_{jk} a_{k1} \; ;$$

that is, multiply the correlation matrix by the trial values to obtain the new set of numbers a'_{j1}. Then divide every number a'_{j1} by the largest one of these to get the next set of trial values. For simplicity of notation, again represent these new values by a_{j1} in the tabular arrangement. Multiply $\mathbf{R}$ by these new values to obtain the new a'_{j1} and a_{j1} and continue this process until successive values of a_{j1} are practically constant. When the squaring of $\mathbf{R}$ has been carried to the stage indicated in step **9**, the values of a_{j1} usually will satisfy (7.13) immediately:

(7.13^{bis}) $a'_{j1} = \lambda a_{j1}$,

that is, the values a'_{j1} will be directly proportional to the corresponding values a_{j1}.

In Table D.6 the first column of arbitrary numbers a_{j1} are the values $a_{j1}^{(8)}$, determined by the squaring process in step **9**. These numbers are then

TABLE D.6

CALCULATION OF THE F_1 COEFFICIENTS

Variable j	a_{j1}	a'_{j1}	a_{j1}	$a_{j1} = a_{j1}\sqrt{\lambda_1}/\sqrt{\Sigma a_{j1}^2}$
1	1.0000	4.4556	1.0000	.858
2	.9893	4.4083	.9894	.849
3	.9434	4.2038	.9435	.810
4	.9618	4.2852	.9618	.825
5	.8698	3.8757	.8698	.747
6	.7423	3.3076	.7423	.637
7	.6531	2.9099	.6531	.561
8	.7214	3.2142	.7214	.619

$$\lambda_1 = 4.4556 , \qquad \sum_{j=1}^{8} a_{j1}^2 = 6.0487$$

$$\sqrt{\lambda_1}/\sqrt{\Sigma a_{j1}^2} = .85827$$

multiplied by $\mathbf{R}$ to get a'_{j1}. For example,

$$a'_{11} = .854(1.0000) + .846(.9893) + \ldots + .382(.7214) = 4.4556 .$$

After all the values a'_{j1} have been obtained, they are divided by the largest of them ($a'_{11} = 4.4556$) in the calculation of the new quantities a_{j1}. Since the maximum discrepancy between the old and the new values a_{j1} is only .0001, these numbers are accepted as stationary.

11. The value of a'_{11} corresponding to $a_{11} = 1.0000$ is the first characteristic root λ_1. Then the coefficients of the first factor can be calculated by means of

$$(7.7^{\text{bis}}) \qquad a_{j1} = \frac{a_{j1}\sqrt{\lambda_1}}{\sqrt{a_{11}^2 + a_{21}^2 + \ldots + a_{n1}^2}} \qquad (j = 1, 2, \ldots, n).$$

In the example, $\lambda_1 = 4.4556$ and the coefficients a_{j1} are given in the last column of Table D.6.

12. A check on the final determination of the a_{j1} is provided by the fact that

$$\sum_{j=1}^{n} a_{j1}^2 = \lambda_1 .$$

In other words, the sum of the contributions of the first factor to the total communality must be equal to the first characteristic root. The value of λ_1 from the analysis is 4.4556 and the sum of the squares of the coefficients is 4.455, so that the check is satisfied (within rounding errors).

TABLE D.7

PRODUCT MATRIX: $Q_1 = \|a_{j1}a_{k1}\|$

	1	2	3	4	5	6	7	8	E_{j1}	$a_{j1}D_1$
1	.736	....	....	....	....	....	....	....	5.067	5.067
2	.728	.721	....	....	....	....	....	....	5.014	5.014
3	.695	.688	.656	....	....	....	....	....	4.783	4.784
4	.708	.700	.668	.681	....	....	....	....	4.873	4.872
5	.641	.634	.605	.616	.558	....	....	....	4.411	4.412
6	.547	.541	.516	.526	.476	.406	....	....	3.763	3.762
7	.481	.476	.454	.463	.419	.357	.315	....	3.312	3.313
8	.531	.526	.501	.511	.462	.394	.347	.383	3.655	3.656

13. Before additional factors can be determined, the first-factor residuals are required. A table of products of the first-factor coefficients may be prepared to facilitate the calculation of these residuals. The elements $_1p_{jk}$ ($=_1p_{kj}$) of the product matrix $Q_1 = \|_1p_{jk}\| = \|a_{j1}a_{k1}\|$ are obtained as follows: the values in the first column are the respective products of a_{11} by itself and every other a_{j1} ($j = 2, 3, \ldots, n$), the values in the diagonal and below it in the second column are the respective products of a_{21} by itself and all remaining coefficients a_{j1} ($j = 3, 4, \ldots, n$), and so on for the values in and below the diagonal in all the other columns. Since the product matrix is symmetric, it is not necessary to write the values above the diagonal. The matrix Q_1 for the given data is presented in Table D.7.

To assist the reader, a summary of the notation referring to the various matrices employed in the principal-factor method is presented in Table D.8.

TABLE D.8

NOTATION

	Original Correlations	First-Factor Products	First-Factor Residuals	Second-Factor Products	Second-Factor Residuals
Element................	r_{jk}	$_1p_{jk}$	$_1r_{jk}$	$_2p_{jk}$	$_2r_{jk}$
Matrix.................	$\mathbf{R}$	$\mathbf{Q}_1$	$\mathbf{R}_1$	$\mathbf{Q}_2$	$\mathbf{R}_2$
Sum of elements in row j of matrix................	S_j	E_{j1}	S_{j1}	E_{j2}	S_{j2}
The eth power of matrix..	$\mathbf{R}^e$	$\mathbf{Q}_1^e$	$\mathbf{R}_1^e$	$\mathbf{Q}_2^e$	$\mathbf{R}_2^e$
Sum of elements in row j of eth power of matrix.....	$S_j^{(e)}$	$E_{j1}^{(e)}$	$S_{j1}^{(e)}$	$E_{j2}^{(e)}$	$S_{j2}^{(e)}$

14. To check the calculation of the elements of the product matrix $\mathbf{Q}_1$, first obtain the sums of the complete rows (or columns), that is,

$$E_{j1} = \sum_{k=1}^{n} a_{j1}a_{k1} \qquad (j = 1, 2, \ldots, n),$$

and compare with the corresponding values of $a_{j1}D_1$, where

$$D_1 = \sum_{k=1}^{n} a_{k1}.$$

The sum of the first-factor coefficients for the given data is $D_1 = 5.906$. Then the check, say, for the elements of the third row and column is given by the agreement of

$$E_{31} = .695 + .688 + .656 + .668 + .605 + .516 + .454 + .501 = 4.783$$

and

$$a_{31}D_1 = .810(5.906) = 4.784,$$

and the remaining elements of $\mathbf{Q}_1$ are similarly checked. The values E_{j1} and $a_{j1}D_1$ are also recorded in Table D.7.

15. Subtract the values in $\mathbf{Q}_1$ from the corresponding entries in $\mathbf{R}$ to get the matrix of first-factor residuals $\mathbf{R}_1$. This matrix is presented in Table D.9, and is written out in full to simplify later multiplications with it. The sums of the rows, S_{j1}, are given in a column alongside the matrix $\mathbf{R}_1$. These

TABLE D.9

MATRIX OF FIRST-FACTOR RESIDUALS: $\mathbf{R}_1$

	1	2	3	4	5	6	7	8	S_{j1}	$a_{j2}^{(1)}$
1	.118	.118	.110	.151	−.168	−.149	−.180	−.149	−.149 −	.6082
2	.118	.176	.193	.126	−.258	−.215	−.199	−.111	−.170 −	.6939
3	.110	.193	.177	.133	−.225	−.197	−.217	−.156	−.182 −	.7429
4	.151	.126	.133	.102	−.180	−.197	−.136	−.146	−.147 −	.6000
5	−.168	−.258	−.225	−.180	.312	.286	.311	.167	.245	1.0000
6	−.149	−.215	−.197	−.197	.286	.281	.226	.183	.218	.8898
7	−.180	−.199	−.217	−.136	.311	.226	.206	.192	.203	.8286
8	−.149	−.111	−.156	−.146	.167	.183	.192	.196	.176	.7184

sums should be equal to the differences between the sums of the respective rows of $\mathbf{R}$ and $\mathbf{Q}_1$, that is,

$$S_{j1} = S_j - E_{j1}.$$

16. To obtain the best set of trial values for the calculation of the second-factor coefficients, an appropriate power of $\mathbf{R}_1$ should be employed. It is not necessary, however, to perform repeated squarings on $\mathbf{R}_1$ to get this power, because it can be obtained more simply by means of the formula

(7.21^{bis}) $$\mathbf{R}_1^e = \mathbf{R}^e - \lambda_1^{e-1}\mathbf{Q}_1.$$

Furthermore, since the actual entries of $\mathbf{R}_1^2$, or any higher power of $\mathbf{R}_1$, are not required for the determination of trial values if the sums of the rows are known, additional labor can be saved by means of formula (7.21). The values $S_j^{(2)}$ and E_{j1} may be considered as elements of the matrices $\mathbf{R}^2$ and $\mathbf{Q}_1$, respectively. Then, according to (7.21),

$$S_{j1}^{(2)} = S_j^{(2)} - \lambda_1 E_{j1},$$

so that $S_{j1}^{(2)}$, the sum of the elements in row j of the matrix $\mathbf{R}_1^2$, can be obtained without calculating the individual entries in $\mathbf{R}_1^2$.

Construct Table D.10, in which each block contains the derivation of the trial values from the power of $\mathbf{R}_1$ represented by the superscript on a_{j2}. In the first block the values of S_j and E_{j1} are copied from Tables D.1 and D.7, and the sums S_{j1} are obtained by subtraction. Then the trial values $a_{j2}^{(1)}$ are calculated by dividing the corresponding sums S_{j1} by the largest one of them (in absolute value), that is, by $S_{51} = .245$. Record the values of $S_j^{(2)}$ from Table D.2 in the second block of Table D.10, retaining only two decimal places since all the work is based upon three significant figures, and

TABLE D.10
DETERMINATION OF TRIAL VALUES FOR THE CALCULATION OF THE F_2 COEFFICIENTS

Variable j	S_j	E_{j1}	S_{j1}	$a_{j2}^{(1)}$	$S_j^{(2)}$	$\lambda_1 E_{j1}$	$S_{j1}^{(2)}$	$a_{j2}^{(2)}$
1......	4.918	5.067	−.149	− .608	22.37	22.58	−.21	− .57
2......	4.844	5.014	−.170	− .694	22.07	22.34	−.27	− .73
3......	4.601	4.783	−.182	− .743	21.04	21.31	−.27	− .73
4......	4.726	4.873	−.147	− .600	21.50	21.71	−.21	− .57
5......	4.656	4.411	.245	1.000	20.02	19.65	.37	1.00
6......	3.981	3.763	.218	.890	17.10	16.77	.33	.89
7......	3.515	3.312	.203	.829	15.07	14.76	.31	.84
8......	3.831	3.655	.176	.718	16.54	16.29	.25	.68

TABLE D.11
CALCULATION OF THE F_2 COEFFICIENTS

Variable j	a_{j2}	a_{j2}'	a_{j2}	a_{j2}'	a_{j2}	a_{j2}'	a_{j2}	$a_{j2} = a_{j2}\sqrt{\lambda_2}/\sqrt{\Sigma a_{j2}^2}$
1......	− .57	− .865	− .580	− .8856	− .5851	− .8852	− .5851	− .328
2......	− .73	−1.100	− .737	−1.1152	− .7368	−1.1148	− .7369	− .414
3......	− .73	−1.097	− .735	−1.1118	− .7345	−1.1112	− .7345	− .412
4......	− .57	− .902	− .605	− .9129	− .6031	− .9129	− .6034	− .339
5......	1.00	1.492	1.000	1.5136	1.0000	1.5129	1.0000	.561
6......	.89	1.348	.903	1.3666	.9029	1.3660	.9029	.507
7......	.84	1.300	.871	1.3144	.8684	1.3142	.8687	.488
8......	.68	.987	.662	1.0005	.6610	1.0001	.6610	.371

$$\lambda_2 = 1.5129, \qquad \sum_{j=1}^{8} a_{j2}^2 = 4.8027$$

$$\sqrt{\lambda_2}/\sqrt{\Sigma a_{j2}^2} = .56126$$

one additional figure is sufficient to assure the accuracy of the three figures. Compute the products $\lambda_1 E_{j1}$, with the value $\lambda_1 = 4.4556$ taken from Table D.6, and again keep four figures. The sums $S_{j1}^{(2)}$ are obtained simply by subtraction, and the corresponding $a_{j2}^{(2)}$ are then determined. These values are truly significant to only one decimal place, and in the one significant figure they agree with $a_{j2}^{(1)}$. If the calculations in the next block were attempted, it would be evident that corresponding values of $S_j^{(4)}$ and $\lambda_1^3 E_{j1}$ are equal to three significant figures. For example, $S_1^{(4)} = 448$ and $\lambda_1^3 E_{11} = 448$. Hence the sums $S_{j1}^{(4)}$ (that is, $S_j^{(4)} - \lambda_1^3 E_{j1}$) are insignificant and $a_{j2}^{(4)}$ cannot be obtained. It therefore follows that the best set of trial values for the calculation of a_{j2} is $a_{j2}^{(2)}$.

17. Employ the numbers $a_{j2}^{(2)}$ as the first set of trial values a_{j2} by which to multiply the matrix $\mathbf{R}_1$ to obtain a_{j2}' in Table D.11. The first of these values, for example, is given by

$$a_{12}' = .118(-.57) + .118(-.73) + .110(-.73) + \ldots - .149(.68) = -.865 .$$

Divide the values a_{j2}' by the largest of them ($a_{52}' = 1.492$) to obtain the next set of trial values, which are also designated by a_{j2} for simplicity. Multiply $\mathbf{R}_1$ by these new values and divide the resulting a_{j2}' by the largest one of them to obtain the next set of trial values. Continue this process until corresponding trial values in successive sets agree to three significant figures. In the computations, after the first or second iterations, keep four figures if three significant figures are desired for the factor coefficients. Three iterations of the form (7.12) were sufficient, in the present example, for stability in the trial values a_{j2}.

18. The value $a_{52}' = 1.5129$ corresponding to $a_{52} = 1.0000$ is the characteristic root λ_2. Then the coefficients of the second factor can be computed by means of a formula like (7.7), as follows:

$$a_{j2} = \frac{a_{j2}\sqrt{\lambda_2}}{\sqrt{a_{12}^2 + a_{22}^2 + \ldots + a_{n2}^2}} \qquad (j = 1, 2, \ldots, n) .$$

The coefficients a_{j2} are given in Table D.11.

19. The final calculation of the coefficients a_{j2} can be checked by means of the formula

$$\sum_{j=1}^{n} a_{j2}^2 = \lambda_2 .$$

In the example, the sum of the squares of the eight coefficients is 1.511 and $\lambda_2 = 1.5129$, so that the coefficients check.

20. To obtain additional factors proceed with the form of calculation as indicated in steps **13–19.** The notation of Table D.8 will aid in the application of the method, for then the only changes in the preceding steps will be the advancement of the indices.

For the given data it will be shown now that no further factors are required. The products of the second-factor coefficients $_2p_{jk} = a_{j2}a_{k2}$ given in Table D.12, are subtracted from the corresponding residuals $_1r_{jk}$ of Table

TABLE D.12

PRODUCT MATRIX: $Q_2 = \|a_{j2}a_{k2}\|$

	1	2	3	4	5	6	7	8
1	.108							
2	.136	.171						
3	.135	.171	.170					
4	.111	.140	.140	.115				
5	−.184	−.232	−.231	−.190	.315			
6	−.166	−.210	−.209	−.172	.284	.257		
7	−.160	−.202	−.201	−.165	.274	.247	.238	
8	−.122	−.154	−.153	−.126	.208	.188	.181	.138

D.9 to obtain the matrix of second-factor residuals which is presented in Table D.13. These residuals are obviously insignificant and so may be considered as final. Inasmuch as the problem of factor analysis is to account for

TABLE D.13

MATRIX OF SECOND-FACTOR RESIDUALS: R_2

	1	2	3	4	5	6	7	8
1	.010							
2	−.018	.005						
3	−.025	.022	.007					
4	.040	−.014	−.007	−.013				
5	.016	−.026	.006	.010	−.003			
6	.017	−.005	.012	−.025	.002	.024		
7	−.020	.003	−.016	.029	.037	−.021	−.032	
8	−.027	.043	−.003	−.020	−.041	−.005	.011	.058

the total communality variance, a more definite check on the adequacy of a solution is afforded by the extent to which the sum of the contributions of the factors agrees with the original total communality. In the present example, two common factors account for practically 100 per cent of the communality. The percentage contributions of the individual factors are presented in Table 7.4, where the complete principal-factor pattern is exhibited.

APPENDIX E

OUTLINE FOR COMPUTATION OF A CENTROID PATTERN

By the method developed in **8.2**, a centroid pattern can be obtained for any correlation matrix. The details of the numerical calculations are described in the following steps. A centroid solution for the first thirteen of the twenty-four psychological tests of **2.8** is obtained to illustrate the steps in the outline.

1. Determine the best possible estimates of the communalities for the given data. The problem of estimation of communalities is treated in **7.2**. The choice of communalities for the illustrative example is indicated in **8.3**.

2. Put the estimates of the communalities in the principal diagonal of the correlation matrix, writing the correlations in the lower-left half of the table only. The intercorrelations of the thirteen psychological tests are given in Table E.1, in which the communalities are also included.

3. The procedure for the calculation of the coefficients of the first centroid factor is presented in this and the next three steps for the case of a matrix involving very few negative correlations. If a matrix contains a large number of negative correlations, then the procedure of steps **11–27** should be followed. The present example is typical in that it involves a matrix of generally positive correlations.

Obtain the sums of the complete rows (or columns) of the correlation matrix. Although only half of the intercorrelations are written explicitly, the complete sums can be obtained very simply. Thus, for any variable j, add the entries in row j to the diagonal and the entries in column j (including the diagonal value). This sum is represented by

$$S_j = \sum_k r_{jk} \, ,$$

where the summation extends over the n values of k, and r_{jj} is the estimate of the communality h_j^2. Throughout this appendix the symbol Σ will be used to connote summation from 1 to n when a single index is involved; and, when more than one index is involved, the index for which the summation is made will be specified. The sums S_j, for the given data, are presented in Table E.1.

353

TABLE E.1

Calculation of the C_1 Coefficients from the Correlation Matrix R

Variable	1	2	3	4	5	6	7	8	9	10	11	12	13	Check
1	.558													
2	.318	.203												
3	.403	.317	.362											
4	.468	.230	.305	.314										
5	.321	.285	.247	.227	.646									
6	.335	.234	.268	.327	.622	.641								
7	.304	.157	.223	.335	.656	.722	.750							
8	.332	.157	.382	.391	.578	.527	.619	.571						
9	.326	.195	.184	.325	.723	.714	.685	.532	.758					
10	.116	.057	−.075	.099	.311	.203	.246	.285	.170	.554				
11	.308	.150	.091	.110	.344	.353	.232	.300	.280	.484	.449			
12	.314	.145	.140	.160	.215	.095	.181	.271	.113	.585	.428	.531		
13	.489	.239	.321	.327	.344	.309	.345	.395	.280	.408	.535	.512	.599	
S_j	4.592	2.687	3.168	3.618	5.519	5.350	5.455	5.340	5.285	3.443	4.064	3.690	5.103	
a_{j1}	.607	.355	.418	.478	.729	.707	.721	.705	.698	.455	.537	.487	.674	

Check:

$$T = 2\sum_{i \leqq k} r_{ik} - \Sigma r_{ii}$$

$$T = 2(32.125) - 6.936$$

$$= 57.314$$

$$T = 57.314$$
$$\sqrt{T} = 7.5706$$
$$1/\sqrt{T} = .1321$$
$$D_1 = 7.571$$

4. Calculate the total T of all the entries in the correlation matrix. This may be done simply by use of the formula

$$T = \Sigma S_j \, .$$

For the example,

$$T = \sum_{j=1}^{13} S_j = 4.592 + 2.687 + \ldots + 5.103 = 57.314 \, ,$$

and $\sqrt{T} = 7.5706$, $1/\sqrt{T} = .1321$. The sum T may then be checked by means of the formula

$$T = 2\sum_{j \leq k} r_{jk} - \Sigma r_{jj} \, ,$$

where all indices extend over the range 1 to n, and the first term indicates summation for both j and k under the restriction $j \leq k$. This check is also given in Table E.1.

5. The coefficients of the first centroid factor now can be computed by means of formula (8.6), namely,

$$a_{j1} = \frac{S_j}{\sqrt{T}} \qquad\qquad (j = 1, 2, \ldots, n) \, .$$

The factor coefficient for any variable z_j thus is obtained by dividing the sum of the n correlations of this variable with all others (including the communality) by the square root of the sum of all the correlations in the complete matrix. For a large set of variables, it is convenient to calculate the reciprocal of $\sqrt{T}$ and to multiply all the values S_j by it. The factor coefficients for the given data are obtained by multiplying the respective sums S_j by $1/\sqrt{T} = .1321$ and are presented in the last row of Table E.1.

6. A check on the preceding computation is available. Since

$$a_{j1} = \frac{S_j}{\sqrt{T}} \, ,$$

it follows that

$$D_1 = \Sigma a_{j1} = \frac{1}{\sqrt{T}} \sum S_j = \frac{1}{\sqrt{T}} T = \sqrt{T} \, .$$

In the example,

$$D_1 = \Sigma a_{j1} = 7.571 \, ,$$

which agrees, except for errors due to rounding, with the value of $\sqrt{T}$.

7. Before additional factors can be determined, the first-factor residuals are required. A table of products of the first-factor coefficients may be prepared to facilitate the calculation of these residuals, just as in the case of step **13** of Appendix D. The elements $_1p_{jk}$ ($=_1p_{kj}$) of the product matrix $\mathbf{Q}_1$ are obtained as follows: the values in the first column are the respective products of a_{11} by itself and every other a_{j1} ($j = 2, 3, \ldots, n$), the diagonal value and all the entries below it in the second column are the respective products of a_{21} by itself and all remaining coefficients a_{j1} ($j = 3, 4, \ldots, n$), and so on for the values in and below the diagonal in all the other columns. Since the product matrix is symmetric, it is not necessary to write the values above the principal diagonal. The matrix $\mathbf{Q}_1 = \|_1p_{jk}\| = \|a_{j1}a_{k1}\|$ for the given data is presented in Table E.2. For example, the elements in the first column of the product matrix are

$$
\begin{aligned}
_1p_{11} &= a_{11}^2 &&= (.607)^2 &&= .368 , \\
_1p_{12} &= a_{11}a_{21} &&= (.607)(.355) &&= .215 , \\
_1p_{13} &= a_{11}a_{31} &&= (.607)(.418) &&= .254 , \\
_1p_{14} &= a_{11}a_{41} &&= (.607)(.478) &&= .290 , \text{etc.}
\end{aligned}
$$

8. To check the calculations of the products, step **14** of Appendix D can be applied. Employing the same notation as in the principal-factor method, the sums of the complete rows (or columns) of the product matrix $\mathbf{Q}_1$ are designated by

$$ E_{j1} = \sum_k a_{j1}a_{k1} \qquad (j = 1, 2, \ldots, n) , $$

or

$$ E_{j1} = a_{j1}D_1 , $$

which serves as a check on the products of the first-factor coefficients. For the given data the thirteen values of E_{j1} and the corresponding checking values $a_{j1}D_1$ are presented in Table E.2.

9. Subtract the values in the product matrix $\mathbf{Q}_1$ from the corresponding entries in the correlation matrix $\mathbf{R}$ to obtain the matrix of first-factor residuals $\mathbf{R}_1 = \|_1r_{jk}\| = \|r_{jk} - _1p_{jk}\|$. The first-factor residuals are presented in Table E.3. For example,

$$
\begin{aligned}
_1r_{11} &= r_{11} - _1p_{11} = .558 - .368 = .190 , \\
_1r_{29} &= r_{29} - _1p_{29} = .195 - .248 = -.053 ,
\end{aligned}
$$

and all the other residuals, which are given in and below the diagonal in Table E.3, can be obtained in a similar manner.

TABLE E.2

PRODUCT MATRIX: $Q_1 = \|a_{j1}a_{k1}\|$

Variable	1	2	3	4	5	6	7	8	9	10	11	12	13
1	.368												
2	.215	.126											
3	.254	.148	.175										
4	.290	.170	.200	.228									
5	.443	.259	.305	.348	.531								
6	.429	.251	.296	.338	.515	.500							
7	.438	.256	.301	.345	.526	.510	.520						
8	.428	.250	.295	.337	.514	.498	.508	.497					
9	.424	.248	.292	.334	.509	.493	.503	.492	.487				
10	.276	.162	.190	.217	.332	.322	.328	.321	.318	.207			
11	.326	.191	.224	.257	.391	.380	.387	.379	.375	.244	.288		
12	.296	.173	.204	.233	.355	.344	.351	.343	.340	.222	.262	.237	
13	.409	.239	.282	.322	.491	.477	.486	.475	.470	.307	.362	.328	.454
E_{j1}	4.596	2.688	3.166	3.619	5.519	5.353	5.459	5.337	5.285	3.446	4.066	3.688	5.102
$a_{j1}D_1$	4.596	2.688	3.165	3.619	5.519	5.353	5.459	5.338	5.285	3.445	4.066	3.687	5.103

TABLE E.3

First-Factor Residuals: $_1r_{jk}$

Variable	1	2	3	4	5	6	7	8	9	10	11	12	13
1	.190												
2	.103	.077											
3	.149	.169	.187										
4	.178	.060	.105	.086									
5	−.122	.026	−.058	−.121	.115								
6	−.094	−.017	−.028	−.011	.107	.141							
7	−.134	−.099	−.078	−.010	.130	.212	.230						
8	−.096	−.093	.087	.054	.064	.029	.111	.074					
9	−.098	−.053	−.108	−.009	.214	.221	.182	.040	.271				
10	−.160	−.105	−.265	−.118	−.021	−.119	.082	−.036	−.148	.347			
11	−.018	−.041	−.133	−.147	−.047	−.027	−.155	−.079	−.095	.240	.161		
12	.018	−.028	−.064	−.073	−.140	−.249	−.170	−.072	−.227	.363	.166	.294	
13	.080	.000	.039	.005	−.147	−.168	−.141	−.080	−.190	.101	.173	.184	.145
$\sum_k {}_1r_{jk}$	−.004	−.001	.002	−.001	.000	−.003	−.004	.003	.000	−.003	−.002	.002	.001

TABLE E.3'

SIGN CHANGES

Variable	-1	2	3	4	5	6	7	8	9	-10	-11	-12	-13
1	.190												
2	.103	.077											
3	.149	.169	.187										
4	.178	.060	.105	.086									
5	-.122	.026	-.058	-.121	.115								
6	-.094	-.017	-.028	-.011	.107	.141							
7	-.134	-.099	.078	-.010	.130	.212	.230						
8	-.096	-.093	.087	-.054	.064	.029	.111	.074					
9	-.098	-.053	-.108	-.009	.214	.221	.182	.040	.271				
10	-.160	-.105	-.265	-.118	-.021	-.119	.082	-.036	-.148	.347			
11	-.018	-.041	-.133	-.147	-.047	-.027	-.155	-.079	-.095	.240	.161		
12	.018	-.028	.064	-.073	-.140	-.249	-.170	-.072	-.227	.363	.166	.294	
13	.080	.000	.039	.005	-.147	-.168	-.141	-.080	-.190	.101	.173	.184	.145

TABLE E.3″

CALCULATION OF THE C_2 COEFFICIENTS

Variable	−1	2	3	4	5	6	7	8	9	−10	−11	−12	−13	Check
1	.190	−.103	−.149	−.178	.122	.094	.134	.096	.098	.160	−.018	.018	.080	
2		.077	.169	.060	.026	−.017	.099	−.093	−.053	.105	.041	.028	.000	
3			.187	.105	−.058	−.028	.078	.087	−.108	.265	.133	.064	−.039	
4				.086	−.121	−.011	−.010	.054	−.009	.118	.147	.073	−.005	$T_1 = 2\sum_{i \leq k} r_{ijk} - \Sigma r_{1jj}$
5					.115	.107	.130	.064	.214	.021	.047	.140	.147	
6						.141	.212	.029	.221	.119	.027	.249	.168	$T_1 = 2(8.028)$
7							.230	.111	.182	.082	.155	.170	.141	$\qquad\qquad -2.318$
8								.074	.040	.036	.079	.072	.080	
9									.271	.148	.095	.227	.190	$= 13.738$
10										.347	.240	.363	.101	
11											.161	.166	.173	
12												.294	.184	
13													.145	
S_{j1}	.224	.141	.550	.309	.954	1.311	1.360	.729	1.516	1.785	1.446	2.048	1.365	$T_1 = 13.738$
$\epsilon_j S_{j1}$	−.224	.141	.550	.309	.954	1.311	1.360	.729	1.516	−1.785	−1.446	−2.048	−1.365	$\sqrt{T_1} = 3.7065$
														$1/\sqrt{T_1} = .2698$
a_{j2}	−.060	.038	.148	.083	.257	.354	.367	.197	.409	−.482	−.390	−.553	.368	$D_2 = .000$

360

10. A check on the subtractions involved in obtaining the first-factor residuals is afforded by

$$\sum_k {}_1r_{jk} = S_j - E_{j1}.$$

The sum of all the residuals for each of the variables appear in Table E.3 and may be checked with the differences $S_j - E_{j1}$. These numbers always must check exactly, of course, because no statistical discrepancies, such as rounding of numbers, are involved. The sum of the residuals for variable 5, for example, is

$$\Sigma_1 r_{5k} = -.122 + .026 + \ldots -.147 = .000,$$

while $S_5 - E_{51} = 5.519 - 5.519 = .000$.

The preceding check may be obviated, for in the residual-factor space the centroid is at the origin, and hence it is expected that each of the residual sums will be approximately zero. Then the foregoing check may be employed in individual cases where the difference of a particular sum from zero is questionable. Thus, if it is doubted that the largest sum (in absolute value) differs from zero only because of rounding errors, the check may be applied to it. In the example one of the largest sums is $\Sigma_1 r_{7k} = -.004$, and $S_7 - E_{71} = 5.455 - 5.459 = -.004$.

11. To remove the centroid from the origin in the residual-factor space and to increase the contribution of the second factor to the residual variance, certain variables are reflected in the origin. The variables to be reflected are determined from a table similar to Table E.4, in which the number of negative residuals for each variable is recorded and minimized by the reflection of variables. In this table put the numbers of the variables in the stub and allow two rows at the bottom of the table for the totals in the respective columns and the differences between successive totals, which will be useful for checking purposes. The first column* of the table should be headed "Reflected Variable," and a minus sign will be placed in this column opposite any variable which is to be reflected. The remaining columns are introduced successively as an increasing number of variables are reflected.

12. Count the number of negative signs for each variable in the residual matrix of Table E.3 and record in the second column and in the appropriate row of Table E.4. The second column of Table E.4 is headed "Before Reflection," because the values put in this column refer to the number of negative residuals before any variables are reflected. It should be noted that,

---

* Here, and in the remainder of this outline, the column numbers refer to the body of the table, excluding the stub.

although only half of the symmetric residual matrix is written explicitly, the number of negative signs to be considered for each variable is that of the total matrix. In other words, when counting the number of negative signs read across the row and down the column for a specified variable. For example, the number of negative signs, before any reflections, for variable 1 is 7.

13. Add all the entries in the second column of Table E.4 and record the sum in the "Total" row. In the present example this sum is 96. The count

TABLE E.4

NUMBER OF MINUS SIGNS FOR FIRST-FACTOR RESIDUALS AFTER
SUCCESSIVE REFLECTIONS OF VARIABLES

VARIABLE	RE-FLECTED VARIABLE	BEFORE REFLEC-TION	AFTER REFLECTION OF SUCCESSIVE VARIABLES				
			10	11	12	13	1
1.............	—	7	6	5	6	7	5
2.............	....	7	6	5	4	5	6
3.............	....	7	6	5	4	5	6
4.............	....	7	6	5	4	5	6
5.............	....	7	6	5	4	3	2
6.............	....	8	7	6	5	4	3
7.............	....	8	7	6	5	4	3
8.............	....	6	5	4	3	2	1
9.............	....	8	7	6	5	4	3
10.............	—	9	3	2	1	0	1
11.............	—	9	10	2	1	0	1
12.............	—	8	9	10	2	1	0
13.............	—	5	6	7	8	4	3
Total......	....	96	84	68	52	44	40
Difference....	....	....	12	16	16	8	4

of negative signs may be checked by re-counting the negative residuals in Table E.3, which should be equal to one-half of the total recorded in the second column of Table E.4.

14. Pick the variable with the largest number of negative signs to be reflected first. If several variables have the same maximum number of negative signs, any one of them may be arbitrarily selected for reflection. In the example, variables 10 and 11 have a maximum of 9 negative signs, and z_{10} is arbitrarily selected for reflection.

15. Opposite variable 10 in the first column of Table E.4 place a minus sign to indicate that this variable is to be reflected. An adjustment in the number of negative signs for each variable will be made as if variable 10 were reflected in Table E.3, (i.e., as if all the signs for variable 10 were changed) and these results will be recorded in the third column of Table E.4. This column is headed "10," to indicate that the count of negative signs for each variable is that after variable 10 is reflected.

16. For the variable being reflected the adjusted number of negative signs is $(n - 1)$ *minus* the number of negative signs it had before reflection. Upon reflection of a given variable, every residual which was positive becomes negative and every negative residual becomes positive, except that the value in the diagonal of the residual matrix remains unchanged. The value $(n - 1)$ is the total number of entries in a given row and column of (the lower half of) Table E.3, ignoring the diagonal. In the example, $n - 1 = 12$ and the entry for variable 10 in the third column of Table E.4 is $12 - 9 = 3$.

17. It is not necessary to change all the signs of the residuals for the variable being reflected in order to count the number of negative signs for the other variables after the reflection. Instead, consider the sign of each entry except the diagonal in the row and column of Table E.3 for the variable being reflected, and proceed as follows.

a) If the entry for a particular variable, which was not previously reflected, is positive, increase by one the number of negative signs for that variable recorded in the second column of Table E.4 and record the new value for that variable in the third column of Table E.4. For example, the entry for variable 11 in column 10 of Table E.3 is positive, and since z_{11} was not previously reflected, the number of negative signs for it is increased one, from 9 to 10, in Table E.4 after variable 10 is reflected.

b) If the entry for a particular variable, which was not previously reflected, is negative, decrease by one the number of negative signs for that variable and record the new value for that variable in the third column of Table E.4. For example, the entry for variable 1 in row 10 of Table E.3 is negative, and since z_1 has not been reflected, the number of negative signs for it is decreased one, and the result 6 is recorded for it in the third column of Table E.4.

The general rules for sign changes are formulated conveniently in Table E.5.

18. The count of negative signs after variable 10 has been reflected can be checked by the following procedure. Add all the entries in the third column of Table E.4, getting 84; and subtract this total from the preceding one, obtaining 12 for the difference. This difference should be twice the difference between the number of negative signs for variable 10 before and after reflection. In the example,

$$12 = 2(9 - 3) ,$$

and so the arithmetical work involved in the third column of Table E.4 is checked.

19. Pick the variable having the largest number of negative signs in the third column of Table E.4 as the next one to be reflected. This is variable 11, which has 10 negative signs. Put a minus sign opposite variable 11 in the first column and the number "11" at the head of the fourth column of Table E.4 to indicate that this variable is being reflected. Then adjust the number of negative signs for each variable as if variable 11 were reflected in Table E.3, and record these results in the fourth column of Table E.4. The adjustments are made according to the procedure outlined in steps **16** and **17.**

TABLE E.5

RULES FOR SIGN-CHANGE ADJUSTMENTS

	Entry in Row (or Column) of Reflected Variable Is Positive	Entry in Row (or Column) of Reflected Variable Is Negative
Not previously reflected (or reflected an even number of times)	Increase one	Decrease one
Previously reflected once (or any odd number of times)	Decrease one	Increase one

For example, the entry for variable 1 in row 11 of Table E.3 is negative (second column of Table E.5), and, since z_1 has not been reflected (first row of Table E.5), the rule for the sign adjustment is given in the upper-right cell of Table E.5. The number of negative signs for z_1 is reduced from 6 to 5, which is recorded in the fourth column of Table E.4. Another example, that of variable 10, may be considered. The entry for variable 10 in row 11 of Table E.3 is positive, and, since z_{10} was previously reflected once, the rule for the sign adjustment is given in the lower-left cell of Table E.5. The number of negative signs for variable 10 is then changed from three to two.

Check the values in the fourth column of Table E.4 by the method indicated in step **18.**

20. If zero values should appear in any of the correlation or residual tables, they may be treated as positive numbers in making sign adjustments for the reflection of variables. The diagonal values of the residual tables are not considered in the count of negative signs, for, if a variable is reflected, its "self-correlation" remains unchanged.

21. It may happen that a variable which had already been reflected may again appear as the variable with a maximum number of negative signs after several other variables are reflected. In this case the variable is reflected again, changing the minus to plus in the first column of Table E.4, and the number of minus signs is adjusted for each of the variables.

22. The reflection of variables is continued until each variable has less than $n/2$ negative residuals. In the example $n = 13$, so that the reflections are carried to the point where there are six or fewer negative signs for each variable. It will be noted that upon reflection of variable 1, the entries in the last column of Table E.4 are six or less.

23. The variables having minus signs in the first column of Table E.4 now may be actually reflected in Table E.3. In order to make the procedure perfectly clear, two additional tables, E.3′ and E.3″, are included. In practice, however, these additional tables may be obviated by incorporating them in Table E.3. That procedure is indicated by Table E.7, in which the third-factor coefficients are calculated.

24. First place a minus sign before the column number of each variable which is to be reflected, i.e., before variables 1, 10, 11, 12, and 13 in Table E.3′. This is done for the convenience of the subsequent sign changes in this table.

The signs of the residuals $_1r_{jk}$ may be changed according to the following formula:

$$r_{1jk} = \epsilon_j \epsilon_k (_1r_{jk}) .$$

It will be recalled that the epsilons are merely algebraic symbols for the plus or minus signs. Hence, if neither z_j nor z_k was reflected, or if both variables were reflected, then $r_{1jk} = {}_1r_{jk}$; but, if only one or the other of z_j and z_k was reflected, then $r_{1jk} = -{}_1r_{jk}$. First go through the upper half of Table E.3, one row at a time, and insert minus signs according to the above rules. A convenient procedure is to look at each entry of the first column, note the adjusted sign, and when this sign should be minus, record a minus sign in the corresponding cell of the first row of the upper half of the table. Check the total number of minus signs for the first variable with the number given for that variable in the last column of Table E.4. Then proceed to the second column of the lower half of the table, note the sign changes, and record the minus signs in the second row of the upper half of the table. The count of six minus signs for variable 2, in the second column and second row of the upper half of Table E.3′, agrees with that given in the last column of Table E.4. Continue this process of sign changes for every variable in Table E.3′. As an additional check, the total number of minus signs in the upper half of Table E.3′ must be equal to one-half of the total given in the last column of Table E.4.

25. Now, merely copy the values (without any algebraic signs) from the columns of the lower half of Table E.3 into the corresponding rows of the upper half of Table E.3. This is done in Table E.3″ for the example. The values so obtained are the residuals of the reflected variables.

26. The second-factor coefficients are calculated from the values in the upper half of the table.* The sum of the residuals (after reflection) for any variable z_j is

$$S_{j1} = \sum_k r_{1jk} ,$$

and the total of all the reflected residuals is

$$T_1 = \Sigma S_{j1} .$$

The thirteen sums S_{j1} and the total T_1 are presented in Table E.3″. The square root and the reciprocal of the square root of T_1 are also given. The algebraic signs of the sums S_{j1} are changed for the variables that have been reflected, and the resulting values, $_1S_j = \epsilon_j S_{j1}$, are presented in Table E.3″. Finally, by multiplying each $_1S_j$ by $1/\sqrt{T_1}$, the respective coefficients a_{j2} are obtained. These are the coefficients for the observed variables, not the reflected ones.

27. A useful check on the calculation of the second-factor coefficients (and the coefficients of all other factors except the first) is given by the fact that the sum of the coefficients must be approximately zero if a centroid system has been obtained. In the example,

$$D_2 = \Sigma a_{j2} = .000 .$$

Another check, like the one given in step **6** for the first factor, follows from the relation

$$\Sigma \epsilon_j a_{j2} = \frac{\Sigma S_{j1}}{\sqrt{T_1}} = \frac{T_1}{\sqrt{T_1}} = \sqrt{T_1} .$$

The sum of the factor coefficients for the reflected variables must be equal to the square root of the total of all the reflected residuals. The coefficients for the reflected variables are merely those given in the last row of Table E.3″ with the signs changed for all variables which have been reflected. Thus,

$$\Sigma \epsilon_j a_{j2} = .060 + .038 + .148 + \ldots + .368 = 3.706 ,$$

which agrees with the value of $\sqrt{T_1}$.

---

* It may be noted again that this portion of the table was separated out as Table E.3″ for clarification, but in practice only one Table E.3 need be made.

28. Proceed, as in steps **7** through **27,** to determine the third-factor coefficients. The calculations leading to a_{j3} are given in Tables E.6, E.7, and E.8. This procedure is repeated over and over again until sufficient factors are obtained, which account for the total communality.

It is evident from the third-factor residuals, given in Table E.10, that three factors are sufficient to account for the original correlations. Furthermore, the sum of the contributions of the three factors agrees well with the original total communality. This is indicated in Table 8.1, where the centroid pattern for the thirteen psychological tests is presented. The percentage contribution of each factor to the total communality is also given in Table 8.1. The discrepancy between the original and calculated communality for each test is given in the last column of Table 8.1. The sum of the thirteen differences is $-.030$, or -0.4 per cent of the original total communality (6.936). This indicates a very good factorization, with a slight tendency for overfactoring.

PRODUCT MATRIX: $Q_2 = \|a_{j2} a_{k2}\|$

Variable	1	2	3	4	5	6	7	8	9	10	11	12	13
1	.004												
2	−.002	.001											
3	−.009	.006	.022										
4	−.005	.003	.012	.007									
5	−.015	.010	.038	.021	.066								
6	−.021	.013	.052	.029	.091	.125							
7	−.022	.014	.054	.030	.094	.130	.135						
8	−.012	.007	.029	.016	.051	.070	.072	.039					
9	−.025	.016	.061	.034	.105	.145	.150	.081	.167				
10	.029	−.018	−.071	−.040	−.124	−.171	−.177	−.095	−.197	.232			
11	.023	−.015	−.058	−.032	−.100	−.138	−.143	−.077	−.160	.188	.152		
12	.033	−.021	−.082	−.046	−.142	−.196	−.203	−.109	−.226	.267	.216	.306	
13	.022	−.014	−.054	−.031	−.095	−.130	−.135	−.072	−.151	.177	.144	.204	.135
E_{j2}	.000	.000	.000	.002	.000	−.001	−.001	.000	.000	.000	.000	.001	.000
$a_{j2} D_2$	.000	.000	.000	.000	.000	.000	.000	.000	.000	.000	.000	.000	.000

TABLE E.7

Second-Factor Residuals and the Calculation of the C_3 Coefficients

Variable	-1	-2	-3	-4	5	6	7	8	9	10	11	12	-13	Check
1	.186	.105	.158	.183	.107	.073	.112	.084	.073	.189	.041	.015	.058	
2	.105	.076	.163	.057	-.016	.030	.113	.100	.069	.087	.026	.007	.014	
3	.158	.163	.165	.093	.096	.080	.132	-.058	.169	.194	.075	-.018	.093	
4	.183	.057	.093	.079	.142	.040	.040	-.038	.043	.078	.115	.027	.036	$T_2 = 2\sum_{i \leqq k} r_{2,k} - \Sigma r_{2ii}$
5	.107	.016	.096	.142	.049	.016	.036	.013	.109	.103	.053	.002	.052	
6	-.073	-.030	-.080	-.040	.016	.016	.082	.041	.076	.052	.111	-.053	.038	
7	-.112	-.113	-.132	-.040	.036	.082	.095	.039	.032	.095	.012	.033	.006	$T_2 = 2(5.334) - .927$
8	-.084	-.100	-.058	-.038	.013	.041	.039	.035	.041	.059	.002	.037	.008	
9	-.073	-.069	-.169	-.043	.109	.076	.032	.041	.104	.049	.065	-.001	.039	$= 9.741$
10	-.189	-.087	-.194	-.078	.103	.052	.095	.059	.049	.115	.052	.096	.076	
11	-.041	-.026	-.075	-.115	.053	.111	.012	.002	.065	.052	.009	-.050	-.029	
12	-.015	-.007	-.018	-.027	.002	-.053	.033	.037	-.001	.096	-.050	-.012	-.020	
13	.058	.014	.093	.036	-.052	-.038	-.006	-.008	-.039	.076	-.029	-.020	-.010	
$\sum_k 2r_{jk}$	-.004	-.001	.002	.001	.000	-.002	-.003	.003	.000	-.003	-.002	.001	.001	
S_{j2}	1.384	.831	1.342	.895	.762	.520	.803	.195	.786	1.245	.454	.103	.421	$T_2 = 9.741$
$\epsilon_j S_{j2}$	-1.384	-.831	-1.342	-.895	.762	.520	.803	.195	.786	1.245	.454	.103	.421	$\sqrt{T_2} = 3.1211$
a_{j3}	-.443	-.266	-.429	-.287	.244	.167	.257	.062	.252	.399	.145	.033	-.135	$1/\sqrt{T_2} = .3204$ $D_3 = -.001$

TABLE E.8

NUMBER OF MINUS SIGNS FOR SECOND-FACTOR RESIDUALS AFTER SUCCESSIVE REFLECTIONS OF VARIABLES

VARIABLE	RE-FLECTED VARIABLE	BEFORE RE-FLECTION	AFTER REFLECTION OF SUC-CESSIVE VARIABLES				
			1	2	4	13	3
1...........	—	8	4	3	2	1	0
2...........	—	7	8	4	3	2	1
3...........	—	6	7	8	9	10	2
4...........	—	7	8	9	3	2	1
5...........	....	4	3	4	3	2	1
6...........	....	7	6	5	4	3	2
7...........	....	6	5	4	3	2	1
8...........	....	6	5	4	5	4	5
9...........	....	7	6	5	4	3	2
10...........	....	5	4	3	2	1	0
11...........	....	7	6	5	4	5	4
12...........	....	7	6	5	4	3	4
13...........	—	7	8	9	10	2	1
Total....	....	84	76	68	56	40	24
Difference..	....	....	8	8	12	16	16

TABLE E.9

PRODUCT MATRIX: $Q_3 = \|a_{j3}a_{k3}\|$

Variable	1	2	3	4	5	6	7	8	9	10	11	12	13
1	.196												
2	.118	.071											
3	.190	.114	.184										
4	.127	.076	.123	.082									
5	-.108	-.065	-.105	.070	.060								
6	-.074	-.044	-.072	-.048	.041	.028							
7	-.114	-.068	-.110	.074	.063	.043	.066						
8	-.027	-.016	-.027	-.018	.015	.010	.016	.004					
9	-.112	-.067	-.108	-.072	.061	.042	.065	.016	.064				
10	-.177	-.106	-.171	-.115	.097	.067	.103	.025	.101	.159			
11	-.064	-.039	-.062	-.042	.035	.024	.037	.009	.037	.058	.021		
12	-.015	-.009	-.014	-.009	.008	.006	.008	.002	.008	.013	.005	.001	
13	.060	.036	.058	.039	-.033	-.023	-.035	-.008	-.034	-.054	-.020	-.004	.018
E_{j3}	.000	.001	.000	-.001	-.001	.000	.000	.001	.001	.000	-.001	.000	.000
$a_{j3}D_3$	.000	.000	.000	.000	-.000	-.000	-.000	-.000	-.000	-.000	-.000	-.000	.000

371

TABLE E.10
Third-Factor Residuals (Final Residuals)

Variable	1	2	3	4	5	6	7	8	9	10	11	12	13
1	−.010												
2	−.013	.005											
3	−.032	.049	−.019										
4	.056	−.019	−.030	−.003									
5	.001	.081	.009	−.072	−.011								
6	.001	.014	.008	.008	−.025	.012							
7	.002	−.045	.022	.034	−.027	.039	.029						
8	−.057	−.084	−.085	.056	−.002	−.051	.023	.031					
9	.039	−.002	−.061	.029	.048	.034	−.033	−.057	.040				
10	−.012	−.019	−.023	.037	.006	−.015	−.008	.034	−.052	−.044			
11	.023	.013	−.013	−.073	.018	.087	−.049	−.011	.028	−.006	−.012		
12	.000	.002	.032	−.018	−.006	−.059	.025	.035	−.009	.083	−.055	−.013	
13	−.002	−.022	.035	−.003	−.019	−.015	.029	.000	−.005	−.022	.049	−.016	−.008
$\sum_{k} {}_{3}r_{jk}$	−.004	−.002	.002	.002	.001	−.002	−.003	.002	−.001	−.003	−.001	.001	.001

372

APPENDIX F

EVALUATION OF THE ROOTS OF A
POLYNOMIAL EQUATION

In obtaining a derived principal-factor pattern, the solution of a polynomial equation of the third, fourth, or higher degree is required. Several methods are available for computing the roots of such an equation to any desired number of decimal places. Each method, however, requires some preliminary information concerning the root to be calculated. It is necessary to know the limits between which the root lies and that there is no other root between the same limits. Thus it would be sufficient to know that the root is between 5 and 6, provided that there is no other root between these limits. If there were another root within this range, narrower limits would be necessary. When limits are obtained such that only one root is contained in the interval, then the root is said to be *isolated*.

As the first step toward the isolation of the roots of an equation of the mth degree,

$$(F.1) \qquad f(\mu) \equiv \mu^m + a_1\mu^{m-1} + a_2\mu^{m-2} + \ldots + a_{m-1}\mu + a_m = 0 \,,$$

Descartes's rule of signs will be presented. The term "variation of sign" is used to indicate that two consecutive terms of a polynomial or equation have coefficients of unlike signs; and by the variations of sign of an equation is meant all the variations presented by consecutive terms (when written in order of decreasing powers of the variable).

DESCARTES'S RULE. *The number of positive real roots of an equation $f(\mu) = 0$ is either equal to the number of its variations of sign or is less than that number by a positive even integer. The number of negative real roots of $f(\mu) = 0$ is either equal to the number of variations of sign of $f(-\mu) = 0$ or is less than that number by a positive even integer. A root of multiplicity q is here counted as q roots.*

Direct application of Descartes's rule of signs will not isolate the roots of an equation, except to give an upper limit to the number of positive and negative roots. Descartes's rule may be used as a rough check on the derivation of the general characteristic equation (9.10), since all the roots of this equation must be real and positive in factor analysis. This check consists simply in noting that, when the characteristic equation is written in order of decreasing powers of the variable, the signs of the terms must be alternately plus and minus. The number of variations of signs is then equal to the degree of the equation, giving the number of positive real roots. Thus, if the general equation (F.1) is a characteristic equation, then the coefficients must be alternately positive and negative, and the equation may be written in the form (9.10).

For purposes of illustrating the methods of evaluating the roots of a polynomial equation, the third example of **9.3** will be considered. The characteristic equation arising in the process of transforming the averoid to the principal-factor solution is

$$(\text{F.2}) \quad f(\mu) \equiv \mu^4 - 11.0142\mu^3 + 30.5260\mu^2 - 31.7349\mu + 11.1727 = 0 .$$

In this equation there are four variations of sign, indicating four positive real roots.

More exact methods for isolating the roots of a polynomial equation $f(\mu) = 0$ will now be presented. One procedure is to plot the polynomial $f(\mu)$, and by means of this graph to isolate the roots. To obtain a reliable graph, however, the bend points of the curve are required, and, since these points are difficult to obtain for a polynomial of degree greater than three, this method is usually impracticable. A much more effective, analytical procedure is given by Sturm's method.*

The first step in Sturm's method is to divide $f(\mu)$ by the first derivative $f'(\mu)$, obtaining a remainder $r(\mu)$, whose degree is less than that of f'. Denoting the quotient by q_1, this result may be written $f = q_1 f' + r$. Now indicate the negative of this remainder by $f_2(\mu)$, so that $f = q_1 f' - f_2$. Then divide f' by f_2 and denote the remainder with its sign changed by $f_3(\mu)$. Continue this process until a constant remainder is obtained. This procedure may be exhibited as follows:

$$(\text{F.3}) \quad \begin{cases} f = q_1 f' - f_2 , \\ f' = q_2 f_2 - f_3 , \\ f_2 = q_3 f_3 - f_4 , \\ \cdots , \\ f_{m-2} = q_{m-1} f_{m-1} - f_m , \end{cases}$$

where f_m is a constant.

If $f_m = 0$ then f_{m-1} divides f_{m-2} and all the other polynomials f_j, including f' and f, as may be seen by employing equations (F.3) in reverse order. Conversely, any common divisor of f and f' divides f_2 and hence all the other polynomials. Thus if $f_m = 0$, then f_{m-1} is the greatest common divisor of

* L. E. Dickson, *First Course in the Theory of Equations*, pp. 75–78.

f and f', and a root of $f_{m-1}(\mu) = 0$ is a multiple root of $f(\mu) = 0$.* On the other hand, if f_m is a constant different from zero then f and f' have no common divisor involving μ, and $f(\mu) = 0$ has no multiple root. In the remainder of this appendix it will be assumed that $f(\mu) = 0$ has no multiple roots, so that in the sequence of polynomials, $f, f', f_2, \ldots, f_m$, the last one, f_m, is a constant different from zero.

STURM'S THEOREM. *If a and b are real numbers, $a < b$, neither a root of $f(\mu) = 0$, the number of real roots of $f(\mu) = 0$ between a and b is equal to the excess of the number of variations of sign of*

(F.4) $$f(\mu), \ f'(\mu), \ f_2(\mu), \ \ldots, \ f_{m-1}(\mu), \ f_m$$

for $\mu = a$ over the number of variations of sign for $\mu = b$. Terms which vanish are to be dropped out before counting the variations of sign.

The application of Sturm's Theorem to the isolation of the roots of equation (F.2) will now be given. The first derivative of the function in (F.2) is

$$f'(\mu) = 4\mu^3 - 33.0426\mu^2 + 61.0520\mu - 31.7349 ,$$

and the first of equations (F.3) becomes

$$f = (.2500\mu - .6884)f' - f_2 ,$$

where

$$f_2 = 7.4835\mu^2 - 18.2270\mu + 10.6736 .$$

By dividing f' by f_2, the second of equations (F.3) is obtained, as follows:

$$f' = (.5345\mu - 3.1136)f_2 - f_3, \quad \text{where} \quad f_3 = 1.4046\mu - 1.4984 .$$

Continuing this process, it is found that on the next division the remainder is a constant different from zero. The sequence of polynomials (F.4) may then be summarized as follows:

(F.5) $$\begin{cases} f = \mu^4 - 11.0142\mu^3 + 30.5260\mu^2 - 31.7349\mu + 11.1727 , \\ f' = 4\mu^3 - 33.0426\mu^2 + 61.0520\mu - 31.7349 , \\ f_2 = 7.4835\mu^2 - 18.2270\mu + 10.6736 , \\ f_3 = 1.4046\mu - 1.4984 , \\ f_4 = .2615 . \end{cases}$$

* *Ibid.*, p. 61.

The roots of $f(\mu) = 0$ may then be isolated conveniently as indicated in Table F.1.

In selecting trial values of the variable μ, integral values are usually taken, beginning with zero, one, and so on. According to Sturm's Theorem, there is one real root of $f(\mu) = 0$ between 0 and 1 since

$$V_0 - V_1 = 4 - 3 = 1,$$

where $V\mu$ denotes the number of variations of sign of the numbers (F.4) when μ is a particular real number not a root of $f(\mu) = 0$. Trying the next integer—2—it is found that the excess of the number of variations of sign of the polynomials (F.4) for $\mu = 1$ over the number of variations of sign for $\mu = 2$ is two. Consequently, there are two roots between 1 and 2, and

TABLE F.1

ISOLATION OF ROOTS OF $f(\mu) = 0$

TRIAL VALUE	SIGNS					NUMBER OF VARIATIONS	COMMENTS
μ	f	f'	f_2	f_3	f_4	$V\mu$	
0........	+	−	+	−	+	4	One root between $\mu=0$ and $\mu=1$
1........	−	+	−	−	+	3	
2........	−	−	+	+	+	1	Two roots between $\mu=1$ and $\mu=2$
1.5.......	+	−	+	+	+	2	One root between $\mu=1.5$ and $\mu=2$, and one root between $\mu=1$ and $\mu=1.5$
7........	−	+	+	+	+	1	No roots between $\mu=2$ and $\mu=7$
8........	+	+	+	+	+	0	One root between $\mu=7$ and $\mu=8$

hence these roots are not sufficiently isolated. A value of μ halfway between these numbers is arbitrarily taken as the next trial value. It is then found that $V_1 - V_{1.5} = 1$ and $V_{1.5} - V_2 = 1$ so that one root is isolated between 1 and 1.5, and the other between 1.5 and 2.

At this point, three roots are already isolated. Their total contribution to the communality (equal to the sum of the three roots) may be estimated to be less than 4. From the averoid solution of Table 8.10 it is known that the total contribution of the four principal factors will be about 11. Therefore, the remaining factor must contribute upward of 7 to the total communality, or the remaining root of (F.2) is probably greater than 7. Hence, after isolating the three roots in Table F.1, the next trial value of μ is taken as 7. The last root is isolated between $\mu = 7$ and $\mu = 8$.

It may be noted that

(F.6) $$V_a \geqq V_b \quad \text{for} \quad a < b.$$

This relation may serve as a rough check on the computation of Sturm's functions (F.4).

When a particular root of an equation is isolated, it can be computed to any number of decimal places by means of Horner's Method.[*] This method involves successive transformations or reductions of the original equation. Thus, to find the root between 7 and 8 of equation (F.2), set $\mu = 7 + d$, where d is a decimal fraction to be determined. Direct substitution into (F.2) gives the transformed equation for d:

(F.7) $d^4 + 16.9858d^3 + 93.2278d^2 + 148.5417d - 92.0682 = 0$.

To obtain an approximation to the decimal d, ignore for the moment the terms involving d to the second or higher degree. Then from $148.5417d - 92.0682 = 0$, $d = 0.6$. But this value is too large, since all the terms ignored are positive. For $d = 0.5$, the polynomial in (F.7) is still positive, while for $d = 0.4$ it is negative. Hence $d = 0.4 + h$, where h is of the denomination hundredths. The value of the root of (F.2) may then be written as $\mu = 7.4 + h$, or, to simplify the notation, $\mu = 7.4 + d$, where d is now a new decimal of the denomination hundredths.

The method as just described is laborious especially for equations of high degree. If synthetic division[†] is employed instead of direct substitution, however, the work can be organized in the simple form indicated in Table F.2. In this table, the coefficients and constant term of equation (F.2) are recorded in the first row, and the equation is designated by (1). The given polynomial is divided synthetically by $\mu - 7$, and each quotient is also divided by $\mu - 7$. Then the successive remainders are the coefficients of the transformed equation (F.7). These coefficients appear in bold-face type just under the first zigzag line in Table F.2, and the fourth-degree equation with these coefficients is labeled (2). The polynomial (2), again expressed in terms of the variable μ, is divided synthetically by $\mu - .4$, and each quotient is also divided by $\mu - .4$. The remainders are the coefficients of the next transformed equation, which is designated by (3) in the table. Again consider the variable in the transformed equation as d and ignore the terms in d^2, d^3, and d^4 in order to get an approximation to the next decimal. Then from $231.5331d - 16.6224 = 0$, $d = .07$. The polynomial (3) is positive for $d = .07$ and negative for $d = .06$. Hence it is divided by .06. This process is continued, as completely illustrated in Table F.2, until the root of the original equation is calculated to as many decimal places as desired. In the present case the root is given correctly to four decimal places by $\mu_1 = 7.4694$.

[*] *Ibid.*, pp. 86–89.   [†] *Ibid.*, pp. 13–15.

To clarify further the procedure for evaluating a root of an equation, the complete work for the second largest root of (F.2) is presented in Table F.3.

TABLE F.2

CALCULATION OF μ_1 BY HORNER'S METHOD

μ^4	μ^3	μ^2	μ	Constant
(1) 1 − 11.0142	+ 30.5260	− 31.7349	+ 11.1727	7.
7.	− 28.0994	+ 16.9862	− 103.2409	
1 − 4.0142	+ 2.4266	− 14.7487	− 92.0682	
7.	+ 20.9006	+ 163.2904		
1 + 2.9858	+ 23.3272	+ 148.5417		
7.	+ 69.9006			
1 + 9.9858	+ 93.2278	92.0682		
7.		—————— = .6		
(2) 1 + 16.9858		148.5417		

$\mu_1 = 7 + d$

(2) is − for $d = .4$
(2) is + for $d = .5$
(2) is + for $d = .6$

.4	+ 6.9543	+ 40.0728	+ 75.4458	0.4
1 + 17.3858	+ 100.1821	+ 188.6145	− 16.6224	
.4	+ 7.1143	+ 42.9186		
1 + 17.7858	+ 107.2964	+ 231.5331		
.4	+ 7.2743			
1 + 18.1858	+ 114.5707	16.6224		
.4		—————— = .07		
(3) 1 + 18.5858		231.5331		

$\mu_1 = 7.4 + d$

(3) is − for $d = .06$
(3) is + for $d = .07$

.06	+ 1.1187	+ 6.9414	+ 14.3085	0.06
1 + 18.6458	+ 115.6894	+ 238.4745	− 2.3139	
.06	+ 1.1223	+ 7.0087		
1 + 18.7058	+ 116.8117	+ 245.4832		
.06	+ 1.1259			
1 + 18.7658	+ 117.9376	2.3139		
.06		—————— = .009		
(4) 1 + 18.8258		245.4832		

$\mu_1 = 7.46 + d$

(4) is − for $d = .009$
(4) is + for $d = .01$

.009	+ .1695	+ 1.0630	+ 2.2189	0.009
1 + 18.8348	+ 118.1071	+ 246.5462	− .0950	
.009	+ .1696	+ 1.0645		
1 + 18.8438	+ 118.2767	+ 247.6107		
.009	+ .1697			
1 + 18.8528	+ 118.4464	.0950		
.009		—————— = .00038		
(5) 1 + 18.8618		247.6107		

$\mu_1 = 7.469 + d$

(5) is − for $d = .00038$
(5) is + for $d = .00039$

.0004	+ .0072	+ .0450	+ .0941	0.00038
1 + 18.8622	+ 118.4536	+ 247.6557	− .0009	

$\mu_1 = 7.4694$

One important distinction may be noted between the work in Table F.2 and that in Table F.3. Whereas the constant terms in the successive transformed equations of Table F.2 are all negative, those in Table F.3 are all positive. In obtaining an approximation to the decimal at each stage, a different rule must then be applied. In the case of a negative constant (Table F.2), the value d is selected which makes the polynomial negative just before turning positive. When the constant term is positive (Table F.3), however, the value d is selected which just leaves the polynomial positive before turning negative.

TABLE F.3

CALCULATION OF μ_2 BY HORNER'S METHOD

	μ^4	μ^3	μ^2	μ	Constant	
(1)	$1 -$ 11.0142	$+$ 30.5260	$-$ 31.7349	$+$ 11.1727	$\lfloor$1.5	
	1.5	$-$ 14.2713	$+$ 24.3821	$-$ 11.0292		$\mu_2 = 1.5 + d$
	$1 -$ 9.5142	$+$ 16.2547	$-$ 7.3528	$+$ .1435		
	1.5	$-$ 12.0213	$+$ 6.3501			
	$1 -$ 8.0142	$+$ 4.2334	$-$ 1.0027			
	1.5	$-$ 9.7713				
	$1 -$ 6.5142	$-$ 5.5379	$\dfrac{.1435}{1.0027} = .1$		(2) is $+$ for $d = .09$	
	1.5				(2) is $-$ for $d = .1$	
(2)	$1 -$ 5.0142					
	.09	$-$ .4432	$-$ .5383	$-$ .1387	$\lfloor$0.09	
	$1 -$ 4.9242	$-$ 5.9811	$-$ 1.5410	$+$ .0048		$\mu_2 = 1.59 + d$
	.09	$-$ .4351	$-$ .5775			
	$1 -$ 4.8342	$-$ 6.4162	$-$ 2.1185			
	.09	$-$ .4270				
	$1 -$ 4.7442	$-$ 6.8432	$\dfrac{.0048}{2.1185} = .002$		(3) is $+$ for $d = .002$	
	.09				(3) is $-$ for $d = .003$	
(3)	$1 -$ 4.6542					
	.002	$-$ .0093	$-$ .0137	$-$ .0043	$\lfloor$0.002	
	$1 -$ 4.6522	$-$ 6.8525	$-$ 2.1322	$+$ .0005		$\mu_2 = 1.592 + d$
	.002	$-$ .0093	$-$ .0137			
	$1 -$ 4.6502	$-$ 6.8618	$-$ 2.1459			
	.002	$-$ .0093				
	$1 -$ 4.6482	$-$ 6.8711	$\dfrac{.0005}{2.1459} = .00023$		(4) is $+$ for $d = .00023$	
	.002				(4) is $-$ for $d = .00024$	
(4)	$1 -$ 4.6462					
	.0002	$-$ .0011	$-$ .0016	$-$ .0005	$\lfloor$0.00023	
	$1 -$ 4.6460	$-$ 6.8722	$-$ 2.1475	$+$ .0000		$\mu_2 = 1.5922$

The two remaining roots, as isolated in Table F.1, can be computed in a manner similar to that of Tables F.2 or F.3. The values of the four roots may be summarized as follows:

$$(\text{F.8}) \qquad \begin{cases} \mu_1 = 7.4694 \,, \\ \mu_2 = 1.5922 \,, \\ \mu_3 = 1.0934 \,, \\ \mu_4 = 0.8591 \,. \end{cases}$$

The sum of these roots is 11.0141, which agrees with the total contribution (11.015) of the four averoid factors of Table 8.10. This is to be expected, because the total contribution of the four principal factors must be equal to the total contribution of the averoid factors, the former solution being merely a rotation of the latter in the same common-factor space. The relative size of the contributions of successive factors is different, however, in the two cases.

APPENDIX G

SOLUTION OF SIMULTANEOUS LINEAR EQUATIONS

G.1. *General Procedure*

The problem of solving a set of simultaneous linear equations arises in at least four distinct phases of factor analysis, which will be discussed in the following sections of this appendix. In general, a system of n equations of the first degree in n unknowns can be solved by means of determinants.* While the determinantal method has some undisputed theoretical advantages, a more economical procedure is desired, especially when dealing with a large number of variables. The systems of equations which appear in factor analysis have symmetric determinants of coefficients and so lend themselves to special methods of solution. Gauss's method of substitution† produces a routine scheme for the solution of such a set of equations, including a complete check on the arithmetical work.

For convenience of the theoretical work, a system of only three equations in three unknowns will be employed. The procedure illustrated, however, is applicable to a system of any number of equations, provided the determinant of coefficients is symmetric. Let the equations be

$$(\text{G.1}) \qquad \begin{aligned} aX + bY + cZ - g &= 0, \\ bX + dY + eZ - h &= 0, \\ cX + eY + fZ - k &= 0, \end{aligned}$$

in which X, Y, Z are the unknowns and the remaining letters are constants. Solving the first of these equations for X,

$$(\text{G.2}) \qquad X = -\frac{b}{a}Y - \frac{c}{a}Z + \frac{g}{a},$$

and substituting this value into the last two of equations (G.1), they become

$$(\text{G.3}) \qquad \begin{cases} \left(d - \dfrac{b^2}{a}\right)Y + \left(e - \dfrac{bc}{a}\right)Z = \left(h - \dfrac{bg}{a}\right), \\[2mm] \left(e - \dfrac{bc}{a}\right)Y + \left(f - \dfrac{c^2}{a}\right)Z = \left(k - \dfrac{cg}{a}\right). \end{cases}$$

---

* See, e.g., Maxime Bocher, *Introduction to Higher Algebra*, 1935, p. 43.

† This method has been referred to as the "Doolittle Solution" in many textbooks on statistics. Convenient forms for the solution of a set of normal equations, arising in the problem of curve-fitting, were devised by M. H. Doolittle and are presented in T. W. Wright and J. F. Hayford, *The Adjustment of Observations*, 1906, pp. 101–24.

Let

$$d_1 = d - \frac{b^2}{a}, \quad e_1 = e - \frac{bc}{a}, \quad f_1 = f - \frac{c^2}{a}, \quad h_1 = h - \frac{bg}{a}, \quad k_1 = k - \frac{cg}{a},$$

then equations (G.3) may be written in the simpler form

(G.4)
$$\begin{cases} d_1Y + e_1Z = h_1, \\ e_1Y + f_1Z = k_1. \end{cases}$$

From the first of these equations,

(G.5)
$$Y = -\frac{e_1}{d_1}Z + \frac{h_1}{d_1},$$

and, upon substituting this value in the second equation, it becomes

(G.6)
$$\left(f_1 - \frac{e_1^2}{d_1}\right)Z = k_1 - \frac{e_1h_1}{d_1}.$$

Setting

$$f_2 = f_1 - \frac{e_1^2}{d_1} \quad \text{and} \quad k_2 = k_1 - \frac{e_1h_1}{d_1},$$

the value of Z may be written explicitly as follows:

(G.7)
$$Z = \frac{k_2}{f_2}.$$

Then substituting this value of Z into (G.5), the value of Y is determined, and, finally, using these values of Y and Z in (G.2), the unknown X is determined.

The substitutions of the last paragraph can be put in a routine outline form as indicated in Table G.1. In this form the coefficients and constant terms of equations (G.1) are recorded in the appropriate columns of lines 1, 3, and 7. Since the coefficients of X, Y, and Z in (G.1) constitute a symmetric determinant, and since the method of solution causes terms to the left of the principal diagonal to become zero as the variables are eliminated, these terms are omitted in Table G.1. If there were more equations in the system, there would be additional blocks in the table, each successive block including one additional line of calculations.

The directions for the remaining lines of Table G.1 are self-evident. Specific directions for checking the arithmetic, however, have not been in-

cluded. The sum of the entries in each line should be obtained. This value
should agree, except for rounding errors, with the corresponding expression

TABLE G.1
OUTLINE FOR GAUSS'S METHOD OF SUBSTITUTION

Line L_j	X	Y	Z	Constant	Check	Directions
			Forward Solution			
1.........	a	b	c	$-g$	Σ_1	From (G.1)
2.........	-1	$-\dfrac{b}{a}$	$-\dfrac{c}{a}$	$\dfrac{g}{a}$	$-\dfrac{1}{a}\Sigma_1$	$-\dfrac{1}{a}\cdot L_1$
3.........		d	e	$-h$	Σ_2	From (G.1)
4.........		$-\dfrac{b^2}{a}$	$-\dfrac{bc}{a}$	$\dfrac{bg}{a}$	$-\dfrac{b}{a}\Sigma_1'$	$-\dfrac{b}{a}\cdot L_1\cdot\Sigma_1'=\Sigma_1-a$
5.........		d_1	e_1	$-h_1$	Σ_2'	L_3+L_4
6.........		-1	$-\dfrac{e_1}{d_1}$	$\dfrac{h_1}{d_1}$	$-\dfrac{1}{d_1}\Sigma_2'$	$-\dfrac{1}{d_1}\cdot L_5$
7.........			f	$-k$	Σ_3	From (G.1)
8.........			$-\dfrac{c^2}{a}$	$\dfrac{cg}{a}$	$-\dfrac{c}{a}\Sigma_1''$	$-\dfrac{c}{a}\cdot L_1\cdot\Sigma_1''=\Sigma_1-a-b$
9.........			$-\dfrac{e_1^2}{d_1}$	$\dfrac{e_1 h_1}{d_1}$	$-\dfrac{e_1}{d_1}\Sigma_2''$	$-\dfrac{e_1}{d_1}\cdot L_5\cdot\Sigma_2''=\Sigma_2'-d_1$
10.........			f_2	$-k_2$	Σ_3'	$L_7+L_8+L_9$
11.........			-1	$\dfrac{k_2}{f_2}$	$-\dfrac{1}{f_2}\Sigma_3'$	$-\dfrac{1}{f_2}L_{10}$
			Back Solution			
From L_{11}......	$Z=\dfrac{k_2}{f_2}$					Entry in "Constant" column
From L_6......	$Y=-\dfrac{e_1}{d_1}Z+\dfrac{h_1}{d_1}$					Use entries in "Z" and "Constant" columns
From L_2......	$X=-\dfrac{b}{a}Y-\dfrac{c}{a}Z+\dfrac{g}{a}$					Use entries in "Y," "Z," and "Constant" columns

in the check column. The entries in the check column for lines 1, 3, and 7
are merely the sums of the elements in these lines and are checked if the
remaining checks (employing these values) are satisfied. For example, the

sum of the elements in line 5 is $(d_1 + e_1 - h_1)$, and this should agree with the check sum

$$\Sigma_2' = \Sigma_2 - \frac{b}{a}\,\Sigma_1' \,.$$

Now, if this check is satisfied, and the sum of the elements in line 4 is checked, then the sum Σ_2 must be correct.

In the back solution of Table G.1 the actual values of X, Y, and Z are determined. The value of Z, as given by equation (G.7), is obtained directly from the last line of the forward solution. Knowing the value of Z, the determination of Y can be effected by means of the values given in line 6 and agrees with formula (G.5). Finally, employing the values of Y and Z, the value of X as given in equation (G.2) can be obtained from the entries in line 2 of Table G.1. After X, Y, Z have been calculated, the back solution can be checked by substituting these values into (G.1).

G.2. *Application to Solution of Derived Principal-Factor Pattern*

In transforming the averoid solution of Table 8.10 into a principal-factor pattern, systems of equations of the form (9.8) must be solved for the direction cosines of the principal factors. To illustrate Gauss's method of substitution in this situation, consider the following system of equations for the direction cosines of the first principal factor:

$$\text{(G.8)} \quad \begin{cases} -.0288\lambda_{11} - .3136\lambda_{21} - .2753\lambda_{31} + .0360\lambda_{41} = 0\,, \\ -.3136\lambda_{11} - 6.0744\lambda_{21} + .0413\lambda_{31} - .3222\lambda_{41} = 0\,, \\ -.2753\lambda_{11} + .0413\lambda_{21} - 6.3707\lambda_{31} - .0917\lambda_{41} = 0\,, \\ .0360\lambda_{11} - .3222\lambda_{21} - .0917\lambda_{31} - 6.3895\lambda_{41} = 0\,, \end{cases}$$

where the coefficients are taken from (9.22) with the value of μ $(= 7.4694)$ given by the largest root in (F.8).

The rank of the matrix of coefficients of (G.8) is three, and the first three equations may be used to solve for the first three unknowns, λ_{11}, λ_{21}, λ_{31}, in terms of the last unknown, λ_{41}. For all values of the latter, the expressions for the three unknowns will satisfy the given four equations. Then, by employing the auxiliary condition,

$$\text{(G.9)} \qquad\qquad \lambda_{11}^2 + \lambda_{21}^2 + \lambda_{31}^2 + \lambda_{41}^2 = 1\,,$$

unique values for the four unknowns can be determined.

The forward solution of the first three of equations (G.8) by Gauss's method of substitution is presented in Table G.2. In lines 1, 3, and 7 of this table are recorded the coefficients of the first three of equations (G.8). The constant terms are $.0360\lambda_{41}$, $-.3222\lambda_{41}$, and $-.0917\lambda_{41}$, but for simplicity λ_{41} is omitted in each case and put at the head of the column. The directions for calculating the elements in the other lines of this table are similar to those given in Table G.1.

TABLE G.2

FORWARD SOLUTION FOR DIRECTION COSINES OF
FIRST PRINCIPAL-FACTOR AXIS

Line	λ_{11}	λ_{21}	λ_{31}	Constant (λ_{41})	Check
1............	$-.0288$	$-.3136$	$-.2753$	$.0360$	$-.5817$
2............	$-1.$	-10.8889	-9.5590	1.2500	-20.1979
3............	....	-6.0744	$.0413$	$-.3222$	-6.3553
4............	....	3.4148	2.9977	$-.3920$	6.0205
5............	....	-2.6596	3.0390	$-.7142$	$-.3348$
6............	....	$-1.$	1.1427	$-.2685$	$-.1258$
7............	....	....	-6.3707	$-.0917$	-6.4624
8............	....	....	2.6316	$-.3441$	2.2875
9............	....	....	3.4727	$-.8161$	2.6566
10............	....	....	$-.2664$	-1.2519	-1.5183
11............	....	....	$-1.$	-4.6993	-5.6993

The values of λ_{11}, λ_{21}, and λ_{31} in terms of λ_{41} can be obtained by means of the back solution. From line 11 of Table G.2, $\lambda_{31} = -4.6993\lambda_{41}$. Then, employing this value, the calculation from line 6 becomes

$$\lambda_{21} = 1.1427\lambda_{31} - .2685\lambda_{41} = -5.6384\lambda_{41}.$$

From line 2,

$$\lambda_{11} = -10.8889\lambda_{21} - 9.5590\lambda_{31} + 1.2500\lambda_{41},$$

and using the values of λ_{21} and λ_{31} just calculated, this expression reduces to $\lambda_{11} = 107.57\lambda_{41}$. Substituting these values of λ_{11}, λ_{21}, and λ_{31} into equation (G.9), this condition becomes

$$11626\lambda_{41}^2 = 1,$$

from which,

$$\lambda_{41} = \pm.0092744.$$

Using the positive value of λ_{41}, all the direction cosines are determined uniquely, as follows:

$$\text{(G.10)} \quad \begin{cases} \lambda_{11} = .9976 , \\ \lambda_{21} = -.0523 , \\ \lambda_{31} = -.0436 , \\ \lambda_{41} = .0093 . \end{cases}$$

There are several checks which may be applied. First of all, the sum of the squares of the direction cosines (G.10) must be equal to unity, i.e.,

$$\sum_{s=1}^{4} \lambda_{s1}^2 = .9999 .$$

Then, of course, the λ's must satisfy the equations from which they were solved and also the fourth equation of (G.8). Employing the values (G.10) in equations (G.8), the left-hand members become .0000, .0000, .0001, and $-.0027$, respectively. These values are considered sufficiently close to zero to afford a satisfactory check. The greater discrepancy in the check of the fourth equation is due to the fact that the latter was not employed in the solution of the λ's. Hence, the values (G.10) may be accepted as the direction cosines of the first principal axis with respect to the four averoid axes.

The direction cosines of the remaining principal axes can be obtained in a similar manner by employing the values of μ_2, μ_3, and μ_4 of (F.8) successively in (9.22). Three sets of equations of the type (G.8) are thus obtained, and from these and auxiliary conditions like (G.9) the values of λ_{s2}, λ_{s3}, and λ_{s4} ($s = 1, 2, 3, 4$) can be determined. The complete sets of direction cosines are given in Table G.3. Upon multiplying the averoid pattern of Table 8.10 by this matrix of transformation, the derived principal-factor pattern of Table 9.1 is obtained.

TABLE G.3

MATRIX OF TRANSFORMATION

	P_1	P_2	P_3	P_4
A_1........	.9977	$-.0543$	.0293	.0302
A_2........	$-.0523$	$-.8274$	$-.2603$	.4944
A_3........	$-.0436$	$-.1395$	.9533	.2660
A_4........	.0093	.5413	$-.1500$	.8270

G.3. *Application to the Derivation of a Pattern from a Structure*

After a structure, in terms of correlated factors, is obtained, there still remains the problem of determining the factor pattern. As indicated in step 6 of **11.3,** the coefficients of the factor pattern may be calculated from sets of equations of the form

(G.11)
$$
\begin{cases}
b_{j1} \quad + b_{j2}r_{\gamma_1\gamma_2} + \ldots + b_{jm}r_{\gamma_1\gamma_m} = r_{j\gamma_1}, \\
b_{j1}r_{\gamma_2\gamma_1} + b_{j2} \quad + \ldots + b_{jm}r_{\gamma_2\gamma_m} = r_{j\gamma_2}, \\
\cdot \quad \cdot \quad \cdot \quad \cdot \quad \cdot \quad \cdot \quad \cdots \quad \cdot \quad \cdot \quad \cdot \quad \cdot \\
b_{j1}r_{\gamma_m\gamma_1} + b_{j2}r_{\gamma_m\gamma_2} + \ldots + b_{jm} \quad = r_{j\gamma_m}.
\end{cases}
$$

For each j $(j = 1, 2, \ldots, n)$ there are m such equations for the determination of the coefficients $b_{j1}, b_{j2}, \ldots, b_{jm}$ of the m common factors. The terms in the right-hand members of these equations are the known structure elements.

The calculation of the b's for any variable z_j can be performed by Gauss's method of substitution as indicated in Table G.1. Furthermore, since the determinant of coefficients of (G.11) is the same for all values of j, the work can be so organized that the solution for all the b's can be made simultaneously. For the illustrative example of **11.3** there are just two factors and eight variables, plus two composite variables. The factor coefficients for these variables are calculated in Table G.4. The determinant of coefficients of the unknowns (with the elements below the diagonal omitted) appears in lines 1 and 3 of Table G.4, while the constant terms of equations (G.11) are also recorded in lines 1 and 3 for each variable z_j. In the directions these elements are designated as correlations with γ_1 or γ_2. The directions for the calculation of the other elements in the forward solution are similar to those given in Table G.1.

The back solutions for the values of b_{j1} and b_{j2} are calculated from lines 6 and 2 in the manner indicated in Table G.1, with one exception. Since the constant terms are not brought over to the same side of the equation, as is done in (G.1), the negatives of the values in the constant columns of lines 6 and 2 must be employed. Thus, for $j = 1$ the factor coefficients are given by

$$
b_{12} = \quad .051
$$
$$
b_{11} = -.484b_{12} + .919 = .894 .
$$

In a similar manner, all the other factor coefficients are calculated. The values b_{j1}, b_{j2} may be checked upon substitution into equations (G.11). For the illustration, the coefficients of the first variable may be checked by substituting $b_{11} = .894$ and $b_{12} = .051$ in the expression

$$
b_{11} + b_{12}r_{\gamma_1\gamma_2}
$$

TABLE G.4

CALCULATION OF A PATTERN FROM A STRUCTURE

LINE	DIRECTIONS	γ_1	γ_2	CONSTANTS										CHECK
				z_1	z_2	z_3	z_4	z_5	z_6	z_7	z_8	u_1	u_2	
								Forward Solution						
1....	$r_{\gamma_1 k}$	1.	.484	.919	.943	.907	.893	.455	.374	.312	.412	.977	.455	8.131
2....	$-L_1$	-1.	-.484	-.919	-.943	-.907	-.893	-.455	-.374	-.312	-.412	-.977	-.455	-8.131
3....	$r_{\gamma_2 k}$	......	1.	.484	.435	.399	.454	.932	.813	.740	.724	.473	.940	7.394
4....	$-.484L_1$	......	-.234	-.445	-.456	-.439	-.432	-.220	-.181	-.151	-.199	-.473	-.220	-3.450
5....	L_3+L_4	......	.766	.039	-.021	-.040	.022	.712	.632	.589	.525	.000	.720	3.944
6....	$L_5/(-.766)$	......	-1.	-.051	.027	.052	-.029	-.930	-.825	-.769	-.685	.000	-.940	-5.150
								Back Solution						
From line 6.........			b_{j2}	.051	-.027	-.052	.029	.930	.825	.769	.685	.000	.940	......
From line 2.........			b_{j1}	.894	.956	.932	.879	.005	-.025	-.060	.080	.977	.000	......

and noting that the result

$$.894 + .051(.484) = .919$$

agrees with $r_{1\gamma_1}$.

G.4. *Application to the Estimation of Factors*

Gauss's method of substitution can be adapted to the solution of the regression coefficients in the estimation of factors. The linear regression of any factor F_s on the n variables is given by

$$(12.6^{\text{bis}}) \qquad \overline{F}_s = \beta_{s1}z_1 + \beta_{s2}z_2 + \ldots + \beta_{sn}z_n \qquad (s = 1, 2, \ldots, m) .$$

The normal equations for the determination of the β's are

$$(12.7^{\text{bis}}) \qquad \begin{cases} \beta_{s1} + r_{12}\beta_{s2} + \ldots + r_{1n}\beta_{sn} = t_{1s} , \\ r_{21}\beta_{s1} + \quad \beta_{s2} + \ldots + r_{2n}\beta_{sn} = t_{2s} , \\ \qquad \cdot \quad \cdot \quad \cdot \quad \cdot \quad \cdot \quad \cdot \cdot \cdot \quad \cdot \quad \cdot \quad \cdot \quad \cdot \\ r_{n1}\beta_{s1} + r_{n2}\beta_{s2} + \ldots + \quad \beta_{sn} = t_{ns} , \end{cases}$$

where $t_{js} = r_{z_j F_s}$. The coefficients of the β's are the elements of the symmetric matrix of observed correlations. Then the scheme for Gauss's method of substitution of Table G.1 can be followed in the present case.

Since each set of normal equations for the estimation of the successive common factors involves the same matrix of coefficients, all the factors can be estimated simultaneously. Furthermore, this means that several sets of factors, obtained by different methods of analysis, can be predicted at the same time. To illustrate, the two principal factors and the two oblique factors for the example of eight physical variables are estimated. The complete work, including checks, is shown in Table G.5. The observed correlations are taken from Table 7.1; the correlations of the variables with the two principal factors P_1 (General Physical Growth) and P_2 (Body Type) are taken from Table 7.4; and the correlations with the two oblique factors γ_1 (Lankiness) and γ_2 (Stockiness) are taken from the factor structure of Table 11.2.

After the β's are determined in the "back solution," the equation of estimation of any factor may be written. Thus, for the second principal factor, the equation of estimation is

$$\overline{P}_2 = -.261z_1 - .267z_2 - .247z_3 - .116z_4 + .606z_5$$
$$+ .207z_6 + .088z_7 + .161z_8 ,$$

TABLE G.5

ESTIMATION OF FACTORS

LINE	\multicolumn{8}{VARIABLES}								PRINCIPAL FACTORS		OBLIQUE FACTORS		CHECK
	1	2	3	4	5	6	7	8	P_1	P_2	γ_1	γ_2	

LINE	1	2	3	4	5	6	7	8	P_1	P_2	γ_1	γ_2	CHECK
								Forward Solution					
1...	1.	.846	.805	.859	.473	.398	.301	.382	.858	− .328	.919	.484	6.997
2...	−1.	− .846	− .805	− .859	− .473	− .398	− .301	− .382	− .858	.328	− .919	− .484	−6.997
3...		1.	.881	.826	.376	.326	.277	.415	.849	− .414	.943	.435	5.914
4...		− .716	− .681	− .727	− .400	− .337	− .255	− .323	− .726	.277	− .777	− .409	−5.074
5...		.284	.200	.099	− .024	− .011	.022	.092	.123	− .137	.166	.026	.840
6...		−1.	− .704	− .349	.085	.039	− .077	− .324	− .433	.482	− .585	− .092	−2.958
7...			1.	.801	.380	.319	.237	.345	.810	− .412	.907	.399	4.786
8...			− .648	− .691	− .381	− .320	− .242	− .308	− .691	.264	− .740	− .390	−4.147
9...			.141	− .070	.017	.008	− .015	− .065	− .087	.096	− .117	− .018	− .392
10...			.211	.040	.016	.007	− .020	− .028	.032	− .052	.050	− .009	.247
11...			−1.	− .190	− .076	− .033	.095	.133	− .152	.246	− .237	.043	−1.171
12...				1.	.436	.329	.327	.365	.825	− .339	.893	.454	4.290
13...				− .738	− .406	− .342	− .259	− .328	− .737	.282	− .789	− .416	−3.733
14...				− .035	.008	.004	− .008	− .032	− .043	.048	− .058	− .009	− .125
15...				− .008	− .003	− .001	.004	.005	− .006	.010	− .010	.002	− .007
16...				.219	.035	− .010	.064	.010	.039	.001	.036	.031	.425
17...				−1.	− .160	.046	− .292	− .046	− .178	− .005	− .164	− .142	−1.941
18...					1.	.762	.730	.629	.747	.561	.455	.932	5.816
19...					− .224	− .188	− .142	− .181	− .406	.155	− .435	− .229	−1.650
20...					− .002	− .001	.002	.008	.010	− .012	.014	.002	.021
21...					− .001	− .001	.002	− .002	− .002	.004	− .004	.001	.001
22...					− .006	.002	− .010	− .002	− .006	− .000	− .006	− .005	− .033
23...					.767	.574	.582	.456	.343	.708	.024	.701	4.155
24...					−1.	− .748	− .759	− .595	− .447	− .923	− .031	− .914	−5.417
25...						1.	.583	.577	.637	.507	.374	.813	4.491
26...						− .158	− .120	− .152	− .341	.131	− .366	− .193	−1.199
27...						− .000	.001	.004	.005	− .005	− .006	.001	.012
28...						− .000	.001	.001	− .001	.000	− .002	.000	− .001
29...						− .003	.000	.000	.002	.000	.002	.001	.008
30...						− .429	− .435	− .341	− .257	− .530	− .018	− .524	−2.534
31...						.413	.089	.045	.103	− .004	.098	.777
32...						−1.	− .080	− .215	− .109	− .249	.010	− .237	−1.880
33...							1.	.539	.561	.488	.312	.740	3.640
34...							− .091	− .115	− .258	.099	− .277	− .146	− .788
35...							− .002	− .007	− .009	.011	− .013	− .002	− .022
36...							− .002	− .003	.003	− .005	.005	− .001	− .003
37...							.019	− .003	− .011	− .000	− .011	− .009	− .053
38...							− .442	− .346	− .260	− .537	− .018	− .532	−2.135
39...							− .003	− .007	− .004	− .008	.000	− .008	− .030
40...							.441	.058	.022	.048	− .002	.042	.609
41...							−1.	− .132	− .050	− .109	.005	− .095	−1.381
42...								1.	.619	.371	.412	.724	3.126
43...								− .146	− .328	.125	− .351	− .185	− .885
44...								− .030	− .040	.044	− .054	− .008	− .088
45...								− .004	.004	− .007	.007	− .001	− .001
46...								− .000	− .002	− .000	− .002	− .001	− .005
47...								− .271	− .204	− .421	− .014	− .417	−1.327
48...								− .019	− .010	− .022	.001	− .021	− .071
49...								− .008	− .003	− .006	.000	− .006	− .023
50...								.522	.036	.084	− .001	.085	.726
51...								−1.	− .069	− .161	.002	− .163	−1.391

Back Solution

		P_1	P_2	γ_1	γ_2	
From line 51: $\beta_{s8} = -e_s$ (e_s = element in col. s)		.069	.161	− .002	.163	......
From line 41: $\beta_{s7} = -.132\beta_{s8} - e_s$		.041	.088	− .005	.073	......
From line 32: $\beta_{s6} = -.080\beta_{s7} - .215\beta_{s8} - e_s$		.091	.207	− .009	.208	......
From line 24: $\beta_{s5} = -.748\beta_{s6} - .759\beta_{s7} - .595\beta_{s8} - e_s$		.307	.606	.043	.606	......
From line 17: $\beta_{s4} = -.160\beta_{s5} + .046\beta_{s6} + \ldots - .046\beta_{s8} - e_s$		.118	− .116	.158	.026	......
From line 11: $\beta_{s3} = -.190\beta_{s4} - .076\beta_{s5} + \ldots + .133\beta_{s8} - e_s$		.116	− .247	.203	− .072	......
From line 6: $\beta_{s2} = -.704\beta_{s3} - .349\beta_{s4} + \ldots - .324\beta_{s8} - e_s$		.314	− .267	.391	.135	......
From line 2: $\beta_{s1} = -.846\beta_{s2} - .805\beta_{s3} + \ldots - .382\beta_{s8} - e_s$		.177	− .261	.275	− .048	......

and a particular value of this factor can be obtained by substituting the values of the variables for a given individual. The β's, being a solution of a system of normal equations of the type (12.7), must satisfy such equations. Hence the "back solution" can be checked by substituting the β's in equations of the type

$$(G.12) \qquad \beta_{s1}r_{j1} + \beta_{s2}r_{j2} + \ldots + \beta_{s8}r_{j8} = r_{z_jF_s} \qquad (j = 1, 2, \ldots, 8),$$

where F_s is any one of the factors. Employing the first line of Table G.5 (that is, $j = 1$), this check for each of the four factors is given by

$$\sum_{k=1}^{8} \beta_{P_1k}r_{1k} = \quad .858 = r_{z_1P_1},$$

$$\sum_{k=1}^{8} \beta_{P_2k}r_{1k} = \quad -.328 = r_{z_1P_2},$$

$$\sum_{k=1}^{8} \beta_{\gamma_1k}r_{1k} = \quad .919 = r_{z_1\gamma_1},$$

$$\sum_{k=1}^{8} \beta_{\gamma_2k}r_{1k} = \quad .484 = r_{z_1\gamma_2}.$$

As a measure of the accuracy of estimation of a factor F_s by means of its regression on the variables, the coefficient of multiple correlation R_s may be computed. This is given by

$$(12.28^{\text{bis}}) \qquad R_s^2 = \beta_{s1}t_{1s} + \beta_{s2}t_{2s} + \ldots + \beta_{sn}t_{ns}.$$

The multiple correlation can be calculated directly from the values in Table G.5, by multiplying the β's by the first entries in each block for a given factor, summing, and taking the square root. Thus, for the first principal factor

$$R_{P_1} = \sqrt{.177(.858) + .314(.849) + \ldots + .069(.619)} = \sqrt{.96277} = .981.$$

The multiple correlation coefficients for the other factors can be calculated in a similar manner and are given by

$$R_{P_2} = .941, \qquad R_{\gamma_1} = .980, \qquad \text{and} \qquad R_{\gamma_2} = .962.$$

G.5. *Application to the Calculation of the Inverse of a Matrix*

In the shortened method of estimation of oblique factors the inverse of the matrix of correlations among the common factors is required. The solution of this problem can be accomplished by the methods of this appendix. For simplicity, suppose there are three common factors and let the matrix of their intercorrelations be denoted by

$$\phi = \begin{Vmatrix} 1 & r_{12} & r_{13} \\ r_{21} & 1 & r_{23} \\ r_{31} & r_{32} & 1 \end{Vmatrix}.$$

From the definition of the inverse of a matrix, it follows that

$$(G.13) \qquad \phi\phi^{-1} = I.$$

If the elements of the symmetric matrix ϕ^{-1} are denoted by e's, equation (G.13) may be written in full as follows:

$$(G.14) \qquad \begin{Vmatrix} 1 & r_{12} & r_{13} \\ r_{21} & 1 & r_{23} \\ r_{31} & r_{32} & 1 \end{Vmatrix} \cdot \begin{Vmatrix} e_{11} & e_{12} & e_{13} \\ e_{21} & e_{22} & e_{23} \\ e_{31} & e_{32} & e_{33} \end{Vmatrix} = \begin{Vmatrix} 1 & 0 & 0 \\ 0 & 1 & 0 \\ 0 & 0 & 1 \end{Vmatrix},$$

in which $r_{jk} = r_{kj}$ and $e_{jk} = e_{kj}$. The problem is to determine the elements of the inverse matrix from the known correlations.

The matrices in the left-hand member of equation (G.14) may be multiplied and the resulting nine elements set equal to the corresponding elements of the identity matrix on the right. This yields nine algebraic equations for the solution of the nine e's (the symmetry of the matrix serving as a check on the calculation of the elements off the diagonal). These equations may be grouped in the three sets:

$$(G.15_1) \qquad \begin{cases} 1 \cdot e_{11} + r_{12}e_{21} + r_{13}e_{31} = 1, \\ r_{21}e_{11} + 1 \cdot e_{21} + r_{23}e_{31} = 0, \\ r_{31}e_{11} + r_{32}e_{21} + 1 \cdot e_{31} = 0; \end{cases}$$

$$(G.15_2) \qquad \begin{cases} 1 \cdot e_{12} + r_{12}e_{22} + r_{13}e_{32} = 0, \\ r_{21}e_{12} + 1 \cdot e_{22} + r_{23}e_{32} = 1, \\ r_{31}e_{12} + r_{32}e_{22} + 1 \cdot e_{32} = 0; \end{cases}$$

$$(G.15_3) \qquad \begin{cases} 1 \cdot e_{13} + r_{12}e_{23} + r_{13}e_{33} = 0, \\ r_{21}e_{13} + 1 \cdot e_{23} + r_{23}e_{33} = 0, \\ r_{31}e_{13} + r_{32}e_{23} + 1 \cdot e_{33} = 1. \end{cases}$$

It will be noted that each set of three equations involves the same matrix of coefficients—namely, the correlation matrix ϕ. Hence, the work can be so organized that the solution for all the e's can be made simultaneously.

To illustrate the procedure for calculating the inverse of a matrix, a very simple example will be employed. Consider the following matrix of intercorrelations of the two oblique factors, γ_1 and γ_2, from the analysis of the eight physical variables:

$$\phi = \begin{Vmatrix} 1.000 & .484 \\ .484 & 1.000 \end{Vmatrix}.$$

The inverse of this matrix can be computed by means of Gauss's method of substitution. Construct Table G.6, putting the elements of ϕ (excluding those below the diagonal) in lines 1 and 3 of the left-hand portion, and the identity matrix in the right-hand portion of the main body of the table.

TABLE G.6

CALCULATION OF THE INVERSE OF A MATRIX

Line	Directions	γ_1	γ_2	Identity Matrix		Check
1.........	$r_{\gamma_1 k}$	1.	.484	1.	0	2.484
2.........	$-L_1$	−1.	− .484	−1.	0	−2.484
3.........	$r_{\gamma_2 k}$	......	1.	0	1.	2.000
4.........	$-.484L_1$	......	− .234	− .484	0	− .718
5.........	$L_3 + L_4$	......	.766	− .484	1.	1.282
6.........	$-L_5/.766$	......	−1.	.632	−1.305	−1.673

Inverse

	γ_1	γ_2		
From L_2 and L_6: Calculate e_{11} and e_{12}..........	1.306	− .632	....
From L_6: Calculate e_{21} and e_{22}................	− .632	1.305	....

The calculations are similar to those in the preceding sections of this appendix, with the left-hand portion identical to that in Table G.4. The order of recording the elements obtained in the "back solution" is reversed from that of the preceding examples, however. The calculations from the last line of the "forward solution," although performed first, are put in the last line of the "back solution." This is continued, in reverse order, until the calculations from line 2 of the "forward solution" are recorded in the first line of the "back solution." In this manner, the final inverse matrix is disclosed in the natural order at the bottom of the table.

TABLE H.1

STANDARD ERRORS OF FACTOR COEFFICIENTS

$$\sigma_a = \frac{1}{2\sqrt{N}}\sqrt{\frac{3}{\rho} - 2 - 5\rho + 4\rho^2}$$

N	.10	.12	.14	.16	.18	.20	.22	.24	.26	.28	.30	.35	.40	.45	.50	.55	.60	.65	.70	.75
20	.587	.530	.485	.448	.417	.390	.366	.345	.326	.309	.293	.258	.227	.201	.177	.155	.134	.115	.097	.079
30	.479	.433	.396	.366	.340	.318	.299	.282	.266	.252	.239	.210	.186	.164	.144	.126	.110	.094	.079	.065
40	.415	.375	.343	.317	.295	.276	.259	.244	.231	.218	.207	.182	.161	.142	.125	.109	.095	.081	.068	.056
50	.371	.335	.307	.283	.264	.247	.232	.218	.206	.195	.185	.163	.144	.127	.112	.098	.085	.073	.061	.050
60	.339	.306	.280	.259	.241	.225	.211	.199	.188	.178	.169	.149	.131	.116	.102	.089	.077	.066	.056	.046
70	.314	.283	.259	.239	.223	.208	.196	.184	.174	.165	.157	.138	.122	.107	.094	.083	.072	.061	.052	.042
80	.293	.265	.242	.224	.208	.195	.183	.173	.163	.154	.146	.129	.114	.100	.088	.077	.067	.057	.048	.040
90	.277	.250	.229	.211	.196	.184	.173	.163	.154	.146	.138	.121	.107	.095	.083	.073	.063	.054	.046	.037
100	.262	.237	.217	.200	.186	.174	.164	.154	.146	.138	.131	.115	.102	.090	.079	.069	.060	.051	.043	.035
110	.250	.226	.207	.191	.178	.166	.156	.147	.139	.132	.125	.110	.097	.086	.075	.066	.057	.049	.041	.034
120	.240	.216	.198	.183	.170	.159	.150	.141	.133	.126	.120	.105	.093	.082	.072	.063	.055	.047	.039	.032
130	.230	.208	.190	.176	.163	.153	.144	.135	.128	.121	.115	.101	.089	.079	.069	.061	.053	.045	.038	.031
140	.222	.200	.183	.169	.158	.147	.138	.130	.123	.117	.111	.097	.086	.076	.067	.058	.051	.043	.036	.030
150	.214	.193	.177	.164	.152	.142	.134	.126	.119	.113	.107	.094	.083	.073	.065	.056	.049	.042	.035	.029
160	.207	.187	.171	.158	.147	.138	.129	.122	.115	.109	.104	.091	.080	.071	.062	.055	.047	.041	.034	.028
170	.201	.182	.166	.154	.143	.134	.126	.118	.112	.106	.100	.088	.078	.069	.061	.053	.046	.039	.033	.027
180	.196	.177	.162	.149	.139	.130	.122	.115	.109	.103	.098	.086	.076	.067	.059	.052	.045	.038	.032	.026
190	.190	.172	.157	.145	.135	.126	.119	.112	.106	.100	.095	.084	.074	.065	.057	.050	.044	.037	.031	.026
200	.186	.168	.153	.142	.132	.123	.116	.109	.103	.098	.093	.081	.072	.064	.056	.049	.042	.036	.031	.025
250	.166	.150	.137	.127	.118	.110	.104	.098	.092	.087	.083	.073	.064	.057	.050	.044	.038	.032	.027	.022
300	.151	.137	.125	.116	.108	.101	.095	.089	.084	.080	.076	.067	.059	.052	.046	.040	.035	.030	.025	.020
350	.140	.127	.116	.107	.100	.093	.088	.083	.078	.074	.070	.062	.054	.048	.042	.037	.032	.027	.023	.019
400	.131	.118	.108	.100	.093	.087	.082	.077	.073	.069	.065	.058	.051	.045	.040	.035	.030	.026	.022	.018
450	.124	.112	.102	.094	.088	.082	.077	.073	.069	.065	.062	.054	.048	.042	.037	.033	.028	.024	.020	.017
500	.117	.106	.097	.090	.083	.078	.073	.069	.065	.062	.059	.052	.045	.040	.035	.031	.027	.023	.019	.016

TABLE H.2
STANDARD ERRORS OF GENERAL-FACTOR RESIDUALS

$$\sigma_{\bar{r}} = \frac{(1-\rho)}{\sqrt{2N}} \sqrt{5 + 8\rho + 2\rho^2}$$

N \ ρ	.10	.15	.20	.25	.30	.35	.40	.45	.50	.55	.60	.65	.70	.75
20	.343	.336	.327	.317	.305	.292	.277	.261	.244	.225	.205	.184	.161	.138
30	.280	.274	.267	.258	.249	.238	.226	.213	.199	.184	.167	.150	.132	.112
40	.243	.237	.231	.224	.215	.206	.196	.185	.172	.159	.145	.130	.114	.097
50	.217	.212	.207	.200	.193	.184	.175	.165	.154	.142	.130	.116	.102	.087
60	.198	.194	.189	.183	.176	.168	.160	.151	.141	.130	.118	.106	.093	.079
70	.183	.180	.175	.169	.163	.156	.148	.139	.130	.120	.110	.098	.086	.074
80	.172	.168	.163	.158	.152	.146	.138	.130	.122	.113	.103	.092	.081	.069
90	.162	.158	.154	.149	.144	.137	.131	.123	.115	.106	.097	.087	.076	.065
100	.154	.150	.146	.142	.136	.130	.124	.117	.109	.101	.092	.082	.072	.062
110	.146	.143	.139	.135	.130	.124	.118	.111	.104	.096	.087	.078	.069	.059
120	.140	.137	.133	.129	.124	.119	.113	.107	.099	.092	.084	.075	.066	.056
130	.135	.132	.128	.124	.120	.114	.109	.102	.096	.088	.080	.072	.063	.054
140	.130	.127	.124	.120	.115	.110	.105	.099	.092	.085	.078	.070	.061	.052
150	.125	.123	.119	.116	.111	.106	.101	.095	.089	.082	.075	.067	.059	.050
160	.121	.119	.116	.112	.108	.103	.098	.092	.086	.080	.073	.065	.057	.049
170	.118	.115	.112	.109	.105	.100	.095	.090	.084	.077	.070	.063	.055	.047
180	.114	.112	.109	.106	.102	.097	.092	.087	.081	.075	.068	.061	.054	.046
190	.111	.109	.106	.103	.099	.095	.090	.085	.079	.073	.067	.060	.052	.045
200	.109	.106	.103	.100	.096	.092	.088	.083	.077	.071	.065	.058	.051	.044
250	.097	.095	.092	.090	.086	.082	.078	.074	.069	.064	.058	.052	.046	.039
300	.089	.087	.084	.082	.079	.075	.071	.067	.063	.058	.053	.047	.042	.036
350	.082	.080	.078	.076	.073	.070	.066	.062	.058	.054	.049	.044	.039	.033
400	.077	.075	.073	.071	.068	.065	.062	.058	.054	.050	.046	.041	.036	.031
450	.072	.071	.069	.067	.064	.061	.058	.055	.051	.050	.046	.041	.036	.031
500	.069	.067	.065	.063	.061	.058	.055	.052	.049	.045	.041	.037	.032	.028

TABLE H.3

SUPPLEMENTARY TABLE FOR COMPUTING
STANDARD ERRORS OF RESIDUALS

ρ_i	$\frac{3}{2} - \rho_i - \frac{5}{2}\rho_i^2 + 2\rho_i^3$	ρ_i	$\frac{3}{2} - \rho_i - \frac{5}{2}\rho_i^2 + 2\rho_i^3$
.03......	1.467804	.32......	.989536
.04......	1.456128	.33......	.969624
.05......	1.444000	.34......	.949608
.06......	1.431432	.35......	.929500
.07......	1.418436	.36......	.909312
.08......	1.405024	.37......	.889056
.09......	1.391208	.38......	.868744
.10......	1.377000	.39......	.848388
.11......	1.362412	.40......	.828000
.12......	1.347456	.41......	.807592
.13......	1.332144	.42......	.787176
.14......	1.316488	.43......	.766764
.15......	1.300500	.44......	.746368
.16......	1.284192	.45......	.726000
.17......	1.267576	.46......	.705672
.18......	1.250664	.47......	.685396
.19......	1.233468	.48......	.665184
.20......	1.216000	.49......	.645048
.21......	1.198272	.50......	.625000
.22......	1.180296	.51......	.605052
.23......	1.162084	.52......	.585216
.24......	1.143648	.53......	.565504
.25......	1.125000	.54......	.545928
.26......	1.106152	.55......	.526500
.27......	1.087116	.56......	.507232
.28......	1.067904	.57......	.488136
.29......	1.048528	.58......	.469224
.30......	1.029000	.59......	.450508
.31......	1.009332	.60......	.432000

TABLE H.4

The Probability Integral: Area under the Normal Curve in Terms of Deviates from the Mean

$$\tfrac{1}{2}a = \frac{1}{\sqrt{2\pi}\sigma} \int_0^{x/\sigma} e^{-\frac{1}{2}(x/\sigma)^2} \, dx$$

$\frac{x}{\sigma}$	$\tfrac{1}{2}a$	$\frac{x}{\sigma}$	$\tfrac{1}{2}a$	$\frac{x}{\sigma}$	$\tfrac{1}{2}a$	$\frac{x}{\sigma}$	$\tfrac{1}{2}a$	$\frac{x}{\sigma}$	$\tfrac{1}{2}a$
.00	.0000	.80	.2881	1.60	.4452	2.40	.4918	3.20	.4993
.02	.0080	.82	.2939	1.62	.4474	2.42	.4922	3.22	.4994
.04	.0160	.84	.2995	1.64	.4495	2.44	.4927	3.24	.4994
.06	.0239	.86	.3051	1.66	.4515	2.46	.4931	3.26	.4994
.08	.0319	.88	.3106	1.68	.4535	2.48	.4934	3.28	.4995
.10	.0398	.90	.3159	1.70	.4554	2.50	.4938	3.30	.4995
.12	.0478	.92	.3212	1.72	.4573	2.52	.4941	3.32	.4995
.14	.0557	.94	.3264	1.74	.4591	2.54	.4945	3.34	.4996
.16	.0636	.96	.3315	1.76	.4608	2.56	.4948	3.36	.4996
.18	.0714	.98	.3365	1.78	.4625	2.58	.4951	3.38	.4996
.20	.0793	1.00	.3413	1.80	.4641	2.60	.4953	3.40	.4997
.22	.0871	1.02	.3461	1.82	.4656	2.62	.4956	3.42	.4997
.24	.0948	1.04	.3508	1.84	.4671	2.64	.4959	3.44	.4997
.26	.1026	1.06	.3554	1.86	.4686	2.66	.4961	3.46	.4997
.28	.1103	1.08	.3599	1.88	.4699	2.68	.4963	3.48	.4997
.30	.1179	1.10	.3643	1.90	.4713	2.70	.4965	3.50	.4998
.32	.1255	1.12	.3686	1.92	.4726	2.72	.4967	3.52	.4998
.34	.1331	1.14	.3729	1.94	.4738	2.74	.4969	3.54	.4998
.36	.1406	1.16	.3770	1.96	.4750	2.76	.4971	3.56	.4998
.38	.1480	1.18	.3810	1.98	.4761	2.78	.4973	3.58	.4998
.40	.1554	1.20	.3849	2.00	.4772	2.80	.4974	3.60	.4998
.42	.1628	1.22	.3888	2.02	.4783	2.82	.4976	3.62	.4999
.44	.1700	1.24	.3925	2.04	.4793	2.84	.4977	3.64	.4999
.46	.1772	1.26	.3962	2.06	.4803	2.86	.4979	3.66	.4999
.48	.1844	1.28	.3997	2.08	.4812	2.88	.4980	3.68	.4999
.50	.1915	1.30	.4032	2.10	.4821	2.90	.4981	3.70	.4999
.52	.1985	1.32	.4066	2.12	.4830	2.92	.4982	3.72	.4999
.54	.2054	1.34	.4099	2.14	.4838	2.94	.4984	3.74	.4999
.56	.2123	1.36	.4131	2.16	.4846	2.96	.4985	3.76	.4999
.58	.2190	1.38	.4162	2.18	.4854	2.98	.4986	3.78	.4999
.60	.2257	1.40	.4192	2.20	.4861	3.00	.4987	3.80	.4999
.62	.2324	1.42	.4222	2.22	.4868	3.02	.4987	3.82	.4999
.64	.2389	1.44	.4251	2.24	.4875	3.04	.4988	3.84	.4999
.66	.2454	1.46	.4279	2.26	.4881	3.06	.4989	3.86	.4999
.68	.2517	1.48	.4306	2.28	.4887	3.08	.4990	3.88	.4999
.70	.2580	1.50	.4332	2.30	.4893	3.10	.4990	3.90	.5000
.72	.2642	1.52	.4357	2.32	.4898	3.12	.4991	3.92	.5000
.74	.2703	1.54	.4382	2.34	.4904	3.14	.4992	3.94	.5000
.76	.2764	1.56	.4406	2.36	.4909	3.16	.4992	3.96	.5000
.78	.2823	1.58	.4429	2.38	.4913	3.18	.4993	3.98	.5000

BIBLIOGRAPHY

This bibliography contains all the books and memoirs that are referred to in the text. There also are included the most important articles bearing upon the historical, theoretical, or practical aspects of factor analysis. These papers have been selected because of their special interest, but their selection out of the vast statistical literature cannot avoid being somewhat arbitrary.

The following list of abbreviations will be employed:

AJP = American Journal of Psychology
Amer. Math. M. = American Mathematical Monthly
Amer. M. S. Trans. = Transactions of the American Mathematical Society
BAAS = Report of the British Association for the Advancement of Science
Biom. = Biometrika
BJEP = British Journal of Educational Psychology
BJP = British Journal of Psychology
Bull. S. M. France = Bulletin de la Société mathematique de France
CP = Character and Personality
J. Ab. Soc. Psych. = Journal of Abnormal and Social Psychology
J. Amer. Stat. Assoc. = Journal of the American Statistical Association
JEP = Journal of Educational Psychology
JMS = Journal of Mental Science
N.Y. Acad. S. = Annals of the New York Academy of Sciences
Phil. Trans. Roy. Soc. = Philosophical Transactions of the Royal Society of London,
    Series A
Proc. Edin. M. S. = Proceedings of the Edinburgh Mathematical Society, Second
    Series
Proc. Nat. Acad. Sci. = Proceedings of the National Academy of Sciences
Proc. Roy. Soc. Edin. = Proceedings of the Royal Society of Edinburgh
Proc. Roy. Soc. Lon. = Proceedings of the Royal Society of London, Series A
Psych. = Psychometrika
Psych. Rev. = Psychological Review
SM = Scientific Monthly

AITKEN, A. C. "On the Evaluation of Determinants, the Formation of Their Adjugates, and the Practical Solution of Simultaneous Linear Equations," *Proc. Edin. M. S.,* III (1932), 207–19.

BARCLAY, SHEPARD. *Win at Contract with Any Partner.* New York: D. Appleton & Co., 1933. Pp. xvii+99.

BARTLETT, M. S. "The Statistical Conception of Mental Factors," *BJP,* XXVIII (1937), 97–104.

BLACK, T. P. "The Probable Error of Some Boundary Conditions in Diagnosing the Presence of Group and General Factors," *Proc. Roy. Soc. Edin.,* XLIX (1929), 72–77.

BLISS, G. A. "Mathematical Interpretations of Geometrical and Physical Phenomena," *Amer. Math. M.,* XL (October, 1933), 472–80.

398

BOCHER, MAXIME. *Introduction to Higher Algebra*. New York: Macmillan Co., 1935. Pp. xi+321.

BROWN, WILLIAM, and STEPHENSON, WILLIAM. "A Test of the Theory of Two Factors," *BJP*, XXIII (1933), 352–70.

BURT, CYRIL. "Experimental Tests of General Intelligence," *BJP*, III (1909), 94–177.

———. "General and Specific Factors Underlying the Primary Emotions," *BAAS*, LXXXV (1915), 694–96.

———. *The Distribution and Relations of Educational Abilities*. London: P. S. King & Son, 1917. Pp. xiii+93.

———. "Methods of Factor Analysis with and without Successive Approximations," *BJEP*, VII (1937), 172–95.

———. "The Unit Hierarchy and Its Properties," *Psych.*, III (1938), 151–68.

———. "The Factorial Analysis of Emotional Traits," *CP*, VII (March and June, 1939), 238–54, 285–99.

BUXTON, CLAUDE. "The Application of Multiple Factorial Methods to the Study of Motor Abilities," *Psych.*, III (1938), 85–93.

CAMP, B. H. "The Converse of Spearman's Two-Factor Theorem," *Biom.*, XXIV (1932), 418–28.

CHANT, S. N. F. "Multiple Factor Analysis and Psychological Concepts," *JEP*, XXVI (1935), 263–72.

CURETON, EDWARD E. "The Principal Compulsions of Factor-Analysts," *Harvard Educational Review*, May, 1939, pp. 287–95.

DICKSON, L. E. *First Course in the Theory of Equations*. New York: John Wiley & Sons, Inc., 1922. Pp. vi+168.

———. *Modern Algebraic Theories*. New York: Benj. H. Sanborn & Co., 1930. Pp. ix+276.

DODD, STUART C. "The Theory of Factors," *Psych. Rev.*, XXXV (1928), 211–34, 261–79.

———. "On the Sampling Theory of Intelligence," *BJP*, XIX (1929), 306–27.

DWYER, PAUL S. "The Determination of the Factor Loadings of a Given Test from the Known Factor Loadings of Other Tests," *Psych.*, II (1937), 173–78.

———. "The Contribution of an Orthogonal Multiple Factor Solution to Multiple Correlation," *ibid.*, IV (1939), 163–71.

———. "The Evaluation of Multiple and Partial Correlation Coefficients from the Factorial Matrix," *ibid.*, V (1940), 211–32.

EMMETT, W. G. "Sampling Error and the Two-Factor Theory," *BJP*, XXVI (1936), 362–87.

ENGELHART, MAX D. "The Technique of Path Coefficients," *Psych.*, I (1936), 287–93.

ETHERINGTON, I. M. H. "On Errors in Determinants," *Proc. Edin. M.S.*, III (1932), 107–17.

FERGUSON, GEORGE A. "A Bi-factor Analysis of Reliability Coefficients," *BJP*, XXXI (1940), 172–82.

FISHER, R. A. "Frequency Distribution of the Values of the Correlation Coefficient in Samples from an Indefinitely Large Population," *Biom.*, X (1915), 507–21.

———. "On the Mathematical Foundations of Theoretical Statistics," *Phil. Trans. Roy. Soc.*, CCXXII (1922), 309–68.

———. *The Design of Experiments.* Edinburgh: Oliver & Boyd, 1935. Pp. xi+252.

———. *Statistical Methods for Research Workers.* 6th ed. Edinburgh: Oliver & Boyd, 1936. Pp. xiii+339.

FLANAGAN, JOHN C. *Factor Analysis in the Study of Personality.* Stanford University, Calif.: Stanford University Press, 1940.

FLOOD, MERRILL M. "A Computational Procedure for the Method of Principal Components," *Psych.*, V (1940), 169–72.

FORSYTH, A. R. *Geometry of Four Dimensions*, Vol. I. Cambridge: Cambridge University Press, 1930. Pp. xxix+468.

GARNETT, H. E., and ANASTASI, ANNE. "The Tetrad-Difference Criterion and the Measurement of Mental Traits," *N.Y. Acad. S.*, XXXIII, 235–82.

GARNETT, J. C. M. "On Certain Independent Factors in Mental Measurement," *Proc. Roy. Soc. Lon.*, XCVI (1919), 91–111.

———. "Further Notes on the Single General Factor in Mental Measurements," *BJP*, XXII (1932), 364–72.

GIRSHICK, M. A. "Principal Components," *J. Amer. Stat. Assoc.*, XXXI (1936), 519–28.

———. "On the Sampling Theory of Roots of Determinantal Equations," *Annals of Mathematical Statistics*, X (1939), 203–24.

GOSNELL, HAROLD F., and SCHMIDT, MARGARET. "Factorial and Correlational Analysis of the 1934 Vote in Chicago," *J. Amer. Stat. Assoc.*, XXXI (1936), 507–18.

GUILFORD, J. P. *Psychometric Methods.* New York: McGraw-Hill Book Co., Inc., 1936. Pp. xvi+566.

GUILFORD, J. P., and GUILFORD, RUTH B. "Personality Factors *N* and *GD*," *J. Ab. Soc. Psych.*, XXXIV (April, 1939), 239–48.

GUTTMAN, LOUIS. "Multiple Rectilinear Prediction and the Resolution into Components," *Psych.*, V (1940), 75–99.

HARMAN, HARRY H. "Systems of Regression Equations for the Estimation of Factors," *JEP*, XXIX (1938), 431–41.

———. "Extensions of Factorial Solutions," *Psych.*, III (1938), 75–84.

———. "On the Rectilinear Prediction of Oblique Factors," *ibid.*, VI (1941), 29–35.

HARSH, CHARLES M. "Constancy and Variation in Patterns of Factor Loadings," *JEP*, XXXI (1940), 335–59.

HEYWOOD, H. B. "On Finite Sequences of Real Numbers," *Proc. Roy. Soc. Lon.*, CXXXIV (1931), 486–501.

HOLZINGER, KARL J. *Statistical Methods for Students in Education.* Boston: Ginn & Co., 1928. Pp. viii+372.

———. *Statistical Résumé of the Spearman Two-Factor Theory.* Chicago: University of Chicago Press, 1930. Pp. iv+44.

————. "On Factor Theory," *Conference on Individual Differences in Special and General Abilities*. Washington: National Research Council, 1931.

————. *Preliminary Report on Spearman-Holzinger Unitary Trait Study*, Nos. 1–9. Chicago: Statistical Laboratory, Department of Education, University of Chicago, 1934, 1935, 1936.

————. "Recent Research on Unitary Mental Traits," *CP*, IV (1936), 335–43.

HOLZINGER, KARL J., and HARMAN, HARRY H. "Relationships between Factors Obtained from Certain Analyses," *JEP*, XXVIII (1937), 321–45.

————. "Comparison of Two Factorial Analyses," *Psych.*, III (1938), 45–60.

————. *Review of Educational Research* (December, 1939), Chap. XIII: "Factor Analysis."

HOLZINGER, KARL J., and SWINEFORD, FRANCES. "The Bi-factor Method," *Psych.*, II (March, 1937), 41–54.

————. *A Study in Factor Analysis: The Stability of a Bi-factor Solution.* "Supplementary Educational Monographs," No. 48. Chicago: Department of Education, University of Chicago, 1939.

HOLZINGER, KARL J., assisted by SWINEFORD, FRANCES, and HARMAN, HARRY H. *Student Manual of Factor Analysis.* Chicago: Department of Education, University of Chicago, 1937. Pp. vi+102.

HORST, PAUL. "A Method of Factor Analysis by Means of Which All Coordinates of the Factor Matrix Are Given Simultaneously," *Psych.*, II (1937), 225–36.

HOTELLING, HAROLD. "The Consistency and Ultimate Distribution of Optimum Statistics," *Amer. M. S. Trans.*, XXXII (1930), 847–59.

————. "Analysis of a Complex of Statistical Variables into Principal Components," *JEP*, XXIV (September and October, 1933), 417–41, 498–520.

————. "The Most Predictable Criterion," *ibid.*, XXVI (February, 1935), 139–42.

————. "Simplified Calculation of Principal Components," *Psych.*, I (1936), 27–35.

————. "Relations between Two Sets of Variates," *Biom.*, XXVIII (1936), 321–77.

HUNTINGTON, EDWARD V. "Mathematics and Statistics, with an Elementary Account of the Correlation Coefficient and the Correlation Ratio," *Amer. Math. M.*, XXVI (December, 1919), 421–34.

IRWIN, J. O. "On the Uniqueness of the Factor *g* for General Intelligence," *BJP*, XXII (1932), 359–63.

————. "A Critical Discussion of the Single-Factor Theory," *BJP*, XXIII (1933), 371–81.

JACKSON, DUNHAM. "The Trigonometry of Correlation," *Amer. Math. M.*, XXXI (June, 1924), 275–80.

————. "The Relation of Statistics to Modern Mathematical Research," *Science*, LXIX (January 18, 1929), 49–54.

JORDAN, CAMILLE. "Essai sur la géométrie à *n* dimensions," *Bull. S. M. France*, III (1875), 103–74.

KELLEY, TRUMAN L. *Statistical Method.* New York: Macmillan Co., 1923. Pp. xi+390.

———. *Crossroads in the Mind of Man: A Study of Differentiable Mental Abilities.* Stanford University, Calif.: Stanford University Press, 1928. Pp. viii+238.

———. *Essential Traits of Mental Life.* "Harvard Studies in Education," Vol. XXVI. Cambridge, Mass.: Harvard University Press, 1935. Pp. 146.

———. "Comment on Wilson and Worcester's 'Note on Factor Analysis,' " *Psych.*, V (1940), 117–20.

———. *Talents and Tasks: Their Conjunction in a Democracy for Wholesome Living and National Defense.* "Harvard Education Papers," No. 1. Cambridge, Mass.: Graduate School of Education, Harvard University, 1940. Pp. 48.

KELLEY, T. L., and KREY, A. C. *Tests and Measurements in the Social Sciences.* New York: Charles Scribner's Sons, 1934. Section by Kelley, "Parsimony in the Judgment and Measurement of Character Traits," pp. 403–36.

KELLOGG, CHESTER E. "The Problem of Principal Components: Derivation of Hotelling's Method from Thurstone's," *JEP*, XXVII (October, 1936), 512–20.

———. "The Problem of Principal Components: Derivation of Hotelling's Method from Thurstone's. II. The Argument for Communalities," *ibid.*, pp. 581–90.

LAMB, HORACE. *Hydrodynamics.* 5th ed. Cambridge: Cambridge University Press, 1924. Pp. xvi+687.

LEDERMANN, WALTER. "Some Mathematical Remarks concerning Boundary Conditions in the Factorial Analysis of Ability," *Psych.*, I (1936), 165–74.

———. "On the Rank of the Reduced Correlational Matrix in Multiple-Factor Analysis," *ibid.*, II (1937), 85–93.

———. "Shortened Method of Estimation of Mental Factors by Regression," *Nature*, CXLI (1938), 650.

———. "On a Shortened Method of Estimation of Mental Factors by Regression," *Psych.*, IV (1939), 109–16.

LEV, JOSEPH. "A Note on Factor Analysis by the Method of Principal Axes," *Psych.*, I (1936), 283–86.

LINE, W.; ROGERS, K. H.; and KAPLAN, E. "Factor-Analysis Techniques Applied to Public-School Problems," *JEP*, XXV (1934), 58–65.

LORGE, IRVING, and MORRISON, N., "The Reliability of Principal Components," *Science*, LXXXVII (May 27, 1938), 491–92.

McCLOY, C. H. "A Factor Analysis of Personality Traits To Underlie Character Education," *JEP*, XXVII (1936), 375–87.

McCLOY, C. H.; METHENY, E.; and KNOTT, V. "A Comparison of the Thurstone Method of Multiple Factors with the Hotelling Method of Principal Components," *Psych.*, III (1938), 61–67.

MACKIE, JOHN. "The Probable Value of the Tetrad Difference on the Sampling Theory," *BJP*, XIX (1928), 65–76.

McMAHON, JAMES. "Hyperspherical Goniometry; and Its Application to Correlation Theory for *n* Variables," *Biom.*, XV (1923), 173–208.

MILLER, W. L. "The Relative Ability of the States To Finance Public Education."

Ph.D. dissertation, Department of Education, University of Chicago, 1940.

MOSIER, CHARLES I. "A Factor Analysis of Certain Neurotic Symptoms," *Psych.*, II (1937), 263–86.

MOULTON, F. R. "The Velocity of Light," *SM*, XLVIII, No. 5 (May, 1939), 481–84.

MUIR, THOMAS. *A Treatise on the Theory of Determinants.* New York: Privately published, 1930. Revised and enlarged by WILLIAM H. METZLER.

MULLEN, FRANCES. "Factors in the Growth of Girls Seven to Seventeen Years of Age." Ph.D. dissertation, Department of Education, University of Chicago, 1939.

OSGOOD, WILLIAM F. *Advanced Calculus.* New York: Macmillan Co., 1932. Pp. xvi+530.

PEARSON, KARL, and FILON, L. N. G. "On the Probable Errors of Frequency Constants and on the Influence of Random Selection on Variation and Correlation," *Phil. Trans. Roy. Soc.*, CXCI (1898), 229–311.

PEARSON, K., and MOUL, M. "The Mathematics of Intelligence. I. The Sampling Errors in the Theory of a Generalized Factor," *Biom.*, XIX (1927), 246–92.

PIAGGIO, H. T. H. "The General Factor in Spearman's Theory of Intelligence," *Nature*, CXXVII (1931), 56.

ROFF, MERRILL. "The Relation between Results Obtainable with Raw and Corrected Correlation Coefficients in Multiple Factor Analysis," *Psych.*, II (1937), 35–39.

SNYDER, VIRGIL, and SISAM, C. H. *Analytic Geometry of Space.* New York: Henry Holt & Co., 1914. Pp. xi+289.

SOMMERVILLE, D. M. Y. *An Introduction to the Geometry of N Dimensions.* New York: E. P. Dutton & Co., Inc., 1929. Pp. xvii+196.

SPEARMAN, CHARLES. "General Intelligence, Objectively Determined and Measured," *AJP*, XV (1904), 201–93.

———. "Correlations of Sums and Differences," *BJP*, V (March, 1913), 417–26.

———. *The Abilities of Man.* New York: Macmillan Co., 1927. Pp. vi+416+xxxiv.

———. "Material versus Abstract Factors in Correlation," *BJP*, XVII (1927), 322–26.

———. "The Factor Theory and Its Troubles. V. Adequacy of Proof," *JEP*, XXV (1934), 310–19.

———. "Abilities as Sums of Factors, or as Their Products," *ibid.*, XXVIII (1937), 629–31.

SPEARMAN, C., and HOLZINGER, K. "Note on the Sampling Error of Tetrad Differences," *BJP*, XVI, Part II (October, 1925), 86–89.

STEPHENSON, W. "Correlating Persons instead of Tests," *CP*, IV (1935), 17–24.

———. "The Inverted Factor Technique," *BJP*, XXVI (1936), 344–61.

———. "Methodological Consideration of Jung's Typology," *JMS*, March, 1939.

THOMPSON, J. R. "Boundary Conditions for Correlation Coefficients between Three and Four Variables," *BJP*, XIX (1928), 77–94.

THOMPSON, J. R. "The General Expression for Boundary Conditions and the Limits of Correlation," *Proc. Roy. Soc. Edin.*, XLIX (1929), 65–71.

THOMSON, GODFREY H. "The Tetrad-Difference Criterion," *BJP*, XVII (1927), 235–55.

———. "Hotelling's Method Modified To Give Spearman's *g*," *JEP*, XXV (May, 1934), 366–74.

———. "On Complete Families of Correlation Coefficients, and Their Tendency to Zero Tetrad-Differences: Including a Statement of the Sampling Theory of Abilities," *BJP*, XXVI (1935), 63–92.

———. "Boundary Conditions in the Common-Factor-Space, in the Factorial Analysis of Ability," *Psych.*, I (1936), 155–63.

———. "Some Points of Mathematical Technique in the Factorial Analysis of Ability," *JEP*, XXVII (1936), 37–54.

———. "Methods of Estimating Mental Factors," *Nature*, CXLI (February 5, 1938), 246.

———. "The Influence of Univariate Selection on the Factorial Analysis of Ability," *BJP*, XXVIII (1938), 451–59.

———. "The Estimation of Specific and Bi-factors," *JEP*, XXIX (1938), 355–62.

———. *The Factorial Analysis of Human Ability*. New York: Houghton Mifflin Co., 1939. Pp. xv+326.

THORNDIKE, ROBERT L. "Factor Analysis of Social and Abstract Intelligence," *JEP*, XXVII (1936), 231–33.

THURSTONE, L. L. "Multiple Factor Analysis," *Psych. Rev.*, XXXVIII, No. 5 (September, 1931), 406–27.

———. *The Vectors of Mind*. Chicago: University of Chicago Press, 1935. Pp. xv+266.

———. "The Bounding Hyperplanes of a Configuration of Traits," *Psych.*, I (1936), 61–68.

———. "The Factorial Isolation of Primary Abilities," *ibid.*, pp. 175–82.

———. "The Perceptual Factor," *ibid.*, III (March, 1938), 1–18.

———. "A New Rotational Method in Factor Analysis," *ibid.*, pp. 199–218.

———. *Primary Mental Abilities*. "Psychometric Monographs," No. 1. Chicago: University of Chicago Press, 1938. Pp. 121.

TRYON, R. C. "Multiple Factors *vs.* Two Factors as Determiners of Abilities," *Psych. Rev.*, XXXIX (1932), 324–51.

———. "So-called Group Factors as Determiners of Abilities," *ibid.*, pp. 403–39.

———. *Cluster Analysis*. Berkeley, Calif.: Associated Students Store, University of California, 1930. (Lithoprinted.)

TUCKER, LEDYARD R. "The Role of Correlated Factors in Factor Analysis," *Psych.*, V (1940), 141–52.

TURNBULL, H. W., and AITKEN, A. C. *An Introduction to the Theory of Canonical Matrices*. London and Glasgow: Blackie & Son, 1932. Pp. xiii+192.

VEBLEN, OSWALD, and WHITEHEAD, J. H. C. *The Foundations of Differential Geometry.* "Cambridge Tracts in Mathematics and Mathematical Physics," No. 29. Cambridge: University Press, 1932. Pp. ix+97.

WEBB, EDWARD. *Character and Intelligence.* "*BJP* Monograph Supplement." London, 1915.

WHITTAKER, E. T., and ROBINSON, G. *The Calculus of Observations.* London and Glasgow: Blackie & Son, Ltd., 1924, 1929. Pp. xvi+395.

WILCOX, L. R. "Modularity in the Theory of Lattices," *Annals of Mathematics*, XL (1939), 490–505.

WILSON, E. B. "On Hierarchical Correlation Systems," *Proc. Nat. Acad. Sci.*, XIV (1928), 283–91.

WILSON, E. B., and WORCESTER, JANE. "Note on Factor Analysis," *Psych.*, IV (1939), 133–48.

WOODROW, HERBERT. "The Common Factors in Fifty-two Mental Tests," *Psych.*, IV (1939), 99–108.

WOODROW, HERBERT, and WILSON, LAWRENCE A. "A Simple Procedure for Approximate Factor Analysis," *Psych.*, I (1936), 245–58.

WRIGHT, T. W., and HAYFORD, J. F. *The Adjustment of Observations.* New York: D. Van Nostrand Co., 1906. Pp. ix+298.

YOUNG, GALE. "Matrix Approximation and Subspace Fitting," *Psych.*, II (1937), 21–26.

———. "Factor Analysis and the Index of Clustering," *ibid.*, IV (1939), 201–8.

YULE, G. U., and KENDALL, M. G. *An Introduction to the Theory of Statistics.* 11th ed. London: Charles Griffin & Co., Ltd., 1937. Pp. xiii+570.

INDEX

INDEX

[The numbers refer to pages.]

Matrix—*continued*
  nonsingular, 305, 308, 319
  notation, 19, 165–67, 217–18, 220–21, 265, 303–4
  one-rowed, 304
  order of, 278, 287
  orthogonal, 49, 217–18, 222
  pattern; *see* Pattern matrix
  postmultiplication of, 227, 279, 294, 306–7, 325
  premultiplication of, 278–79, 287, 290–91, 306–7
  principal diagonal, 280
  product by scalar, 307
  product by transpose, 58, 317–19
  rank of symmetric, 65
  of reproduced correlations, 19, 278
    diagonal elements, 20, 278
  residual, 166–67, 186–87
  scalar, 307
  singular, 305
  square, 303, 305
  sum of, 282, 306
  symmetric, 280, 287, 305, 328, 389, 392
  theorems involving rank of, 45, 46, 58, 316–19
  of transformation, 205, 208, 210, 217, 220–21, 244–45, 290, 294, 386
  transpose of, 19, 58, 280, 285, 291, 304, 305, 308, 319
  triangular, 247
Maximal linearly independent set, 318
Mean value of certain ratios, 124–25, 320–21
Miller, W. L., 198
Minor, 302, 311, 318
Moulton, F. R., 23
Mullen, Frances, 80, 138, 168, 169
Multiple-factor solution
  complexity of variables, 106, 223, 229
  examples, 223–33
  form of, 101–3
  geometric fit, 223–24, 229–30, 232
  rotation of preliminary solution, 102, 180, 222–23
  stability of, 233

Norm, 47
Normal equations, 267, 270–71, 276, 389, 391
Normal law, equation of, 132, 397
Normally distributed factors, 313, 315
Notation
  B-coefficients; *see* *B*-coefficients, notation
  coordinates of points, 43
  elements in different spaces, 59–63
  in Horner's method, 377

  matrix; *see* Matrix notation
  number of combinations, 25
  in principal-factor method, 348
  reflection of variables, 185
  for regression coefficients, 267
  set-theory; *see* Set-theory notations
  summational; *see* Summational notation
N-tuple; *see* Point

Oblique reference system, 235, 238
Oblique reference vectors
  angle between, 236, 243
  correlation between, 237
  direction cosines of, 239–42
  variances of, 242
Oblique solution
  angle between reference axes, 236
  comparison for different initial patterns, 249, 258
  examples
    based upon bi-factor patterns, 255–59
    based upon centroid patterns, 249–55
    of inapplicability, 260–61
  geometric basis, 234–37
  outline for calculation, 237–48
    contributions of factors, 247–48
    direction cosines of axes, 239–42, 323–25
    factor pattern, 246–47
    factor structure, 243–46
    initial orthogonal pattern, 238
    intercorrelations of factors, 242–43, 326
    subsets of variables, 238–39
  parts of, 237
  pattern derived from structure, 246–47, 386–88
  rotation of orthogonal solution, 234, 237
  stability of, 248, 255, 258
Order of rotations, 219, 222
Orthogonal matrix, 49, 217–18, 222
Orthogonal reference vectors
  in bi-factor solution, 117
  in centroid solution, 181
  in multiple-factor solution, 222
  in principal-factor solution, 202
Orthogonal rotations; *see* Orthogonal transformations
Orthogonal solution, 90–91, 181, 202
Orthogonal system, 202, 220, 232
  total contribution of, 233
Orthogonal transformations
  definition of, 49
  in higher-dimensional space, 221–22
  in matrix notation, 217
  notation in, 216–26
  order of, 219
  in plane, 215–18
  to principal-factor axes, 202–14

product of, 219
theoretical development, 215–22
in three-space, 218–21
Osgood, William F., 202, 322

Parametric equations of line, 50, 51
Pattern; *see* Factor pattern
Pattern matrix, 19–20, 208, 326
centroid, 206, 208, 225
common-factor portion, 266, 281, 286
complete, 266
definition of, 19
in estimation of factors, 269
principal, 205, 208, 211
of uniquenesses, 281
Pearson, Karl, 123
Pencil of planes, 99, 117
Pentad criterion, 72
Poincaré, H., 23
Point
arithmetic, 42
geometric, 42
Point representation of variables, 57, 93–94, 159
Polynomial equation
isolation of roots, 373–77
sequence of, 375
solution of, 373–80
Postmultiplication, 227, 279, 294, 325–26
Preferred forms of solution, 8, 265, 289, 296
assumptions and properties of, 106–8
standards for judging, 89–94
composition of variables, 90
contributions of factors, 91
geometric fit, 91–94
parsimony, 90
uncorrelated factors, 90–91
Preferred system of reference, 89
Premultiplication, 278–79, 287, 290–91
Primary abilities, 102, 107
Primary factors; *see* Multiple-factor solution
Principal components; *see* Principal-factor solution
Principal-factor solution
assumption on residuals, 160
complexity of variables, 106
derivation of method, 322–23
derived; *see* Derived principal-factor solution
examples, 168–79
form of, 103–5
iterative method of calculation, 163–68, 342–52
labor of computation, 174–75, 179, 206, 212

orthogonality of coefficients, 163
theoretical development, 159–63
Probability integral, 132, 397
Product of matrices
inverse of, 308
rank of, 58
transpose of, 308
Product matrix, 221
Product of rotations, 219, 221
Projections of lines, 216–17
Projective axiom, 315
"Pythagorean" relation, 15

Radius vector, 54
Reciprocal of matrix; *see* Inverse matrix
Rectangular Cartesian coordinates
elementary formulas in, 47–53
Reduced pattern, 242, 245, 255
Reduced structure, 245, 276
Reference axes; *see* Reference vectors
Reference vectors
centroid, 181
direction cosines of, 164, 202, 208
and linear fit, 92
oblique; *see* Oblique reference vectors
orthogonal; *see* Orthogonal reference vectors
principal, 202
unit, 235, 289
Reflection of axis, 226, 227
Reflection in the origin; *see* Reflection of variables
Reflection of variables, 105, 184–88, 295, 361–66
Regression coefficients, 17, 267, 311
Regression equations, 17, 265, 276–77, 311–13
Relationship between pattern and structure
geometric distinction, 234–37
matrix formulation, 17, 266, 269, 325–27
Relationships among factors, 289–92
example, 292–95
matrix formulation, 291
transformation of coordinates, 292, 294
used in estimating factors, 292
Relative contributions of factors, 91
Reliability, 14–15, 295
Reproduced correlations, 19, 21
from bi-factor solution, 101
matrix of, 19, 278
related to observed correlations, 21, 60, 265
as scalar products, 61
from two-factor solution, 112
from uni-factor solution, 97